# QUANTITY FOOD SANITATION

# QUANTITY
# FOOD SANITATION

**KARLA LONGRÉE, Ph.D.**

*Professor, Department of Institution Management*
*New York State College of Home Economics*
*Cornell University, Ithaca, New York*

**INTERSCIENCE PUBLISHERS**

*a division of John Wiley & Sons*
*New York   London   Sydney*

# PREFACE

Quantity food service is big business. An average of 78 million meals are served every day in the various types of food establishments of the USA. "Eating out" is popular as a social event and necessary in industrial, school, hospital, and related types of food service.

Management entrusted with serving food to the public carries a threefold obligation. The food served must be not only nutritious and attractive, it must also be bacteriologically safe. Food sanitation is an essential part of a food production and service operation since it is closely related to public health. "Sanitary" means "pertaining to health."

The increase in incidence of foodborne illnesses points toward the need of improving the sanitary handling of food. Data are available which show that in 1960, 198 foodborne or waterborne outbreaks were reported which involved well over 9000 cases. Of these, only 5 outbreaks and 48 cases were milkborne, only 11 outbreaks and 1784 cases were waterborne, and the remainder were ascribed to other foods. There is reason to believe that the actual number of incidences of foodborne disease outbreaks is probably several times as high. Reporting of foodborne illnesses is not compulsory in many states of the USA.

The sanitary aspects of preparing and serving food in quantity are very complex and the many foods served complicate the situation.

In spite of the fact that, in general, this country can take pride in a safe and wholesome food supply, the bacteriological quality of many foods is quite variable; some foods are notorious for carrying pathogens capable of causing foodborne illnesses. Exceptions are highly standardized items such as milk. The task of assessing the bacteriological quality of our food supply is complicated by the fact that the food supply becomes increasingly more varied due to the large array of prepared, preportioned, and ready-to-eat foods which are becoming available and are frequently manufactured outside the jurisdiction of local or state health authorities. Food protection programs do not seem to keep pace with the rapid production of new products.

In the food preparation area, perfectly safe, wholesome food materials have another chance to pick up contaminants including microorganisms of public health significance. A food handler can be an important reservoir of food-poisoning organisms. Personnel who are untrained or poorly trained in matters of sanitation and who practice poor habits of personal hygiene represent a menace in the food preparation area. But even when persons preparing food maintain high standards of hygiene, serious trouble may arise when attention is not paid to the control of conditions conducive to bacterial multiplication in the food. These difficulties have often been shown to arise under conditions where food is prepared in quantity, and when no provision was afforded to keep this food cold enough or hot enough until it was served. Such situations are of particular significance in connection with community meal service, camp service, and similar group feedings. When sufficient time is allowed for bacterial multiplication and temperature conditions are favorable, even food prepared by clean persons may turn to poison.

For effective sanitary control, an understanding is needed of the many factors which contribute to foodborne illnesses. These include the important reservoirs of the causative organisms and the conditions under which these organisms will multiply in the food to dangerous numbers.

On the basis of this knowledge, the food service operator will seek to purchase food of high microbial quality, free of harmful bacteria; will see to it that food service personnel handle ingredients, prepare menu items, and hold and serve them in a way which cuts contamination to a minimum; and finally, will prevent contaminants from multiplying through intelligent use of appropriate temperature control.

Preventing foodborne illnesses is an obligation which the food service operator shoulders. The chance for success lies in his or her willingness to understand the facts underlying food protection and to diligently apply the control measures along the way from the purchase of safe food, through the many steps of preparation and holding, to the finished product at serving time.

KARLA LONGRÉE

*Ithaca, New York*

# CONTENTS

CHAPTER **I**

# FOOD SPOILAGE

## Spoilage

The term "spoilage" is somewhat vague. Spoilage is usually thought of as denoting unfitness for human consumption. Spoilage of food may be due to chemical or biological causes; the latter includes action of inherent enzymes, growth of microorganisms, invasion by insects, contamination with trichinae, worms, and the like. About one-fourth of the world's food supply is lost through the action of microorganisms alone.

It is extremely difficult to sharply define "spoilage" because different people have different concepts about edibility, or fitness to eat. It seems that spoilage is usually thought of as being associated with decomposition. In this author's opinion, this concept is too limited since it excludes food which, although not decomposed, harbors certain kinds of bacteria, or their toxins, in numbers or amounts which make the food poisonous and thus unfit for human consumption.

The criteria for assurance in foods of fitness to eat are:
1) The desired stage of development or maturity of the food.
2) Freedom from pollution at any stage in the production and subsequent handling of the food.
3) Freedom from objectionable chemical and physical changes resulting from action of food enzymes; activity of microbes, insects, rodents; invasion of parasites; and damage from pressure, freezing, heating, drying, and the like.
4) Freedom from microorganisms and parasites causing foodborne illnesses.

Enzymatic and microbial activities are undesirable when they are unwanted or uncontrolled. An example is the souring of milk; if unwanted, it is spoilage, yet the same process is purposely used in the production of certain cheeses.

1

## Stability

Foods are frequently classified on the basis of their stability as nonperishable, semiperishable, and perishable. An example of the first group is sugar. Few foods are truly nonperishable. Hermetically sealed, heat-processed, and sterilized (canned) foods are usually listed among the nonperishable items. For all intents and purposes, they belong there. However, canned food may become perishable under certain circumstances, when, by accident, a chance for recontamination following processing is afforded: if the seams of the cans are faulty, or if through rusting or other damage the can is no longer hermetically sealed. Spoilage of canned goods may also take place when the canned items are stored at unusually high temperatures. Bacteria which are extremely resistant to heat must be expected to escape the killing effect of heat applied in routine canning. These thermophilic spore-forming bacteria may multiply at high temperatures, with an optimum near 113°F and higher. Examples of these thermophiles are the *Bacillus* species which cause flat sour spoilage, the *Clostridium nigrificans* causing sulfide spoilage and the *Clostridium thermosaccharolyticum*. It should be emphasized here that the organism causing botulism, *Clostridium botulinum*, is eliminated during the heat treatment given the foods in the canning operation.

Classified as semiperishables are usually the dry foods, such as flour, dry legumes, baked goods, hard cheeses, dried fruits and vegetables, even waxed vegetables. Frozen foods, though basically perishable, may be classified as semiperishables provided they are freezer-stored properly.

The majority of our food materials must be classified as perishables. This group includes meat, poultry, fish, milk, eggs, many fruits and vegetables, and all cooked or "made" food items, except the dry and very acid ones.

## Microorganisms Involved in Spoilage

Microorganisms which may cause food to spoil include molds, yeasts, and bacteria. The contamination with molds, as a rule, is easily detected because of the presence of furry hyphae or threadlike structures which, in many instances, are colored. They often contribute a musty odor and flavor to the food they invade. Some molds are not altogether harmless as was assumed until recently. More will be said about the so-called aflatoxins later on.

Yeasts are unicellular bodies of small sizes which multiply by budding. In general, sugars are the best food for energy for yeasts, carbon dioxide and alcohol being the end products of the fermentation they cause. Spoilage due to yeast may usually be recognized by the presence of bubbles and alcoholic smell and taste.

Bacteria spoil food in many ways and it is not always possible to recognize the spoilage by sight, smell, or taste. Unfortunately, some of the bacteria that are important from a public health point of view may multiply to dangerously high numbers in food without changing the appearance, odor, or taste of the food. This disease-producing food has no decomposed appearance, but is certainly unfit for human consumption, and must be considered to be spoiled.

It is an important fact that almost any food will spoil if it is moist and not frozen. Spoilage must be expected within the temperature range 23-167°F. The various types of microorganisms as well as the genera, species, and strains, vary in their temperature as well as food requirements. Thus, the bacterial flora of a spoiled food item will vary greatly.

Origin of microorganisms varies also. The microorganisms may include the original flora of the particular food, as well as contaminants added in handling, processing, transporting, storing, preparing, and serving.

## Multiplication

The multiplication of spoilage organisms on or in the food materials depends on many factors—the type of organism involved, its ability to gain nourishment from the food, competition from other microorganisms, initial load, and environmental conditions. Some important conditions are composition of the food, available moisture, pH, oxygen tension, and temperature.

## Processing

Many food materials are processed to halt enzyme action and to destroy specific pathogens and spoilage organisms, thus prolonging the keeping quality for hours, days, months, or even years.

Frazier (1958) has summarized the principles of food preservation as follows:

1) Prevention or delay of self-decomposition of the food:
   a) by destruction or inactivation of food enzymes. Example: blanching.
   b) by prevention or delay of chemical reactions. Example: use of an antioxidant.

2) Prevention or delay of microbial decomposition:
   a) by keeping out microorganisms (asepsis).
   b) by removal of microorganisms. Example: filtration.
   c) by hindering the growth and activity of the microorganism by low temperatures, drying, anaerobic conditions, or chemicals.
   d) by killing the microorganism. Examples: heat or radiation. Pasteurization and canning cause thermal destruction of the organisms.

3) Prevention or damage because of insects, animals, mechanical causes, etc.

It is beyond the scope of this book to discuss the principles and methodology of commercial food preservation, such as pasteurization, canning, freezing, freeze drying, dehydration, dehydro freezing, curing, salting, pickling, use of chemical preservatives, radiation, and other methods.

However, the microbial flora of public health significance which may be expected to occur in connection with processed foods will be discussed in Chapter VI.

Persons entrusted with serving meals to the public must be familiar with the signs of incipient spoilage although, as was pointed out above, freedom from such signs is no guarantee of wholesomeness; unfortunately there are forms of illness-producing spoilage which do not give us the comfort of noticeable changes indicating that the food has become poisonous. Whether newly purchased food or stored food is being inspected, signs of incipient spoilage should be familiar to the one doing the job. Maclinn (1952) in *The Rutgers Food Saver* states evidences of quality loss and what he designates to be danger signals for many common foods. Weiser (1962) quotes signs of spoilage listed in an Ohio Department of Health Circular. The reader is referred to these sources.

## References

Frazier, William C. (1958). *Food Microbiology*. McGraw-Hill Book Co., New York.

Maclinn, W. A. (1952). *The Rutgers Food Saver*. Rutgers Univ. Press, New Brunswick, N. J.

Weiser, Harry H. (1962). *Practical Food Microbiology and Technology*. Avi Publishing Co., Westport, Conn.

## Additional Readings

Ball, C. Olin, and F. C. W. Olson. *Sterilization In Food Technology; Theory, Practice and Calculations.* McGraw-Hill Book Co., New York. 1957.

Crisley, F. D. "Factors Affecting the Quality of Processed Foods." Presented at the 24th Klenzade Educational Seminar, Athens, Georgia. *Jour. Environmental Health,* 26(3): 181–186. November-December, 1963.

Dack, G. M. *Food Poisoning. 3rd ed.* Univ. Chicago Press, Chicago. 1956.

Desrosier, Norman W. *The Technology of Food Preservation.* 2nd ed. Avi Publishing Co., Westport, Conn. 1963.

Mossel, D. A. A., and M. Ingram. "The Physiology of the Microbial Spoilage of Foods." *Jour. Appl. Bacteriol., 18:* 233–268. 1955.

Tressler, Donald K., and Clifford F. Evers. *The Freezing Preservation of Foods.* 3rd ed., Avi Publishing Co., Westport, Conn. 1957.

CHAPTER **II**

# SOME BASIC FACTS ON MICROORGANISMS IMPORTANT IN FOOD SANITATION

It is beyond the scope of this book to present a treatise on the elements of food microbiology. However, it was deemed desirable to precede the following chapters with a few brief statements of facts on bacteria and thereby help the reader to reacquaint himself with the terms used in connection with microbiology. Microbiology is only one of the sciences contributing to the understanding and application of food sanitation; examples of others are chemistry, physics, entomology, and epidemiology.

Certain microorganisms and parasites are transmitted through food and may cause illnesses in the persons who ingest the contaminated items. For some microorganisms the food may serve as a mere vehicle of transmission; for others, as a medium in which they multiply to tremendous numbers. Outbreaks of acute gastroenteritis caused by ingestion of food in which certain pathogens have multiplied profusely are popularly referred to as "food poisoning" outbreaks (see Chapter IV).

Microorganisms which may cause foodborne illnesses include bacteria, viruses, rickettsia, and protozoa. Although most of the microorganisms producing foodborne illnesses are bacteria, it should be remembered that less than 1 per cent of all bacteria are enemies of man and many are his friends.

This discussion will be more or less limited to bacteria. Among the bacteria are found some important pathogens transmitted by food, among them those which multiply profusely in food and are capable

6

of causing outbreaks of food infections and food intoxications ("food poisoning").

Bacteria are plants. They are single-celled organisms, and do not contain chlorophyll. The bacterial cell contains a wall through which the cell takes up simple nutrients in solution, which are combined by the cell for its utilization.

## Classification, Size, Shape, Motility, and Endospores of Bacteria

### Classification

In contract to the molds and yeasts, classification of bacteria on a morphological basis is difficult. In fact, bacteria are so small that morphological differences are inadequate as a basis for a workable classification. For larger grouping, some of the morphological characteristics used are shape, size, and grouping of cells. Gram stain and formation of spores are used also. However, finer subdivisions into species and varieties are largely made on the basis of physiological characteristics such as biochemical activities, pathogenicity, metabolic requirements, antigenic reactions, and reactions to the action of bacteriophages which are viruses pathogenic to bacteria. These viruses attack the bacteria and kill them by lysis. Many phages are known, each active against a specific species or even a strain of bacterium. This specificity has an important practical application in the phage typing of bacteria. Thus, types may be distinguished which otherwise are known to look and react alike. Phage typing has been much used to distinguish the salmonellae and staphylococci, among which are forms capable of causing foodborne acute gastroenteric outbreaks.

The standard reference in the field of bacterial classification is Bergey's *Manual of Determinative Bacteriology,* published by the American Society for Microbiology.

### Size

Bacterial cells are very small, with some variation among the different species. The majority of bacteria measure approximately 0.5–1.0 × 2.0–5.0 microns ($\mu$), staphylococci having diameters 0.75 $\mu$ and larger; rods like Salmonellae ranging in width from 0.5 to 1 $\mu$ and in length from 2 to 3 $\mu$. Filamentous bacteria may be extremely long. The single cell is not visible to the naked eye, the visual acuity of the naked eye being approximately 75 $\mu$. One micron equals 1/1000 mm or 1/25,400 inch.

When millions of bacterial cells are suspended in a clear substrate, the suspension will assume a turbid appearance. Thus, one may see the bacteria as a population. Also, when bacteria cover a food surface in the form of a slime they are visible to the human eye. Many times, however, the presence of bacteria cannot be seen in food even if the contaminants are present in sufficient numbers to make a person extremely ill.

## Shape

In general, bacteria fall into three groups: cocci, rods, and spirilla. The rods are also referred to as bacilli. This is an unfortunate term since it may lead to confusion with the genus *Bacillus*, a spore former of the family Bacillaceae. The cocci are spherical; the rods are somewhat elongate; and the spirilla are commalike or corkscrewlike in shape. The spirilla are not represented among the types causing foodborne diseases in man (Fig. 1).

Some bacteria form chains which may be short to quite long. Others cling together in various patterns, sometimes forming sizable aggregates or clumps. Examples among the cocci are: Diplococcus, a pair of cocci; Sarcina, eight spheres arranged in packet form; *Staphylococcus*, a grapelike aggregate of spheres; and *Streptococcus*, a chain of cocci. The rods may occur singly, in pairs, or in chains. The spirilla occur singly.

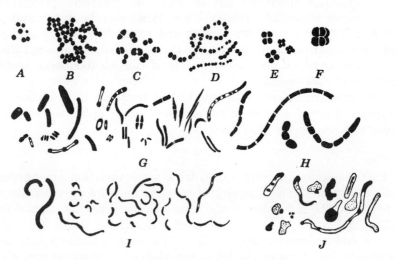

*Fig. 1. Forms of the true bacteria. (A) Single cocci. (B) Staphylococci. (C) Diplococci. (D) Streptococci. (E) Tetrads. (F) Sarcinae. (G) Various forms of bacilli. (H) Streptobacilli. (I) Various forms of spirilla. (J) Involution forms.* Reprinted by permission of The Macmillan Company from *Microbiology*, 5th ed. [Burdon and Williams (1964)]. Copyright, The Macmillan Company, 1964.

## Motility

Some forms of bacteria carry whiplike appendages, termed flagella, by which some locomotion of the cells is made possible. Examples of flagella are shown in Fig. 2. Whereas all spirilla are motile, and practically none of the cocci are, the rods encompass motile as well as nonmotile forms. Examples of motile forms are *Proteus* and *Pseudomonas*. Although the flagella are relatively effective in helping bacteria to move about, they are not of practical importance in disseminating the cells. The distances traveled by bacteria with the aid of flagella are short indeed. Bacteria depend for distant dissemination on other means including dust particles, moisture droplets, direct contact and the like.

## Endospores

Some bacteria may form spores inside the cell wall, these spores being called endospores. One spore is formed in a cell. Of bacterial

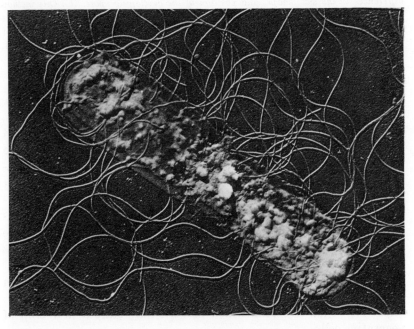

*Fig. 2. Proteus vulgaris. A shadowed electron micrograph especially made to show the flagella. The bacteria were cultivated until they were spreading rapidly over an agar medium. The culture was refrigerated overnight; then the organisms were floated off the agar surface in 5 per cent formalin, and washed twice before being mounted on collodion film. It can be seen that the flagella appear to originate in tiny, spherical bodies about 100 mμ in diameter situated just inside the cell wall.* By permission from Houwink and Van Iterson (1950).

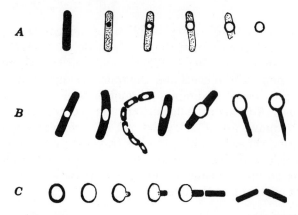

Fig. 3. Bacterial spores. (A) Stages in the formation of a spore. On the left is the vegetative form of the bacillus, on the right the free spore formed from it. (B) The sporulating forms of different kinds of sporebearing bacteria, showing characteristic differences in the size, shape, and position of the developing spore. (C) One method of germination of a spore back to the vegetative form. The newly germinated rod is shown dividing at once into two actively growing bacilli. Reprinted by permission of The Macmillan Company from Microbiology, 5th ed. [Burdon and Williams (1964)]. Copyright, The Macmillan Company, 1964.

genera important in foods, Clostridium and Bacillus are spore formers. In general, bacterial forms other than rods do not produce spores. Examples of bacterial spores are shown in Fig. 3. Spores are formed only in mature cells; they are thick walled and more resistant to high heat, low humidity, and other adverse conditions than vegetative cells.

The heat resistance of spores is very important in the food industry. The heat-resistant spores are used to develop heating temperatures and times for the production of safe canned goods. More will be said about the comparative heat resistance of vegetative cells and spores later on.

Spores may remain dormant for long times, even decades. When conditions become favorable, they will germinate (Fig. 3) into new, sensitive, vegetative cells which in turn may start a new crop of vegetative cells.

### Reproduction and Death of Vegetative Cells

Reproduction of vegetative cells takes places by binary or transverse fission. In some cocci, division may take place along several planes. The rods divide along the short axis only. After a cell has divided into two daughter cells, each of these cells grows somewhat in size, quickly matures, and is ready for a new division. In fact, maturation may take as little 15–30 minutes, this period being called the generation time. The length of generation time varies with the organisms as well as many other factors, among them medium and temperature.

When vegetative bacterial cells divide they multiply. Unfortunately, the term "growth" is also used to denote what in reality represents multiplication.

### The Growth Curve

When bacterial cells multiply under favorable conditions they pass through various phases. When the number of cells is plotted against time, a curve results which illustrates these phases. To determine a growth curve, the investigator makes periodic counts of the number of cells and then he plots the numbers per gram or milliliter of medium logarithmically on the ordinate, and units of time on the abscissa. A typical growth curve is illustrated in Fig. 4.

Some bacteria produce toxins. The toxins may be excreted into the surrounding medium or food (exotoxins), or retained within the

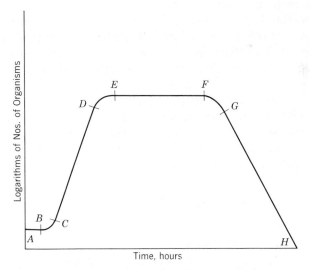

*Fig. 4. Growth curve of microorganism. A to B, lag phase; B to C, phase of positive acceleration; C to D, logarithmic phase; D to E, phase of negative acceleration; E to F, maximum stationary phase; F to G, accelerated death phase; and G to H, death phase. Adapted from Frazier (1958).*

cell (endotoxins) and finally liberated when the cells disintegrate. Toxins capable of causing gastroenteritis or inflammation of the lining of the stomach and intestines are enterotoxins.

During the first phase no multiplication occurs. The phase is designated as stationary or as "lag" phase (A to B). It is possible for a decline to occur, because some of the cells may fail to adjust to the new environment. The second phase (B to C) is that of "positive acceleration," during which the rate of multiplication is continuously increasing. The lag phase and the stage of continued increase are usually combined and referred to as "lag phase." Factors affecting this combination lag phase are: size of inoculum—if the inoculum is large, the lag phase is brief; age of cells—if the cells are young, the lag phase is brief; and general environmental conditions—if favorable, the lag phase is brief.

Perishable food items should be kept at temperatures conducive to holding the bacteria which are present in the "lag phase" as long as possible. This involves two major efforts: to keep the bacterial load low and to regulate the temperature of the food in such a fashion that it is far removed from the growth optimum. In a food service operation, suitable food is available to the bacteria at all times. Therefore, few alterations can be made in environment, except changes in temperature.

During the third phase (C to D) the rate of cell increase is constant. This phase is referred to as the "logarithmic (or log) phase," since the number of bacteria increases in a geometric progression. If the logarithms of the numbers are plotted against time, a straight line results.

A generation time of 20–30 minutes is common for the bacteria which grow well at moderate and high temperatures, whereas the cold-loving bacteria have longer generation times.

The number of generations of bacteria during the logarithmic phase is calculated as follows:

$$n = \frac{\log c - \log b}{\log 2}$$

$n$ = number of generations
$\log c$ = log of number of bacteria/ml at point $D$
$\log b$ = log of number of bacteria/ml at point $C$
$\log 2$ = log of 2

The duration of the logarithmic phase is affected by the factors controlling growth.

The fourth phase (*D* and *E*) is that of "negative acceleration," since the rate of multiplication is constantly decreasing. The fifth phase (*E* to *F*) is the maximum stationary phase; the increase and decrease cancel each other and thus the number of cells remains constant.

The length of the stationary phase is strongly affected by the kind of organism, depletion of nutrients, and accumulation of waste products of cells. The reasons for the stationary phase are not completely understood.

The sixth phase (*F* to *G*) is the "accelerated death phase," and the seventh (*G* to *H*) is the "final death phase" during which the number of viable cells decreases at a steady rate. Eventually, all the cells of a culture die and become autolyzed or self-dissolving.

Some important factors affecting bacterial multiplication and death are, besides kind of organism and its previous history: composition of substrate, moisture, osmotic pressure, oxygen tension, pH, temperature, and presence of inhibitors. Size of initial inoculum and competition from other microorganisms have been shown to be other important factors.

## Factors Affecting Growth

### FOOD

Requirements for growth will vary with the kind of bacterium, sometimes down to the various strains of a species. Some bacteria have an extremely wide range and can multiply in many kinds of food; others are quite specific in their food requirements. Bacteria vary in their need for vitamins and other accessory growth factors in the medium. Although all bacteria need vitamins, some are able to synthesize the vitamins they need from other compounds present in the substrate.

Accessory growth factors are substances which do not furnish building materials or energy to the cells, but which are essential to growth. They are effective in minute or trace quantities. These substances are also called essential metabolites; they range from simple ionic forms such as $Cu^{++}$, $Mn^{++}$, and $F^{+++}$ to complex organic materials.

The bacteria responsible for foodborne illnesses happen to thrive well in many of the foods man eats, especially in food items of proteinaceous nature.

### MOISTURE AND OSMOTIC PRESSURE

Bacteria need food of high moisture content, in general. But the minimum moisture content necessary to support bacterial growth is not a definite value. By comparison, yeasts require high moisture for growth, and molds may develop on substrates of lower moisture content than is required by yeasts and bacteria. If the air surrounding the food is humid, molds may develop on substrates of rather low water content.

It has been emphasized that the amount of available moisture, not total moisture, affects bacterial multiplication. The available moisture may be expressed as "water activity" $(a_w)$. Water activity is calculated by dividing the vapor pressure of the solution by the vapor pressure of the solvent; thus a value of 1.00 is assigned to pure water.

A medium of high osmotic pressure may adversely affect the bacterial cells by drawing water from the cells to an extent damaging to their metabolic processes. Sugar and salt are used in food preservation for this reason. Sensitivity to osmotic pressure varies with the kind of bacteria, whether the cells are vegetative or spores, and some other factors. Some microbial forms are very resistant to high osmotic pressure. Some molds and yeasts grow in substrates of extremely high sugar content. Most bacteria are not highly sensitive to salt concentrations between approximately 0.5 and 3 per cent. Some bacterial forms are quite tolerant to salt, among them *Staphylococcus aureus*, food-poisoning organism. Organisms tolerant to salt are called haloduric (salt resistant). Some bacteria are actually salt loving and may be important in the spoilage of highly salted foods or brines of 20–30 per cent salt content. These organisms are called halophilic (salt loving).

Water may become less available through the presence of solutes like salt and sugar as well as through the action of hydrophilic (water-loving) colloids. Water may also be tied up through freezing. In frozen foods the water is in the solid state and thus unavailable. Removal of water by dehydration is a common form of food preservation.

Once dried, some forms of microbes die more easily than others. Spores may survive longer periods of desiccation than vegetative cells. Even sensitive species can be kept viable in the dried condition if the cells are rapidly frozen, followed by rapid desiccation in a vacuum. This method of preserving bacteria, viruses, toxins, and enzymes is known as lyophilization.

OXYGEN TENSION

Microorganisms vary in their response to oxygen. This characteristic has been used to classify them into three (or four) groups: the strict aerobes, which require free oxygen—to this group belong the molds, yeasts, and some bacteria; the strict anaerobes, which will multiply only where air is excluded except when strong substances are present or when associated with aerobic organisms; and the facultative forms which multiply with or without free oxygen. Many bacteria belong here, among them some important food-poisoning kinds. Some bacteria grow in the presence of minute quantities of oxygen; these organisms are classified as microaerophilic by some authors.

## pH

The degree of acidity or alkalinity of a medium, or food, is expressed as the hydrogen ion concentration. The pH value represents the reciprocal of the negative logarithm of the hydrogen ion concentration. The pH scale extends from 0 to 14, a pH value of 7 expressing neutrality. Acid materials possess pH values below 7; basic or alkaline materials have pH values above 7. A difference of 1 pH unit corresponds to a tenfold difference in hydrogen ion concentration. The relationships between hydrogen ion and hydroxyl ion concentrations of pH and reaction is shown in Table 1.

**Table 1. Relationships between Hydrogen Ion and Hydroxyl Ion Concentrations, pH, and Reaction [Adapted from Burdon and Williams (1964)]**

| Hydrogen ion concentration [H$^+$] (moles/liter) | Logarithm of hydrogen ion concentration | Hydroxyl ion concentration [OH$^-$] (moles/liter) | pH | Reaction |
|---|---|---|---|---|
| 1.0 | −0 | 0.000,000,000,000,01 | 0.0 | Acid |
| 0.1 | −1 | 0.000,000,000,000,1 | 1.0 | Acid |
| 0.01 | −2 | 0.000,000,000,001 | 2.0 | Acid |
| 0.001 | −3 | 0.000,000,000,01 | 3.0 | Acid |
| 0.000,1 | −4 | 0.000,000,000,1 | 4.0 | Acid |
| 0.000,01 | −5 | 0.000,000,001 | 5.0 | Acid |
| 0.000,001 | −6 | 0.000,000,01 | 6.0 | Acid |
| 0.000,000,1 | −7 | 0.000,000,1 | 7.0 | Neutral |
| 0.000,000,01 | −8 | 0.000,001 | 8.0 | Alkaline |
| 0.000,000,001 | −9 | 0.000,01 | 9.0 | Alkaline |
| 0.000,000,000,1 | −10 | 0.000,1 | 10.0 | Alkaline |
| 0.000,000,000,01 | −11 | 0.001 | 11.0 | Alkaline |
| 0.000,000,000,001 | −12 | 0.01 | 12.0 | Alkaline |
| 0.000,000,000,000,1 | −13 | 0.1 | 13.0 | Alkaline |
| 0.000,000,000,000,01 | −14 | 1.0 | 14.0 | Alkaline |

The molds and yeasts are quite acid tolerant, and some forms are able to grow in media of pH values below 2. Bacteria vary greatly in their reaction to pH. Some bacteria are quite sensitive to the pH of the substrate in which they are suspended, others are not. In general, bacteria may be expected to multiply within the pH range 4–10. However, the optimum pH for the majority of microorganisms is near neutral, which is 6.5–7.5.

Some acid-forming bacteria are favored by a slightly acid medium. They are important in the food industry in that they are used in producing various acids in foods such as fermented milk, sauerkraut, butter, and cheeses. Certain proteolytic bacteria can grow in alkaline media such as egg white.

It is an important fact that slightly acid, neutral, and slightly alkaline food materials will support multiplication of the organisms causing food infections and food poisoning.

The food materials of pH near the neutral point are mostly the animal foods: meats and meat products, seafood, eggs, milk, etc. Of the vegetables, some are rather low in acid; examples are corn, peas, and hominy. A very acid vegetable is the tomato, which is actually a fruit. The fruits are at the high-acid end of the scale, the citrus fruit being among the very acid fruits (Table 2).

Some food materials have a rather stable pH. The compounds which resist changes in pH are called buffers. Proteins have excellent buffering power.

Acid is used in food preservation to suppress bacterial multiplication. Within certain limits, acidification can also be used to suppress bacterial multiplication in menu items. This aspect will be given attention in Chapter XI.

Acidity is not only important in relation to bacterial multiplication it is also a factor in thermal death of bacteria. In canning, very acid foods may be given a relatively light heat treatment.

TEMPERATURE

Microorganisms have their specific temperature requirements for growth. At the *optimum temperature* a cell multiplies and grows most readily; at the *minimum temperature* it multiplies but ceases below that point; and at the *maximum temperature* it multiplies, but ceases above that point. It is well not to think of these temperatures as sharp points, since the medium in which the cells are suspended, as well as other factors, cause some degree of variation in optimum, minimum, and maximum temperatures of multiplication.

Table 2.  Hydrogen Ion Concentration and pH of Some Common Foods [Adapted from American Home Economics Association (1964)]

| Hydrogen ion concentration | pH | Average values for common foods |
|---|---|---|
| $1.0 \times 10^{-2}$ | 2.0 | Limes |
| $8.0 \times 10^{-3}$ | 2.1 | |
| $6.3 \times 10^{-3}$ | 2.2 | Lemons |
| $5.0 \times 10^{-3}$ | 2.3 | |
| $4.0 \times 10^{-3}$ | 2.4 | |
| $3.2 \times 10^{-3}$ | 2.5 | |
| $2.5 \times 10^{-3}$ | 2.6 | |
| $2.0 \times 10^{-3}$ | 2.7 | |
| $1.6 \times 10^{-3}$ | 2.8 | |
| $1.3 \times 10^{-3}$ | 2.9 | Vinegar, plums |
| $1.0 \times 10^{-3}$ | 3.0 | Gooseberries |
| | 3.1 | Prunes, apples, grapefruit (3.0–3.3) |
| | 3.2 | Rhubarb, dill pickles |
| | 3.3 | Apricots, blackberries |
| | 3.4 | Strawberries, lowest acidity for jelly |
| | 3.5 | Peaches |
| | 3.6 | Raspberries, sauerkraut |
| | 3.7 | Blueberries, oranges (3.1–4.1) |
| | 3.8 | Sweet cherries |
| | 3.9 | Pears |
| $1.0 \times 10^{-4}$ | 4.0 | Acid fondant, acidophilus milk |
| | 4.1 | |
| | 4.2 | Tomatoes (4.0–4.6) |
| | 4.3 | |
| | 4.4 | Lowest acidity for processing at 100°C |
| | 4.5 | Buttermilk |
| | 4.6 | Bananas, egg albumin, figs, isoelectric point for |
| | 4.7 | casein, pimientos |
| | 4.8 | |
| | 4.9 | |
| $1.0 \times 10^{-5}$ | 5.0 | Pumpkins, carrots |
| | 5.1 | Cucumbers |
| | 5.2 | Turnips, cabbage, squash |
| | 5.3 | Parsnips, beets |
| | 5.4 | Sweet potatoes, bread |
| | 5.5 | Spinach |
| | 5.6 | Asparagus, cauliflower |
| | 5.7 | |
| | 5.8 | Meat, ripened |
| | 5.9 | |
| $1.0 \times 10^{-6}$ | 6.0 | Tuna |
| | 6.1 | Potatoes |
| | 6.2 | Peas |

(*continued*)

**Table 2** (*continued*)

| Hydrogen ion concentration | pH | Average values for common foods |
|---|---|---|
| $1.0 \times 10^{-6}$ | 6.3 | Corn, oysters, dates |
| | 6.4 | Egg yolk |
| | 6.5 | |
| | 6.6 | Milk (6.5–6.7) |
| | 6.7 | |
| | 6.8 | |
| | 6.9 | Shrimp |
| $1.0 \times 10^{-7}$ | 7.0 | Meat, unripened |
| | 7.1 | |
| | 7.2 | |
| | 7.3 | |
| | 7.4 | |
| | 7.5 | |
| | 7.6 | |
| | 7.7 | |
| | 7.8 | |
| | 7.9 | |
| $1.0 \times 10^{-8}$ | 8.0 | Egg white (7.0–9.0) |
| | 8.1 | |
| | 8.2 | |
| | 8.3 | |
| | 8.4 | |

On the basis of their growth response to the various temperatures, bacteria have been classified into groups.

The thermophilic (heat-loving) bacteria have high optimum temperatures from 113 to 140°F (45–60°C) and a maximum of 167°F (75°C). The mesophilic (intermediate) bacteria have optimum growth temperatures between approximately 68 and 113°F (20 and 45°C). The psychrophilics are usually referred to as bacteria that are able to grow relatively rapidly at 32°F (0°C) or lower down to 19°F (–7°C), but usually have optima at 50–68°F (10–20°C), although a few have considerably lower optima, below 50°F (10°C). Lately, an effort has been made to more accurately define this group by dividing it into the truly psychrophilics which perfer low temperatures for growth and psychrotrophics which multiply fairly well at temperatures of 41°F (5°C) and below whatever their optimum temperatures might be (Mossel and Zwart, 1960; Eddy, 1960).

It should be reemphasized that much overlapping occurs within all the groups mentioned above. Organisms may vary greatly regarding the temperature range within which they are able to multiply. For example, some mesophilic bacteria may grow at very low temperatures and others at very high temperatures, although their optimum is in the medium-temperature range.

When the maximum growth temperature of a bacterial cell is exceeded, the bacterium may survive for a while until eventually death takes place.

The heat resistance of microorganisms varies with genus, species, and strain. Therefore, only approximate data can be given. In general, spores of microorganisms are more heat resistant than vegetative cells.

In the case of the yeasts, the vegetative cells are usually killed by applying moist heat of 122–136°F (50–58°C) for 10–15 minutes; spores require exposure to 140°F (60°C) for the same length of time. In case of the molds, vegetative cells and spores are usually killed by moist heating at 140°F (60°C) for 5–10 minutes. Some heat-resistant forms require a more rigorous heat treatment; among these are many species of the common molds.

The resistance to heat varies very widely among the different bacteria. A few generalizations seem in order. Cocci are usually more heat resistant than rods, with exceptions. Bacteria which require high temperatures for optimum growth are likely to be resistant to heat, and so are bacteria which are shielded by capsules. Even strains of the same species may vary regarding response to heat. The heat resistance of bacterial spores varies with the species and the physiological condition of the spores. The concentration of cells has a definite effect on resistance to heat in that the higher the concentration or the larger the load, the greater is the heat treatment required for their destruction.

Age has an effect on heat resistance in that young cells in the lag or log stage are more easily killed than cells in the stationary growth phase. Old cells are again more easily killed. The previous history of cells, the temperature at which they were grown, seems to have an effect on their heat resistance also.

The type of medium in which the microbial cells are exposed has a profound effect on heat resistance. Microorganisms are killed more easily in moist than in dry media; in acid rather than neutral or somewhat alkaline media with exceptions; in the presence of antiseptic or germicidal substances; and in the absence of certain protective substances. The effect of certain protective substances has been established for specific organisms and generalizations cannot be made. Among protective substances are colloidal materials, especially proteins and fats, sodium chloride, and sugar.

The effect of substrates on the thermal death point of three bacteria as reported by Brown and Peiser (1916) is shown by the data in Table 3. Thermal death point is the temperature necessary to kill all of the organisms exposed to heat in 10 minutes.

Table 3. Effect of Protective Substances on Heat Resistance [Adapted from Brown and Peiser (1916)]

|  | Thermal death point, °C | | |
|---|---|---|---|
|  | S. lactis | E. coli | L. bulgaricus |
| Cream | 69–71 | 73 | 95 |
| Whole milk | 63–65 | 69 | 91 |
| Skim milk | 59–63 | 65 | 89 |
| Whey | 57–61 | 63 | 83 |
| Broth | 55–57 | 61 | ? |

Thermal death is a time–temperature effect. In general, as the temperature applied to the microorganisms is increased, the time needed to achieve death decreases. For example, milk can be effectively pasteurized at 145°F (63°C) by maintaining this temperature for 30 minutes, or at 161°F (72°C) by a 15-second exposure. Both temperature and time of heat application affect death of microorganisms.

Therefore, the heat resistance of microorganisms is usually expressed as thermal death time, which is the time required at a specified temperature to kill a specified number of vegetative cells, or spores, under highly specified conditions. In the older literature the term thermal death point refers to the temperature necessary to kill all the organisms within a period of 10 minutes. This term is inexact because not all cells die at the very same instant.

Thermal death depends on the heat resistance of the organisms, the age and previous history of the organism, the temperature it is exposed to, the length of time for which heat is applied, the presence of moisture, the nature of the medium in which the cells are suspended, the number of vegetative cells or spores in the medium, and some other factors. There are differences in heat resistance within a given population.

The food processing industry has developed time–temperature schedules for various products to satisfy the requirements of killing important contaminants of public health significance while preventing loss of culinary quality due to intense or prolonged heating.

Resistant forms are sometimes called "thermodurics." This is a practical term and serves to denote survivors resisting the heat treatments applied to foods in routine heat-processing operations.

At low temperatures the lag phase is prolonged, and when cell division has begun, generation times are very long and the bacterial population builds up at a very slow rate.

Below the freezing point, the degree of killing varies not only with type of organism, but with the nature of the surrounding medium. Vegetative cells are killed more readily than spores.

Low temperatures are used in refrigeration and in the storage of frozen foods. Low temperatures are, in general, inhibitors, whereas their killing power is limited. Above the freezing point little multiplication takes place except for the psychrophiles.

To prevent perishable foods from remaining within the temperature range of bacterial multiplication is one of the most important duties of the food service manager in his endeavors to prepare and serve wholesome food to the public.

INHIBITORS

Inhibitors may have a pronounced effect on bacterial multiplication and death. Inhibitors may be a part of the food; they may have developed as a product of the microorganism's metabolism; they may have developed during processing; or they may have been purposely added by the processor.

Some examples of inhibitors that are a natural part of the food are: benzoic acid in cranberries, lactenins and anticoliform factors in freshly drawn milk, and lysozyme in egg whites.

Inhibitory substances developed by microorganisms during their multiplication may accumulate and become toxic. An example is alcohol produced in the growth and fermentation of yeast, in fruit juices, or in the production of wine. Substances not inhibitory to the organism producing them may be inhibitory to other organisms. This fact is very important when different kinds of microorganisms are in competition while growing. Other inhibitory substances include acids, peroxides, and antibiotics.

Seldom will a contaminant find itself without competition from other kinds of microorganisms with which it will interact in some way. These interactions fall into three general categories: metabiosis, synergism, and antagonism.

In a metabiotic relationship, one type of microorganism makes conditions favorable for the growth of the other. Many examples of these interactions are known such as fermentations and decompositions of raw food materials, and the reader is referred to books on food microbiology. One organism succeeds another, although some overlapping may occur.

In the natural souring of milk, a variety of different bacteria produce the acid at the early stage of souring. During the later stages, usually one *Streptococcus* survives.

In a synergetic relationship, organisms act cooperatively and achieve what neither can do alone. Colors may be produced in the medium which are different from what either organism can produce by itself. An item of interest in food sanitation concerns the food-poisoning organism *Clostridium botulinum*. The toxin *C. botulinum*, Type E, when produced in a fish product was found to be greatly activated by the activity of another *Clostridium* which released an enzyme which enhanced the toxicity of the Type E toxin (Sakaguchi and Tohyama, 1955).

In an antagonistic relationship the microorganisms are in life-or-death competition which may be for nutrients, change of pH to the disadvantage of the other, and even the production of antibiotics by one to the disadvantage of the other. An example of interest from a public health point of view is this: *Staphylococcus aureus* is adversely affected by a mixed population in milk, cream fillings, chicken pies, and other menu items (Peterson et al., 1962a, b). Graves and Frazier (1963) found that of 870 cultures of predominant microorganisms isolated from foods, over 25% were inhibitory to *S. aureus;* the remainder, however, had no stimulatory effects. According to Kraft and Ayres (1966), fluorescing spoilage organisms attained large populations on refrigerated chicken even when *S. aureus* initially outnumbered these spoilage organisms 100 : 1.

*Clostridium botulinum* may be adversely affected by other bacteria, which may limit the germination of spores and vegetative growth of this food poisoning organism or may destroy its toxin as rapidly as it forms. An antibiotic active against *C. botulinum* is formed by *Brevibacterium lineus,* a bacterium important in the ripening of Limburger cheese (Grecz, 1961).

Inhibitory substances may develop during heat processing of foods. Examples are the substances resulting from the heating of lipids.

Substances that are purposely added to foods by the processor to inhibit microbial growth are so manifold that a detailed discussion of these is beyond the scope of this book. Inhibiting agents may be physical or chemical in nature, or a combination. The chemicals may be inorganic or organic in nature. Inorganic chemicals used to inhibit microbial multiplication are, before all, certain inorganic acids and their salts. Gases, peroxides, halogens, metals, and alkalis and their salts are being used also. Of the organic substances, these should be mentioned: organic acids and their salts, alcohols, antibiotics, sugars, and formaldehyde. Many new compounds have been developed in recent years, and many are being developed right now. Many compounds are not permitted to be added to the food itself, but are used to impregnate the wrapping materials.

The effect of the various agencies employed in inhibiting or killing microorganisms is affected by such factors as their concentration and time of action, and by the kinds, numbers, age, and previous history of the microorganisms to which they are applied, as well as by the medium surrounding the microorganism. A protective action may be expected from the presence of colloidal matter or solids. More will be said about this later on.

"Antiseptic" and "bacteriostatic" denote a property ascribed to an agency which inhibits the growth or activity of microorganisms or bacteria, respectively. "Germicidal" or "disinfectant" denotes a property ascribed to an agency which kills the vegetative form of the organism, either by heat or chemical action. "Sterilization" denotes a process to free a substance of all living things, including spores, be it by physical agencies like heat, by chemical disinfectants, or by removing the microorganisms from the substance. "Sanitizing" reduces the microbial population to safe low levels as determined by public health requirements; usually 99.9% of the bacterial population should be exterminated.

Irradiation at various frequencies can be used to eliminate microorganisms from food materials. Irradiation of foods is not yet widely used and will therefore not be discussed. Radiation applied in doses sufficiently large to ensure sterilization tends to have undesirable side effects on food, causing objectionable changes in color, odor, and flavor.

Ionizing radiation (X-rays, gamma rays, cathode rays) can be successfully used if combined with other methods of killing microorganisms using smaller doses which do not impair food quality. Irradiation is now successfully used in killing some animal parasites in certain foods.

For a discussion of the effect of radiation on bacteria, the reader is referred to Pelczar and Reid (1965), Chapter 20. The preservation of foods by radiation is thoroughly discussed in a book published by

**Table 4. Genera of Bacteria Important in Food Bacteriology[a]**

| | |
|---|---|
| *Pseudomonadaceae* | *Brevibacteriaceae* |
| Pseudomonas | Brevibacterium |
| Acetobacter | |
| Halobacterium | *Lactobacillaceae* |
| Photobacterium | *Steptococcus |
| | Subgroups: |
| Alcaligenes | lactic |
| Achromobacter | viridans |
| Flavobacterium | enterococcus |
| | pyogenic |
| *Enterobacteriaceae* | Leuconostoc |
| *Escherichia | Lactobacillus |
| Aerobacter | |
| Erwinia | *Proprionibacteriaceae* |
| Serratia | Proprionibacterium |
| *Proteus | |
| *Salmonella | *Corynebacteriaceae* |
| *Shigella | Microbacterium |
| | *Corynebacterium |
| *Brucellaceae* | |
| *Pasteurella | *Bacillaceae* |
| *Brucella | Bacillus |
| | *Clostridium |
| *Micrococcaceae* | |
| Micrococcus | |
| *Staphylococcus | |

[a] Genera which include species known to be foodborne pathogens are marked with an asterisk.

the National Academy of Sciences (1965), which is a collection of papers presented before an international conference on the subject.

Some genera of bacteria important in food bacteriology are listed in Table 4. Genera containing foodborne pathogens are denoted in the table with an asterisk.

## Other Microorganisms Important in Food Sanitation

### Fungi

These are chlorophyll-free microorganisms which include, among other members, the molds and yeasts.

#### MOLDS

Mold growth appears as cottony, powdery, or fuzzy tufts and patches, often highly colored. Most molds smell "moldy." The tufts or patches are the mycelium which consists of threadlike structures called hyphae; on these hyphae spores are produced (Fig. 5). There is a great variation in the mode of spore formation. In contrast to spore-forming bacteria, in which only one spore is formed in one cell, the mold spores serve as reproductive bodies and disseminate the organism. Practically all molds form spores of some kind.

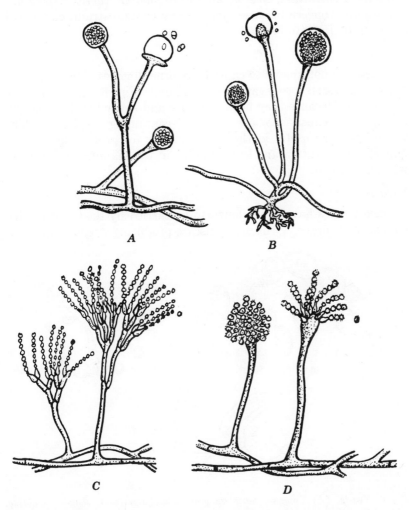

*Fig. 5. The fruiting bodies (structures for formation of asexual reproductive spores) in common molds. (A) Mucor. (B) Rhizopus. (C) Penicillium. (D) Aspergillus.* Reprinted by permission of The Macmillan Company from *Microbiology*, 5th ed. [Burdon and Williams (1964)]. Copyright, The Macmillan Company, 1964.

In general, molds are not choosy regarding the substrate on which they grow, whether it is moist or dry, acid or non-acid, high or low in salt or sugar. Molds may grow over an extremely wide range of temperature. Therefore, one finds molds on practically all foods at almost any temperature under which foods are held.

Among the molds important in food spoilage are species of *Aspergillus, Penicillium, Mucor,* and *Rhizopus.* Of these, *Aspergillus* has aroused concern because some species contain strains capable of releasing toxins into foods.

### YEASTS

Yeasts are not known to cause foodborne illnesses. The yeasts are one-celled bodies propagating by budding (Fig. 6), and are very ubiquitous. Because they need moisture and sugar for their metabolism, they cause spoilage of sugar-containing foodstuffs. The yeasts are very useful in the food industry for processing food requiring fermentation and leavening, as in the manufacture of beer, wine, and bread.

### Viruses

Since viruses have been shown to be carried by food, a brief discussion is in order. Viruses are disease-producing agents and occur

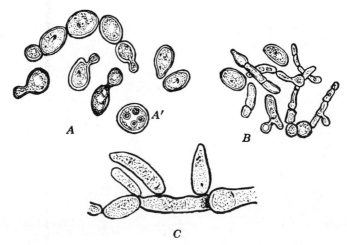

*Fig. 6. Yeasts. (A) Common harmless yeast (Saccharomyces), showing budding. (A') An ascospore, a special reproductive body sometimes formed by true yeasts. (B) Blastomyces, a pathogenic yeast. (C) Candida albicans, a yeastlike fungus causing thrush.* Reprinted by permission of The Macmillan Company from *Microbiology,* 5th ed. [Burdon and Williams (1964)]. Copyright, The Macmillan Company, 1964.

only in living cells. They are of extremely small size and most forms will pass through filters which will retain bacteria. They are very specific in their host relationship, and consist essentially of a few molecules of genetic material. These genetic materials are nucleic acids, which are, in a simple virus, coated with relatively inert protein materials. Viruses are acellular, have no cytoplasm, nucleus, cell wall, or cell membrane. They do not undergo fission. The more complex viruses contain nucleoproteins and other compounds such as carbohydrates, lipids, trace metals, and substances of vitamin-like nature.

An electron microscope* is required to study their structure. It has been found that they are of various shapes and sizes (10–300 m$\mu$) (Fig. 7); some are shaped like cocci or rods, some have peculiar "tails." Some viruses are shown to be of crystalline structure. Examples of human diseases caused by viruses are influenza, measles,

*In an electron microscope, structures of 10 m$\mu$ are visible, whereas with the ordinary light microscope the limit of visibility is approximately 200 m$\mu$.

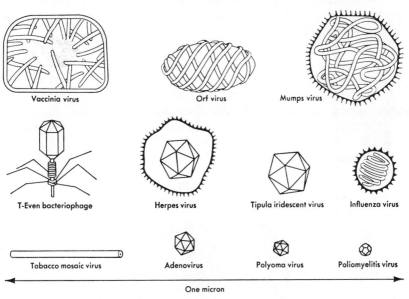

Vaccinia virus      Orf virus      Mumps virus

T-Even bacteriophage      Herpes virus      Tipula iridescent virus      Influenza virus

Tobacco mosaic virus      Adenovirus      Polyoma virus      Poliomyelitis virus

One micron

*Fig. 7. Relative sizes and structure of viruses. Drawings represent the objects magnified 175,000 times. The herpes virus, adenovirus, polyoma and poliomyelitis viruses, and tipula iridescent virus (an insect virus) have a polyhedral structure and possess cubic symmetry. The tobacco mosaic virus and the internal components of the mumps and influenza viruses have helical symmetry. The others have a more complex structural symmetry. From R. W. Horne: The Structure of Viruses. Copyright © 1963 by Scientific American, Inc. All rights reserved.*

mumps, poliomyelitis, chicken pox, yellow fever, the common cold (in part), and hepatitis.

## Rickettsiae

The rickettsiae are rodlike, ovoid, or spherical in shape, and are much smaller than bacteria. Like the viruses they multiply in living tissues only (Fig. 8). They are, in size, intermediate between the large viruses and the bacteria. They range in size $0.5 \times 2 \mu$, at the most, and can be seen with the ordinary microscope. They are believed to multiply by fission, and their mode of nutrition and multiplication is not fully understood. Examples of human diseases caused by rickettsiae are: typus fever, Q fever, and Rocky Mountain spotted fever.

Some members of the rickettsiae have been shown to have a definite metabolic activity. They are susceptible to antibiotics; in this respect they resemble the larger viruses, the small viruses being resistant to antibiotics. Rickettsiae are primarily parasites of insects, and some are pathogenic to their insect hosts. Many of them are pathogenic to man, to whom they are transmitted by the bite of the insects carrying the rickettsiae—the so-called vectors.

## Protozoa

The protozoa need mentioning since certain forms may be carried by food and may cause illness when ingested. Protozoa are one-celled animal-like forms, usually of microscopic size (Fig. 9).

Protozoa are widely distributed in nature, especially in sea water, but also in lakes, ponds, and streams. Soil, especially soil rich in organic matter, contains large numbers of these animals. Nearly

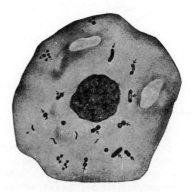

*Fig. 8. Epithelial cell showing rickettsiae in the cytoplasm. Typical rickettsiae are indicated by arrows (about ×3000). By permission from Frobisher (1962).*

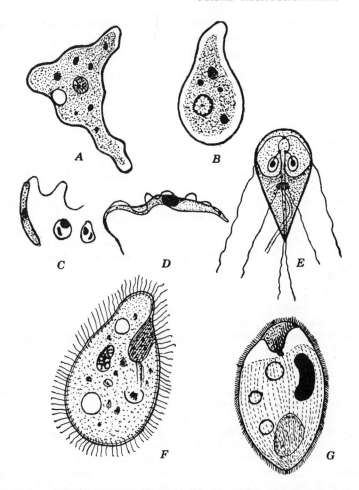

*Fig. 9. Various protozoa. (A) A harmless amoeba. (B) Endamoeba histolytica, the cause of amoebic dysentery. (C) Forms of Leishmania, a kind of protozoan causing sores in the skin. (D) A trypanosome, a flagellated protozoan of the type causing African sleeping sickness. (E) Giardia (lamblia) intestinalis, a common intestinal parasite of man. (F) Colpoda, a harmless ciliated protozoan common in nature. (G) Balantidium coli, a ciliate sometimes found in the intestine of man.* Reprinted by permission of The Macmillan Company from *Microbiology*, 5th ed. [Burdon and Williams (1964)]. Copyright, The Macmillan Company, 1964.

all animals carry protozoa in their intestinal tract, most of them harmless. *Entamoeba histolytica* is a pathogenic form which has been shown to cause amoebiasis or amoebic dysentery and is spread by water and food. Amoebae multiply by fission.

*Giardia lamblia* is an inhabitant of the human intestinal tract; it may possibly cause an enteritis known as giardiasis. The organisms may get into food and water with human feces. This is also true for *Balantidium coli*, another disease-producing protozoan capable of causing intestinal disorders.

## References

American Home Economics Association. (1964). *Handbook of Food Preparation*, revised ed.

American Society for Microbiology. (1957). *Bergey's Manual of Determinative Bacteriology*. 7th ed. Williams and Wilkins Co., Baltimore, Md.

Bigelow, W. D., and P. H. Cathcart. (1941). "Relation of Processing to the Acidity of Canned Foods." *National Canners Assoc. Bulletin 17-L.*

Brown, C. W., and K. Peiser. (1916). "Keeping Qualities of Butter." *Michigan Agricultural Experiment Station Bulletin 30.*

Burdon, K. L., and R. P. Williams. (1964). *Microbiology*. 5th ed. Macmillan Co. New York.

Eddy, B. P. (1960). "The Use and Meaning of the Term 'Psychrophilic'." *Jour. Appl. Bacteriol., 23*: 189–190.

Frazier, William Carroll. (1958). *Food Microbiology*. McGraw-Hill Book Co., New York.

Frobisher, Martin. (1962). *Fundamentals of Microbiology*. 7th ed. W. B. Saunders Co., Philadelphia, London.

Graves, R. P., and W. C. Frazier. (1963). "Food Microorganisms Influencing the Growth of *Staphylococcus aureus*." *Appl. Microbiol., 11*: 513–516.

Grecz, N. (1961). "Natural Antibiotics in Limburger Type Cheese and Its Possible Use in Food Preservation." Activities Report, *Quartermaster Food and Container Institute for the Armed Forces, 13*: 152–159.

Horne, R. W. (1963). "The Structure of Viruses." *Scientific American, 208* (1): 48.

Houwink, A. L., and W. Van Iterson. (1950). "Electron Microscopical Observations on Bacterial Cytology. II. A Study on Flagellation." *Biochimica et Biophysica Acta*, 5: 10–44.

Kraft, Allen A., and J. C. Ayres (1966). "Competitive Growth of Microorganisms and Fluorescence Development on inoculated chicken." *Jour. Food Sci., 31* (1): 111–117.

Mossel, D. A. A., and H. Zwart. (1960). "The Rapid Tentative Recognition of Psychrophilic Types Among Enterobacteriaceae Isolated from Foods." *Jour. Appl. Bacteriol., 23*: 185–188.

National Academy of Sciences, Nat. Research Council (1965). *Radiation Preservation of Foods*. Publ. 1273. Washington, D.C.

Pelczar, M. J., Jr., and R. D. Reid, (1965). *Microbiology*. 2nd ed. McGraw-Hill Book Co., New York.

Peterson, A. C., J. J. Black, and M. F. Gunderson. (1962a). "Staphylococci in Competition. I. Growth of naturally occurring mixed populations in precooked frozen foods during defrost." *Appl. Microbiol., 10*: 16–22.

Peterson, A. C., J. J. Black, and M. F. Gunderson. (1962b). "Staphylococcus in Competition. II. Effects of total numbers and proportion of staphylococci in mixed cultures on growth in artificial culture media." *Appl. Microbiol.*, *10*: 23-30.

Sakaguchi, G., and Y. Tohyama. (1955). "Studies on the Toxin Production of *Clostridium botulinum* Type E. I. A strain of genus *Clostridium* having the action to promote Type E botulinal toxin production in a mixed culture." *Jap. Jour. Med. Sci. and Biol.*, *8*: 247-253.

Sakaguchi, G., and Y. Tohyama. (1955). "Studies on the Toxin Production of *Clostridium botulinum* Type E. II. The mode of action of the contaminant organisms to promote toxin production of Type E organisms." *Jap. Jour. Med. Sci. and Biol.*, *8*: 255-262.

## Additional Readings

Foster, Edwin M. *Dairy Microbiology*. Prentice Hall, Englewood Cliffs, N. J. 1957.

Ingraham, John L. "New Concepts of Psychrophilic Bacteria." Low Temperature Microbiology Symposium, Proceedings, 1961. Campbell Soup Co., Camden, N. J., 1962.

Salle, Anthony J. *Fundamental Principles of Bacteriology*. 5th ed. McGraw-Hill Book Co., New York. 1961.

Sarles, William Bowen, William Carroll Frazier, Joe Bransford Wilson, and Stanley Glenn Knight. *Microbiology*. Harper and Brothers, New York. 1956.

CHAPTER **III**

# FOODBORNE ILLNESSES:

## GROUP I. POISONOUS PLANTS AND ANIMALS

## GROUP II. AGENTS FOR WHICH FOOD SERVES AS A VEHICLE

Essential to successful food protection is a fundamental knowledge of the facts underlying foodborne illnesses, namely, the causative agents and the reasons for their presence and multiplication in the food.

Foodborne illnesses are usually referred to as "food poisoning," a somewhat misleading term, since gastrointestinal upsets following ingestion of food may be due to a variety of causes, some of them being poisons. Because of the overwhelming importance of foodborne illnesses caused by bacteria or their toxins, attention will be concentrated on these, with a brief mention of some of the other causes, and with no discussion of allergies and nutritional deficiencies.

"Ptomaine poisoning" is an outdated term sometimes used to denote foodborne illnesses. In the past it was a common mistake to confuse food poisoning with putrefaction and to assign the term "ptomaine poisoning" to gastrointestinal upsets which were actually caused by a variety of agents. The ptomaine theory of food poisoning is an erroneous one.

Foodborne illnesses may result from consumption of water, milk, other beverages, and solid food items in uncooked or cooked form, provided they contain the disease-producing agent in sufficient quantity. The quantity required to produce illness varies with the susceptibility of the individual and a number of other factors. The causative agents may be: (1) a native part of the offending food,

32

such as poisonous plants and animals; (2) chemicals, which may be purposely added during processing in order to assure keeping quality or to enhance certain quality characteristics, or which may be accidentally added to the food materials at any stage of production, harvesting, transport, processing, storage, preparation, and service; (3) radionuclides, resulting from atomic fission; (4) trichinae; (5) pathogenic microorganisms such as protozoa, viruses, rickettsiae, and bacteria; the latter may or may not profusely multiply in the food and may or may not release exotoxins into the food.

For the sake of simplification of discussion, the causes of gastrointestinal disturbances following the ingestion of food are divided into three groups:

Group I.   Poisonous plants and animals.
Group II.  Agents for which the food is simply a vehicle of transmission.
Group III. Microbial pathogens which multiply profusely in the food causing explosive gastrointestinal upsets. (To be discussed in Chapter IV.)

## AGENTS INVOLVED IN FOODBORNE ILLNESSES

### Group I: Poisonous Plants and Animals

## Plants

Some forms of mushrooms are extremely poisonous. Mushroom poisoning is relatively uncommon in this country, but, for example, *Amanita* species have been mistaken for edible mushrooms. The active principles in poisonous mushrooms are phalloidine and other alkaloids. Potato poisoning from green potatoes has been reported in the literature. The active principle is solanine, a glyco-alkaloid. As reported by Dack (1956) it has been estimated that at least 8 kg (17.6 lb) of potatoes would have to be consumed at one time to cause symptoms of poisoning in man. Rhubarb poisoning has occurred from eating rhubarb leaves, the active principle being oxalic acid. Snakeroot poisoning has resulted from drinking milk drawn from cows which fed on snakeroot; the active principle is trematol. Favism is caused by fava beans (Vicia fava); it is uncommon. Ergot poisoning is produced by the fungus *Claviceps purpurea* which forms its fruit bodies on rye. If these bodies are not removed before the grain is ground, the ergot will poison the flour. Ergot poisoning is now very rare in this country.

Thanks to the high quality food supply in the United States, poisonings from toxic plants are now very rare.

## Animals

### *Poisonous Shellfish*

Paralytic shellfish poisoning may result from eating mussels (Mytilus) and clams (Saxidomus) which have become poisonous by feeding on poisonous food plankton, *Gonyaulax catenella*. The active principle is an alkaloid. Certain areas along the Pacific Coast of the United States and Canada, the Bay of Fundy, and in the Gulf of the St. Lawrence are commercially valuable shellfish areas where this trouble has been important. The toxin is not inactivated by cooking.

### *Poisonous Fish*

Ichthyosarcotoxism may be caused by several kinds of fish. Dack (1956) states that according to an authority on the subject, Halstead, there are six distinctly different clinical entities involved. It has not been established whether the poison is ingested by the fish or manufactured in its metabolism. The following groups of fish are involved: tetraodon, ciguatera, gymnothorax, scombroid, elasmobranch, and fresh water fish; they are all found in warm or tropical climates.

### Group II: Agents for which Food Serves as a Simple Vehicle of Transmission

A variety of agents belong here: chemicals, radionuclides, trichinae, and those pathogenic microorganisms for which the food serves as a vehicle of transmission to man. For the agents included in Group II, food is a mere vehicle for the pathogens, as are hands, money, doorknobs, and the like. The microorganisms included in this group do not profusely multiply in the food. They are usually not associated with the food supply, although exceptions and borderline cases do exist.

### Chemicals

Many chemicals may become a poison when ingested in large amounts. Chemicals which are quite harmless when present in traces have caused severe illness or death when ingested in large amounts.

### *Herbicides, Fungicides, Pesticides, Germicides*

Chemicals such as herbicides, fungicides, pesticides, and germicides when ingested in large amounts, may cause poisoning. However, in the USA spray schedules have been carefully worked out to avoid adherence of deleterious deposits to the crops at the time of harvest. Regulations pertaining to interstate commerce protect the consumer from dangerous levels of spray residues. When locally grown produce is purchased, this safeguard may not be present.

## Additives

Many chemicals are used in processing of foods and are a part of modern food technology. They are referred to as additives. The number of additives is vast and their purposes vary. The reader is referred to Desrosier (1959), Chapter 10.

In this country much concern has focused on the problem of additives as a possible menace to health. The National Academy of Sciences has given the matter much consideration. Internationally, the World Health Organization (WHO) and the Food and Agriculture Organization (FAO) have worked at the problem. A joint committee of these international organizations defined additives as non-nutritive substances added intentionally to food, generally in small quantities, to improve its appearance, flavor, texture, or storage properties. Regarding storage, some of the additives are very effective in perserving the shelf life of some foods. On the other hand, their use may disguise faults of unsanitary processing.

Legal control over the use of additives is extremely important. In the USA the Food and Drug Administration has listed the additives approved by that office and the Meat Inspection Division of the USDA has provided a listing of additives permissible in meat and meat products. The Department of Health, Education, and Welfare establishes tolerances for the residues of toxic pesticides that may safely remain on crops which are marketed in interstate commerce. The same agency establishes safe conditions for use of additives in food processing or handling. It is required that the person who desires to promote a poisonous chemical for use with food that may leave small amounts in the food, must establish the safety of the uses he proposes. At present, no satisfactory protection is afforded to the consumer regarding foods for which no definite standards of identification have been set up by the Food and Drug Administration.

In the United States, chemical preservatives added to food must be listed on the label, even if the amount is quite small.

## Antibiotics

Certain antibiotics have been approved by the Food and Drug Administration for use in the preservation of poultry in specified concentrations. Approved are chlortetracycline (aureomycin) and oxytetracycline (terramycin).

Thatcher (1958) has summarized the use of antibiotics in food materials. He states that antibiotics must be effective under commercial conditions and storage methods, must be stable in foods for certain periods to exercise effective bacteriostasis, must have a "broad-spectrum" antibacterial action, must be nontoxic within limits of safety, must be noncarcinogenic, and must be nonallergenic.

## Metals

Metals may get into food by using utensils, pots, and pans of unsuitable material. For example, cookingware containing cadmium (plated utensils), antimony (grey enamelware), and zinc may render food poisonous. Shelves in refrigerators may contain cadmium. Food such as meats placed directly on such shelves may be rendered poisonous. Tin has been indicted where tinned milk cans were used to store highly acid fruit punch or juices; zinc used in galvanized food containers may render acid foods poisonous, examples being fruit juices and acid salads. The cadmium, tin, and zinc are dissolved through the action of the acid, and containers containing cadmium, tin, and zinc which make contact with food are unsuitable for food preparation. Unfortunately, potentially hazardous containers are sometimes used "in a pinch" when community meals are served.

Copper has caused gastric upsets when it was in contact with acid food and carbonated liquids.

## Miscellaneous Poisonous Chemicals

Miscellaneous poisonous chemicals may get into food "by accident," and some of the descriptions of such poisonings make gruesome reading. Such incidences may be due to actual accidents, but in most instances they are the result of negligence. When rat poison is mixed into breadcrumbs, when sodium fluoride is confused with baking powder and dishwashing compound with paprika, when liquid detergent is taken for cooking oil, something is radically wrong with the housekeeping.

## Radionuclides

Fallout in connection with testing of atomic weapons has caused concern in recent years. Radionuclides are products of atomic fission; some of the important sources of radionuclides in connection with fallout are strontium-89, strontium-90, iodine-131, and cesium-137.

Among foods, milk and plant foods are the most important vehicles of transmission of radionuclides to man.

Eisenbud (1963), in his discussion of the distribution of radio-activity in foods, states that doubtlessly every living cell every-where in the world today contains some of the radioactive substances produced by the tests of nuclear and thermonuclear weapons, but that the radioactivity of nature is probably no less ubiquitous than the radioactivity produced by man. Some radionuclides occur natur-ally. The element delivering the largest share, 20%, is potassium.

Radionuclides originating from fallout may contaminate grass, vegetable crops, and fruits. The mode of contamination from fallout varies. Radionuclides may form deposits on foilage or other plant parts; man or animal becomes contaminated eating these deposits along with the plant parts. Radionuclides may be translocated from foilage to other parts of the plant. Another mode of plant contamina-tion is by way of soil. Radionuclides may contaminate the soil first, then the root system, and eventually the whole plant. Milk becomes contaminated when contaminated vegetation is consumed by cows. Factors affecting the biological availability of radionuclides for plants were discussed by Menzel (1963). The effects of radioactive contamination of the environment on public health are presented by Chadwick (1962).

The symptoms in the person ingesting radionuclides depend on the nature of the source and the tendency of certain radionuclides to concentrate in the tissues of important organs. Symptoms there-fore vary. Also, the age of the person and his resistance to the toxic effect of the radionuclides are said to play a role in the severity of illness resulting from ingesting radionuclides.

Through the past years much progress has been made by the federal government in developing effective radiation surveillance. In this effort, many agencies have participated, including the U.S. Public Health Service and the U.S. Atomic Energy Commission. Protective measures have been discussed by Read (1963). Research is seeking answers to questions on how to minimize the effects of fallout in connection with contamination: means of reducing the uptake of radionuclides from soil, preventing entry of radionuclides to animals, and removal of radionuclides from milk and food.

## Trichinae

*Trichinella spiralis* is the cause of trichinosis, which is a not un-common but preventable disease of public health significance. The trichinae belong to the round worms, *Nematoda*. Trichinosis occurs usually as a sporadic disease, but outbreaks have been reported when many persons were served a disease-producing menu item. The early stages of trichinosis have been confused with food poisoning (Dack, 1956). *Trichinella* is classified among the Helminths, which are parasitic worms of medical significance.

The trichina larvae in the tissues give rise to the pathologic picture. The main source of the parasite is infested pork, other reported sources being bear and rabbit meat. Possibly an early clue to the existence of trichinosis in man and pork is the Mosaic rule against eating pork. Trichinosis has a worldwide distribution, being especially prevalent in countries where pork is eaten in the raw state, and least frequently found where eating of pork is prohibited, as in Jewish and Mohammedan countries.

Trichinosis has been found to have seasonal incidences. In the seasons during which much pork is consumed, more frequent in-incidences occur. In the USA the incidence of trichinosis has been shown to be somewhat variable. In 1930, approximately 1 out of 6 persons (17%) in the USA carried the disease. Since then the incidence per year is declining. It has been shown that the prevalence in pigs is in decline also. In a recent study reported by Moldow (1963), larvae were detected in 5 of 100 human diaphragm specimens (5%).

The parasite takes the following path. The pork harboring the larvae is eaten by man. When eaten, the encysted larvae are released and penetrate the duodenum of the human host. They mature within a few days. The females are fertilized and the males die. The female trichinae then invade the mucosa, where they produce hundreds of embryos and subsequently die. This period of discharging embryos may take 5–6 weeks. The young larvae gain entrance to the bloodstream of the human victim and finally encyst in the victim's muscles. After 4–5 months the capsule which encases the embryo will calcify and the embryo will die.

The onset of symptoms is usually about 2 days after the victim has eaten pork contaminated with the larvae. The symptoms of trichinosis vary with the life history of the parasite and with the number of larvae ingested. Intestinal invasion is usually accompanied by abdominal pain, nausea, vomiting, and diarrhea. At this stage the symptoms may resemble those caused by bacterial "food poisoning." When large numbers of larvae invade the bloodstream, fever may result. There may be other symptoms, such as edema of the eyelids, spastic paralysis of the muscles, and edema of face and hands. Death may occur in very severe infections.

In the past it was a practice to inspect meat for trichinae at the processing plants, but this practice led to false security, since the presence of the parasite is difficult to ascertain. The most promising method is to prevent the meat from becoming infected in the first place. The most successful methods to achieve this goal are to cook all garbage fed to hogs, and to control rats and mice since these may be host to the parasites.

Heating to at least 137°F will kill the larvae. In the Food Service Sanitation Manual (U.S. Public Health Service, 1962) a terminal temperature of 150°F is recommended for cooking pork. At this low terminal temperature the meat is still pink. Unless a thermometer is used and used properly, the endpoint of safety cannot be determined accurately. It is, therefore, a good rule to cook pork to doneness, or a grey color, to provide a margin of safety.

Larvae may be destroyed by freezing also; the larvae will be killed if the meat is freezer-stored at 5°F for 20–30 days.

The former Bureau of Animal Industry (USDA) has worked out a processing method for pork products which, when followed, assures a safe product. This procedure involves treating of the meat with a certain percentage of salt, and holding the salted meat in the drying room under refrigeration for 3 weeks. The length of smoking time and the temperatures applied are specified also. The smoking is to be followed by a certain storage period at specified temperatures.

Treatment of infested meat with gamma rays has been shown to meet with some success in that the larvae were rendered incapable of completing their life cycle.

Government regulations cover the manufacture of frankfurters and other processed pork products to assure their freedom from trichinae.

Recontamination of cooked meat from equipment may occur. Pocock et al. (1963) described an outbreak of trichinosis involving a hospital population in Ohio. The most probable source was a ham salad prepared from ground smoked ham. On the basis of an investigation into the preparation and heating procedures it was concluded that the ham was probably sufficiently heated to kill the trichinae, but that recontamination from raw pork took place when the cooked meat was ground.

The control measures to be applied in the institutional kitchen include the procurement of meat from approved sources, rendering pork safe by adequate cooking, and taking precautions against contamination of cooked meat with trichinae originating from raw pork.

Pathogenic Microorganisms

*Protozoa*

*Entamoeba histolytica* is a member of the protoza which belong to the animal kingdom. This species causes a disease in man which is called amoebiasis or amoebic dysentery.

Contamination of food with this pathogen, although worldwide is more prevalent in high-temperature regions. Amoebic dysentery usually occurs sporadically but has been found to occur in epidemics also. It is, in general, spread by man-to-man contact but may be food- and waterborne.

The symptoms vary from mild to violent diarrhea, alternating with constipation, and abdominal pain is usually present. Occasional fatalities do occur.

The amoebae may infect rats and flies. The organisms get into the soil from human and animal feces. Food becomes contaminated from soil, rats, flies, or unclean hands of infested persons, especially if they do not wash their hands after visiting the toilet. Therefore, food handlers may play an important role in the spread of the amoebae.

Raw foods grown on contaminated soil are an important vehicle of the contaminant. Vegetables should be cooked before they are eaten, and fruits should be thoroughly washed and peeled. Infested persons should not handle food.

Giardiasis and balantidiasis are diseases caused by *Giardia lamblia* and *Balantidium coli*. These protozoa cause enteritis with symptoms of diarrhea and in case of giardiasis presence of mucus in the stool. For giardiasis, infection is most common in children. The source of the pathogens is human feces. Food and water may become contaminated from sewage or from feces adhering to the bodies of insects (flies, cockroaches) and rodents (rats, mice), and to the hands of the food handler.

*Viruses*

Viruses can multiply only in the living cell. Outbreaks of associated virus-produced diseases which have been reported point to food as a vehicle in virus transmission, a role discussed by Berg (1964).

Hepatitis as well as poliomyelitis outbreaks have been linked to food contaminated with the virus. These foods were found to have been handled by carriers, to have had contact with sewage, or to have been otherwise grossly mishandled.

An early record of food-associated hepatitis dates back to 1946 when Read et al. linked infectious hepatitis to food eaten at a certain fraternity house. In 1961, a report was made of an outbreak of hepatitis in the Pascagoula area in Mississippi, which was caused by ingestion of raw oysters contaminated by sewage (Mason and Mc-Lean, 1962). Hepatitis was also linked to clams originating in the Raritan Bay area of New Jersey. The clams had been eaten raw (Morbidity and Mortality, 1961, 1962). Other incidences were reported in Morbidity and Mortality, 1964. Outbreaks of hepatitis have been traced to orange juice and potato salad (Eisenstein, 1963). An outbreak of poliomyelitis has been associated with milk contaminated by a carrier; it has been described by Lipari (1951).

Other viruses which are looked upon as being transmitted by food, are the Coxsackie viruses, groups A and B, ECHO polio viruses, and adenoviruses. They are the causes of a variety of illnesses such as respiratory and diarrheal diseases, summer rash, and poliomyelitis. These viruses when ingested tend to cause infection of the gastrointestinal tract. The virus associated with infectious hepatitis in man is known to be excreted in large amounts with the feces of patients suffering from this disease.

Viruses leaving the body with fecal excretions may get onto the hands of the food handler, who then contaminates the foods he touches. It is assumed that such contamination may be a means of starting a nucleus of infection in a community. After the contaminant has been "seeded," an epidemic may then build up by routes other than food. Food must be regarded as an important link in the transmission of the virus, since the infection of even a few persons may give rise to large-scale epidemics.

Animals may carry viruses also. Cattle, swine, and sheep may be infected with a number of viruses, some of these seemingly specific, others not. Viruses which infect animals may be present in the apparently healthy tissues of meat. We have at present little knowledge about the specificity of the viruses and the ability of viruses of other than human origin to cause infection in man. However, it is a known fact that Newcastle disease, a poultry disease caused by a virus, may be contracted by workers handling poultry through splash, causing infection of the workers' eyes.

Also, outbreaks of ornithosis, or psittacosis, are on record, involving patients employed in poultry plants and handling turkey. Berg (1964) has suggested that food, animals, or plants might be investigated as reservoirs of viruses possibly dangerous to man. Important research is now being conducted on the relationships among human and animal viruses. There is at present a lack of knowledge about the ability of viruses to cross from animal to man.

At the time this is written, exact data as to the heat treatment required to inactivate the viruses in food are not available. According to Dack (1963), McKee found that the viruses he worked with withstood heating at 140°F (60°C) for 2 hours. O'Malley et al. (1961) reported that the A-1 virus studied by them was inactivated by heating at 132°F (56°C) for 30 minutes.

Except for some of the larger and more complex types, viruses have been found so far to resist inactivation by antibiotics. Research data are available which show that viruses could be inactivated by certain disinfectants (Dack, 1963). Since the human carrier and sewage are main sources, the control should be directed toward eliminating these sources.

## Rickettsiae

The rickettsiae may be looked upon as being somewhat akin to the bacteria, but they radically differ from bacteria and resemble viruses in that they need the living cell to reproduce and are truly parasitic in nature. Food is not a vehicle of transmission for the rickettsiae, with the exception of the organism causing Q fever.

## Bacteria: Pathogens for which Food Serves Merely as a Vehicle of Transmission

Pathogens causing communicable diseases may be transmitted through food just as they are through other vehicles on or in which bacteria may land. The pathogens are passed on from person to person via food, money, hands, etc. These agents may stem from humans, either acute cases or carriers, or from animals.

It is difficult to arrive at a hard-and-fast rule as to which pathogens transmitted by food should be included in this category or in the category of organisms causing acute gastroenteric outbreaks. The latter category includes the organisms which multiply profusely in the food and cause illnesses of an explosive nature. Infectious diseases and epidemics, however, are characterized as illnesses developing over a period of several days, and contact with relatively small numbers of bacteria brings on the illness.

Examples of pathogens which may be foodborne and belong in the category of pathogens for which food serves merely as a vehicle of transmission are those causing tuberculosis, undulant fever, scarlet fever, septic sore throat, diphtheria, and cholera. Of the pathogens causing these diseases, some are capable of developing powerful exotoxins, the most important being *Streptococcus pyogenes, Coryne-*

*bacterium diphtheriae,* and *Shigella dysenteriae.* These organisms may be sustained in the food which serves as their vehicle in the spread of communicable diseases. They are specific pathogens one would not find in a healthy person, except for the chronic carriers. A carrier is a person who, without apparent symptoms of a communicable disease, harbors and disseminates the specific organisms.

Since some of these pathogens may multiply profusely in milk, the basis for grouping them here may be questioned. However, for all practical purposes, milk nowadays is a food somewhat set apart from other foods because in the USA it is presently marketed under highly controlled regulations of sanitation. Pasteurization temperatures and times are regulated to free milk of the important human pathogens that in the distant past were frequently transmitted through milk.

Examples of borderline cases with respect to grouping into the two categories are the pathogens causing bacillary dysentery, typhoid fever, and paratyphoid fever.

Dack (1956), an authority on "food poisoning," has set the gastrointestinal disturbances caused by these organisms apart from other "food poisoning" forms, as "food poisoning" organisms were classified as those causing illnesses of an explosive nature. However, typhoid and paratyphoid fevers are illnesses that develop over a period of several days, the pathogens are highly infective since a small number of cells may cause the disease in the person who ingests them, and the exclusive host is man.

Since the pathogens causing typhoid and paratyphoid fevers and bacillary dysentery would not be found in a healthy person nor commonly in the food supply delivered to the kitchen, these organisms are included in Group II.

The foods involved in the transmission of pathogens may be many. For animals as well as man, foodstuffs of animal origin are the usual vehicle. In the case of human pathogens, the organisms get into the food when it is handled by a person suffering from the disease producing the pathogen. The pathogens may also be transmitted through sewage and sewage-polluted water. Streams, lakes, and ocean waters that have become polluted with raw sewage in turn contaminate fish and seafood living therein. Sewage may directly contaminate food through faulty plumbing.

PATHOGENS OF ANIMAL AND HUMAN ORIGIN

*Mycobacterium tuberculosis,* especially the bovine type, has caused tuberculosis primarily in children. It is no longer a major problem because of vigilance in detecting and eliminating infected cows, and because of heat treatment during pasteurization of milk and cream. However, the human pathogen may be transmitted by a food handler suffering from tuberculosis.

*Brucella abortus, B. melitensis,* and *B. suis* cause brucellosis, or undulant fever, in man. The organisms stem from cattle, goats, and hogs, respectively. These organisms are killed by proper pasteurization of milk and cream. The organisms have been shown to remain viable in cream stored at 50°F for several days. Control over the disposal of infected milk animals seems the most fundamental measure for eradication of brucellosis from animals and humans.

### PATHOGENS OF HUMAN ORIGIN

For the sake of simplification, the pathogens of human communicable disease are discussed as three groups based on the site of infection: pathogens of the skin; pathogens of the mouth, nasal passages, throat, ear, and chest; and intestinal pathogens.

*Skin.* A discussion of the many diseases of the skin is beyond the scope of this book. Any of the pathogens causing skin diseases may be transmitted through food which serves as a simple vehicle of transmission.

Hemolytic streptococci of Group A which cause erysipelas are worth mentioning because the disease is not uncommon and is very contagious. The organism causes an inflammation of the superficial lymphatic vessels of skin or mucous membranes. Discharges from these lesions carry large loads of the streptococci. Other diseases of the skin include leprosy, lupus, and syphilis.

*Staphylococcus aureus* causes furuncles and carbuncles of the skin and is also associated with acne and common pimples. This organism is not only transmitted through food, it also has the ability to multiply freely in the food. Unfortunately, certain strains release a toxin into the food that is capable of causing gastroenteric outbreaks or true food poisoning. Therefore, the organism will be further discussed later on.

*Mouth, Nose, Throat.* From the mouth, nose, and throat a great number of pathogens may be transmitted through food. The food handler's saliva and discharges are the source of the pathogens.

Hemolytic streptococci, Group A, cause sore throat, or pharyngitis, tonsillitis, scarlet fever, and other ailments of the throat. They also cause ear infections. Another important bacterial infection of the mouth and throat is Vincent's angina, caused by two kinds of organisms, *Fusobacterium fusiforme* and *spirochetes,* which may be transmitted through food.

Pathogens associated with colds, sinusitis, and influenza, although usually transferred directly from one person to another, may be transmitted through food also. Among these pathogens may be viruses and *Staphylococcus aureus.*

*Corynebacterium diphtheriae* is the pathogen causing diphtheria, and it may be transmitted through food. Diphtheria was once among the most feared of all communicable diseases. Its pathogen causes severe inflammation of the throat and other portions of the upper respiratory tract. Other vital organs, the heart and the kidneys in particular, are poisoned by a very powerful toxin secreted by the bacterial cells.

Pathogens associated with bronchial and lung diseases may also be transferred through food. The principle specific diseases of the lungs are tuberculosis, mentioned earlier, and pneumonia caused by *Diplococcus pneumoniae.* Some other organisms involved in pneumonia are *S. aureus, Klebsiella pneumoniae, Streptococcus pyogenes* and viruses.

**Intestinal Tract.** Pathogens of intestinal origin have a good chance to contaminate food when it is touched by contaminated hands. A food handler may transmit these pathogens to ingredients and menu items when he does not wash his hands properly after visiting the toilet. Important bacterial pathogens of the intestinal tract are those causing cholera, bacillary dysentery, and typhoid and paratyphoid fevers.

*Vibrio comma,* the causative organism of cholera, infects the human intestinal tract. Cholera is a disease characterized by vomiting, diarrhea, and severe prostration. Patients often die from severe dehydration. Since about 1875 cholera epidemics have no longer been a menace in the United States, but they continue to flourish in the warmer countries of Asia.

The shigellae are frequently transmitted by food. Bacillary dysentery, or shigellosis, may be caused by several species: *Shigella dysenteriae, sonnei,* and *flexneri.* The disease is an acute infection of the intestines, causing diarrhea and bloody stool containing mucus. The period of incubation is commonly less than 4 days, but may be as long as 7 days. Fever and cramps are often present. The organisms are transmitted in the same manner as *Salmonella typhosa.* Of the three shigellae species, *S. dysenteriae* is the only one capable of producing exotoxins.

Transmission is commonly through food and water which have become contaminated with feces, and the food handler may play an important role in the transmission. Any item which has been contaminated by him and is brought in contact with food may serve to transmit the pathogen.

Among the salmonellae is the powerful intestinal pathogen of man, *Salmonella typhosa*, the cause of typhoid fever. This disease presents an interesting chapter in the history of public health in the USA. Before 1900, typhoid fever was one of the principle causes of severe illness and death. At present, it has an insignificant place in mortality statistics of this country. In cities where the water supply is under strict sanitary control, few cases of this disease occur; however, in rural regions, it does occur in isolated cases, mostly as epidemics limited to a family.

The source of infection is the infected human. The pathogen causes an infection of the intestinal tract, especially in the lower ileum. Continued fever is an important symptom, also headache, abdominal pain, and anorexia. The bacteria invade the lymph nodes, then the bloodstream, and eventually various organs and tissues such as the kidneys, liver, bone marrow, and spleen.

The incubation period is from 1 to 3 weeks. The recovered patient may become a carrier and remain a carrier for many months.

Paratyphoid fever is caused by *Salmonella* A, B, and C. These strains are also referred to as *S. paratyphi, S. schottmuelleri,* and *S. hirshfeldii*. The disease is extremely similar to typhoid fever but the symptoms are milder.

To prevent transmission of pathogens the sanitation of food and drink, and sanitary sewage disposal are important. Patients suffering from communicable diseases or carriers should not handle food to be served to others. It is important to ascertain that a person who is employed in food service is not a carrier. It is important to remember that convalescent patients of certain diseases may remain carriers for long periods of time.

### References

Berg, G. (1964). "The Food Vehicle in Virus Transmission." *Health Lab. Sci., 1*: 51–59.

Chadwick, Donald R. (1962). "Effects of Radioactive Contamination of the Environment on Public Health." *Jour. Dairy Sci., 45*(12): 1552–1557.

Dack, G. M. (1956). *Food Poisoning*. 3rd ed. Univ. of Chicago Press, Chicago, Ill.

Dack, G. M., (1963). "Problems in Food Diseases." *In*: Slanetz et al. *Microbiological Quality of Foods*. Proceedings of a Conference held at Franconia, New Hampshire, August, 1962. Pages 41–49.

Derosier, N. W. (1959). *Technology of Food Preservation*. Avi Publishing Co., Westport, Conn.

Eisenbud, Merrill. (1963). "Distribution of Radioactivity in Foods." *Federation Proceedings, 22*(6); 1410–1414.

Eisenstein, A. B., R. D. Aach, W. Jacobsohn, and A. Goldman. (1963). "An Epidemic of Infectious Hepatitis in a General Hospital." *Jour. Amer. Med. Assoc., 185*(3): 171–174.

Lipari, M. (1951). "A Milkborne Poliomyelitis Episode." *New York State Jour. Med., 51*(3): 362.

Mason, J. C., and W. R. McLean. (1962). "Infectious Hepatitis Traced to the Consumption of Raw Oysters." *Amer. Jour. Hyg., 75*: 90–111.

Menzel, Ronald C. (1963). "Factors Influencing the Biological Availability of Radionuclides for Plants." *Federation Proceedings, 22*(6): 1398–1401.

Moldow, Raymond E. (1963). "Incidences of Trichinosis." *Jour. Amer. Med. Assoc., 185*: 146–147.

Morbidity and Mortality Weekly Reports, U.S. Department of Health, Education and Welfare; *Public Health Service, 10*(6), Feb. 17, 1961; *10*(17), May 5, 1961; and *11*(23), June 15, 1962.

Morbidity and Mortality Weekly Reports, U.S. Department of Health, Education and Welfare; *Public Health Service, 13*(7), Feb., 1964.

O'Malley, J. P., H. M. Meyer, Jr., and J. E. Smadel, (1961). "Antibody in Hepatitis Patients Against a Newly Isolated Virus." *Proc. Soc. Exp. Biol. Med., 108*: 200–205.

Pocock, D. G., P. R. Schnurrenberger, A. D. Ziegler, F. H. Wentworth, and J. Basche, Jr. (1963). "Trichinosis. A Point Source Outbreak." *Annuals Internat. Med., 59*(3): 323–331.

Read, M. R., H. Bancroft, J. A. Doull, and R. F. Parker. (1946). "Infectious Hepatitis—Presumedly Foodborne Outbreak." *Amer. Jour. Publ. Hlth., 36*(4): 367–370.

Read, Meril S. (1963). "Countermeasures Against Radionuclides in Foods." *Federation Proceedings, 22*(6): 1418–1423.

Thatcher, F. S. (1958). "Antibiotics in Foods—A Review of Some Public Health Aspects." *Canad. Jour. Publ. Hlth., 49*: 58–72.

U.S. Department of Health, Education and Welfare, Public Health Service, "Food Service Sanitation Manual." PHS Pub. No. 934, Washington, D.C. 1962.

## Additional Readings

Ayres, J. C., A. A. Kraft, H. E. Snyder, and H. W. Walker. "Chemical and Biological Hazards in Food." *Canad. Jour. Publ. Hlth., 54*: 237. 1963.

Bartsch, A. F., and E. F. McFarren. "Fish Poisoning: a problem in the food toxication." *Pacific Sci., 16*: 42–56. 1962.

Buchbinder, L. "Current Status of Food Poisoning Control." *U.S. Publ. Hlth. Repts., 76*: 515–520. 1961.

Buck, Robert W. "Mushroom Poisoning Since 1924 in the United States." *Mycologia, 53*(5): 537-538. 1961.

Burdon, Kenneth L., and Robert P. Williams. *Microbiology.* 5th ed. Macmillan Co., New York. 1964.

Cheng, T. C. "Parasitological Problems Associated with Food Protection." *Envir. Hlth., 28*(3): 208–214. 1965.

Dack, G. M. "Current Status of Therapy in Microbial Food Poisoning." *Jour. Amer. Med. Assoc., 172*(9): 929–932. 1960.

Dauer, Carl C. "Summary of Disease Outbreaks and a 10-year resume." *U.S. Publ. Hlth. Repts., 76*(10):  915–922. 1961.

Dewberry, Elliot B. *Food Poisoning, Foodborne Infection and Intoxication;* nature, history and causation, measures for prevention and control. 4th ed. Hill, London, 1959.

Edwards, H. I. "The Etiology and Epidemiology of Paralytic Shellfish Poisoning." *Jour. Milk and Food Tech., 19:* 331–335. 1956.

Eichenwald, Heinz F. "Viral Hepatitis, Clinical, Laboratory and Public Health Aspects." *U.S. Publ. Hlth. Service,* Publication No. 435. 1955.

Esselen, William B., and Arthur S. Levine. "Bacterial Food Poisoning and Its Control." A Review. University of Massachusetts, College of Agriculture Bulletin 493. 1957.

Frazier, William C. *Food Microbiology.* McGraw-Hill Book Co., New York. 1958.

Galton, Mildred M., and James H. Steele. "Laboratory and Epidemiological Aspects of Foodborne Diseases." *Jour. Milk & Food Tech., 24*(4): 104–114. 1961.

Gould, Sylvester E. *Trichinosis. 1st ed.* Charles C. Thomas, Springfield, Ill. 1945.

International Association of Milk and Food Sanitarians. Committee on Communicable Diseases Affecting Man. Procedure for the Investigation of Foodborne Disease Outbreaks. Shelbyville, Indiana. 1957.

Jensen, E. T. (1963). "Shellfish Sanitation." *Association of Food and Drug Officials of the U.S., 27*(3): 106–114.

Jensen, L. B. *Microbiology of Meats.* 3rd ed. The Garrard Press, Champaign, Ill. 1954.

Joseph, J. M. (1965). "Virus Diseases Transmitted Through Food." *Association Food and Drug Officials of the U.S., 29*(1): 10–15.

Lang, E. P. (1963). "What You Should Know About FDA's Radioactivity Program." *Food Engin., 35:* 42–45.

McCrea, J. F. "Literature Survey of Viruses and Rickettsiae in Foods." *U.S. Govt. Res. Repts., 38,* No. 11 S-16. 1963.

Prakash, A. "Sources of Paralytic Shellfish Toxin in the Bay of Fundy." *Jour. Fisheries Res. Board of Canad., 20*(4): 983–996. 1963.

Rivers, T. N. *Viral and Rickettsia Infections in Man.* 3rd ed. Lippincott, Philadelphia. 1959.

Slanetz, L. W. (ed.), C. O. Chichester, A. R. Ganfin, and Z. J. Ordal. *Microbiological Quality of Foods.* Proceedings of a Conference held at Franconia, New Hampshire, August, 1962. Academic Press, New York. 1963.

Tanner, F. W., and L. P. Tanner. *Foodborne Infections and Intoxications. 2nd ed.* The Garrard Press, Champaign, Ill. 1953.

U.S. Department of Health, Education and Welfare, Public Service. "Radioactive Contamination of the Environment: Public Health Action." Prepared by the National Advisory Committee on Radiation. May 1962.

U.S. Public Health Service. "Conference on Viruses and Rickettsiae in Foods." Division of Environmental Engineering and Food Protection, Public Health Service, Washington, D.C. January, 1963.

Wilson, E., M. J. Foter, and K. H. Lewis. "Public Health Aspects of Food Poisoning." *Jour. Milk & Food Tech.*, *20:* 65–71. 1957.

CHAPTER **IV**

# FOODBORNE ILLNESSES:

## GROUP III. PATHOGENS MULTIPLYING PROFUSELY IN FOODS AND CAPABLE OF CAUSING OUTBREAKS OF ACUTE GASTROENTERITIS

Outbreaks of acute gastroenteritis caused by microbial pathogens which multiply profusely in the food are popularly called "food poisoning" outbreaks. These outbreaks are either foodborne intoxications or foodborne infections. The symptoms are violent reactions and include nausea, vomiting, diarrhea, and intestinal cramps.

Using a scientific terminology, the term "food poisoning" should be restricted to incidences in which a poison or toxin causes the illness. Foodborne poisonings or intoxications are, in general, of a more explosive nature than foodborne infections. The time elapsing between partaking of the toxin-containing food and the appearance of the first symptoms may be as short as a couple of hours. In the infectious type of foodborne illness, the symptoms are caused by the activity, within the gastrointestinal system of the victim, of large numbers of bacterial cells, and the incubation time of the infection is longer than that of the intoxication.

Both types of the illnesses under discussion are more explosive in nature than illnesses in which food plays merely the role of a transmitting vector. An exception is botulism, a foodborne intoxication with a long incubation period.

Paramount to effectual sanitary control of menu items prepared in quantity is an understanding of the reservoirs of these potentially dangerous organisms, the conditions favoring contamination of food

50

in the areas where menu items are prepared and served, and the factors allowing for profuse multiplication of the contaminants during preparation and storage of menu items under conditions of quantity food service.

## Incidence of Outbreaks

### Relative Importance of Causative Agents

Important pathogens responsible for foodborne intoxications are *Clostridium botulinum*, a spore former, and *Staphylococcus aureus*. Pathogens frequently responsible for foodborne infections include certain salmonellae and fecal streptococci. Among pathogens of somewhat uncertain etiology is *Clostridium perfringens (welchii)*, which seems to be gaining importance as an agent capable of causing foodborne acute gastroenteritis. Other miscellaneous organisms are under suspicion, among these *Bacillus cereus*, species of the genus *Proteus*, and *Escherichia coli*. Certain halophilic bacteria have been indicted in Japan. Recently, *Aspergillus flavus* strains have been shown to be capable of releasing powerful toxins into food on which these strains grow.

The cause of many outbreaks is unknown. The data in Table 5 (1963) indicate that illnesses of unknown etiology are more frequent than the causes ascribed to staphylococci and salmonellae, which are the agents most frequently identified.

According to Dauer (1961), the fact that the number of *Staphylococcus* incidents suddenly decreased in 1957 while the number of outbreaks of unknown etiology increased is due to the fact that beginning in 1957 only cases confirmed by laboratory examinations were included in the group "Staphylococcus food poisoning."

### Reports from States

Dauer's (1961) data for a 10-year period show that in some states incidences were much higher than in others and that the average number of outbreaks per million of population varied widely. This, of course, does not necessarily indicate that in the states reporting the higher figures the sanitary conditions of food service were lower. It may well mean that in these states reporting was better because of an interest in sanitation.

Approximately 10,000 cases are reported annually in the United States, but there is reason to believe that the actual figures are several times as high. Reporting is compulsory in relatively few states; other circumstances contribute toward the uncertainty re-

Table 5. Foodborne Illnesses Reported in the U.S. from 1957 to 1962[a]

| Food | Botulism | | Staphylococcus | | Salmonella | | Clostridium perfringens | | Trichinosis | | Chemical | | Other | |
|---|---|---|---|---|---|---|---|---|---|---|---|---|---|---|
| | O.[b] | Cases | O. | Cases | O. | Cases | O. | Cases | O. | Cases | O. | Cases | O. | Cases |
| Meat | 1 | 1 | 61 | 2386 | 8 | 1534 | 1 | 21 | 13 | 149 | 4 | 30 | 51 | 1628 |
| Eggs | — | — | 3 | 58 | 3 | 127 | — | — | — | — | — | — | 2 | 140 |
| Poultry | 2 | 3 | 28 | 1563 | 16 | 1633 | 2 | 13 | — | — | 3 | 15 | 39 | 2383 |
| Fish | 5 | 9 | 4 | 91 | 3 | 113 | — | — | — | — | 1 | 1 | 11 | 158 |
| Dairy products | — | — | 18 | 799 | 9 | 122 | — | — | — | — | — | — | 5 | 249 |
| Bakery items | — | — | 34 | 293 | 6 | 328 | — | — | — | — | — | — | 14 | 153 |
| Miscellaneous | 21 | 46 | 58 | 2678 | 24 | 791 | 6 | 266 | — | — | 14 | 245 | 119 | 3675 |
| Total | 29 | 59 | 206 | 7868 | 69 | 4648 | 9 | 300 | 13 | 149 | 22 | 291 | 241 | 8386 |

[a] Morbidity and Mortality Weekly Reports, Public Health Service, U.S. Department of Health, Education and Welfare.
[b] Outbreaks

garding incidence. For example, many family incidents go by without being reported to the health authorities, probably because the individual outbreak is restricted to one family at a time and lacks the dramatic impact of an outbreak at a public gathering where hundreds of people might be involved. Even outbreaks which take place in food service establishments remain largely unreported because of "poor publicity" for the organization, loss of customers and profit, and fear of possible legal involvements.

Difficulties in identification of the causative agent are manifold. They include delayed reporting, inability to secure samples of the suspected menu items, inadequate history of the incident, inadequate facilities for laboratory studies, and poor cooperation of food service personnel.

The U. S. Public Health Service is well aware of the inadequacies of assessing the incidence of the hazards caused by incomplete reporting, incomplete diagnosis, and lack of uniformity in state regulations and works at improving this situation.

Reliable data on gastroenteric episodes are important because they form a basis for successful measures to protect the consumer. It is the duty of the food manager to do his share by reporting foodborne gastroenteric episodes to the appropriate health authorities.

In the early twenties, the Public Health Service began to prepare annual summaries of milkborne episodes reported by the states. In 1938, reports of waterborne and foodborne illnesses were added. Accounts of water-, milk-, and foodborne outbreaks have appeared weekly, beginning in 1951, in "Morbidity and Mortality Weekly Reports." These Reports are now published by the Communicable Disease Center in Atlanta, Georgia.

*Foods Involved*

The data in Table 6 show that the number of outbreaks caused by foods other than milk is greater than the number caused by milk or water. This fact has a bearing on the importance of high sanitary standards when handling food and prepared menu items. There is much room for improvement.

Foodborne illnesses reported in the United States from 1957 to 1962 are combined in Table 5. Meats and poultry are very frequently implicated, but the largest number of incidences is reported for the group of miscellaneous foods.

It has been shown that circumstances often associated with outbreaks of foodborne illnesses are: employees suffering from intestinal upsets, colds, sinusitis, acne, sores, infectious burns, and boils;

Table 6. Waterborne, Milkborne, and Foodborne Disease Outbreaks and Cases
Reported in 1958–1960 [Adapted from Dauer (1961)]

| Year | Source | | | | | |
|------|--------|--|--|--|--|--|
| | Water | | Milk | | Other foods | |
| | Outbreaks | Cases | Outbreaks | Cases | Outbreaks | Cases |
| 1958 | 4 | 445 | 13 | 441 | 239 | 9,925 |
| 1959 | 7 | 206 | 11 | 49 | 322 | 10,595 |
| 1960 | 11 | 1,784 | 5 | 48 | 182 | 7,434 |
| Average | — | 812 | — | 179 | — | 9,318 |

apparently healthy employees who have been recently ill with
intestinal upsets; employees having unsanitary personal habits;
obtaining food from unsafe sources; prolonged holding of cooked
food in warm places; inadequate refrigeration; insufficient heating;
unclean food preparation equipment; presence of flies, cockroaches,
rodents.

*Food Services Involved*

Incidences have been reported from many types of food service
establishments, such as restaurants, hospitals, schools, colleges, and
camps, and from family gatherings, public transportation, and
private clubs, and of course, private homes (Table 7).

Many of the outbreaks of foodborne illness have been traced to
meals served at social gatherings such as picnics, banquets, church
socials, and other community meals. In many instances the occasions
involved food which was prepared and served without the benefit
of adequate facilities for keeping the menu items either hot enough or
cold enough to discourage bacterial multiplication.

## Bacteria Causing Foodborne Intoxications

The two important pathogens causing foodborne intoxications
are *Clostridium botulinum* and *Staphylococcus aureus*.

*Clostridium botulinum*

ORGANISM

The food poisoning referred to as botulism is caused by *Clostridium
botulinum*. Botulism is a disease of humans and animals. An excellent
treatise on botulism has been published, as the Proceedings of a

Table 7. Outbreaks of Certain Foodborne Diseases Reported in 1960, by Type and Source of Food[a] [Adapted from Dauer (1961)]

| Source | Salmonellosis | | Shigellosis | | Staphylococcal food poisoning | | Other[b] | | Gastroenteritis, etiology unknown | |
|---|---|---|---|---|---|---|---|---|---|---|
| | Outbreaks | Cases | Outbreaks | Cases | Outbreaks | Cases | Outbreaks | Cases | Outbreaks | Cases |
| Public eating establishments | 6 | 84 | — | — | 9 | 95 | 1 | 17 | 29 | 791 |
| Private clubs | 1 | 6 | — | — | 1 | 18 | 1 | 100 | 5 | 308 |
| Schools | — | — | 1 | 570 | 4 | 689 | — | — | 3 | 92 |
| Colleges | — | — | 1 | 52 | 1 | 40 | — | — | 1 | 12 |
| Hospitals and institutions | — | — | — | — | 4 | 272 | — | — | 6 | 208 |
| Labor camps | — | — | — | — | — | — | — | — | 3 | 178 |
| Social gatherings | 4 | 320 | — | — | 10 | 695 | 1 | 47 | 13 | 639 |
| Private homes | 4 | 56 | 1 | 19 | 15 | 92 | — | — | 19 | 83 |
| Transportation | — | — | — | — | — | — | — | — | 2 | 32 |
| Picnics | — | — | — | — | 1 | 22 | 2 | 42 | 1 | 164 |
| Other | 1 | 153 | 1 | 105 | 6 | 140 | 1 | 954 | 2 | 129 |
| Not stated | — | — | 1 | 65 | — | — | — | — | — | — |
| Total | 16 | 619 | 5 | 811 | 51 | 2,063 | 6 | 1,160 | 84 | 2,636 |

[a] Milkborne and waterborne outbreaks not included.
[b] Includes two outbreaks each due to Clostridium perfringens infections and paracolon organisms, and one each of Bacillus cereus infection and alpha streptococcal infection.

Symposium, by the U.S. Department of Health, Education and Welfare (1964). A brief summary article was published by Foster et al. (1965). The organism is an anaerobic, gram-positive gas-producing spore former which is able to grow over a wide range of pH and temperatures, and tolerates high salt concentrations.

*C. botulinum* is capable of producing a powerful toxin, a protein. Six types are distinguishable on the basis of the serological specificity of the toxins. Five of the types are now known in a more or less purified form; these are Types A, B, C, D, and E. Type F has not yet been purified. The toxins are exotoxins in the sense that they are released into the medium or food after the death, or lysis, of the cell. The physical and chemical properties of Type A are known best, because extensive studies have been made of this particular toxin. The main features of the different types are shown in Table 8. *C. botulinum* is antigenic, causing the production of antitoxins specific for the type of toxin. The toxins are the active agents causing the food poisoning. They are the most potent toxins known, and may persist in food for long periods of time, especially under low-temperature storage. Spores or vegetative cells will not cause ill effects in the human being when ingested.

DISTRIBUTION AND SOURCE

*Clostridium botulinum* exists as saprophytes in soil, the sediment of lakes and oceans, and the intestinal tract of man and animals. Human botulism is most often caused by Types A, B, and E; animal botulism by Types C and D. Type F is very rare.

Type A, an inhabitant of soil, is most common in the western part of the United States, while Type B, also found in soil, seems to have a wider geographic distribution; both types are proteolytic. Type C causes botulism in fowl, cattle, and some other animals, but is not toxic to man. Type D, not toxic to humans, has caused botulism in cattle in South Africa and possibly in other animals in other parts of the world. These types (C and D) have caused severe losses in domestic and wild animals. Type E is known to cause botulism in man, and has also affected some animals. It is now generally agreed that Type E is of terrestrial, rather than marine, origin (Foster et al., 1965). One episode caused by Type F has been reported from Denmark. In the United States, Type F has been demonstrated in two samples of marine sediment, one off the coast of California and the other off the coast of Oregon (Eklund and Poysky, 1965).

Types A and B have been known for decades to cause food poisoning, and these toxins have been found to be associated with meats

Table 8. Main Feature of the Different Types of *C. Botulinum* [Adapted from Dolman (1964)]

| Type | Differentiated by | Year | Species mainly affected | Most common vehicles | Highest geographic incidence |
|---|---|---|---|---|---|
| A | Leuchs Burke | 1910 1919 | Man; chickens ("limber-neck") | Home-canned vegetables and fruits, meat and fish | Western United States, Soviet Ukraine |
| B | Leuchs Burke | 1910 1919 | Man, horses, cattle | Prepared meats, especially pork products | France, Norway, Eastern United States |
| $C^\alpha$ | Bengston | 1922 | Aquatic wild birds ("western duck sickness") | Fly larvae (*Lucilia caesar*); rotting vegetation of alkaline ponds | Western United States and Canada, South America, South Africa, Australia |
| $C^\beta$ | Seddon | 1922 | Cattle ("Midland cattle disease"), horses ("forage poisoning"), mink | Toxic forage, carrion, pork liver | Australia, South Africa, Europe, North America |
| D | Theiler and Robinson Meyer and Gunnison | 1927 1929 | Cattle ("lamziekte") | Carrion | South Africa, Australia |
| E | Gunnison, Cummings, and Meyer Kushnir | 1936 1937 | Man | Uncooked products of fish and marine mammals | Northern Japan, British Columbia, Labrador, Alaska, Great Lakes region, Sweden, Denmark, USSR |
| F | Moeller and Scheibel Dolman and Murakami | 1960 1961 | Man | Home-made liver paste | Denmark |

and vegetables. Type E has become the major cause of botulism from commercially prepared foods in recent years. It has been known to be a serious contaminant of fish consumed by Eskimos.

## SYMPTOMS

*Clostridium botulinum* affects the nervous system; the symptoms appear from 2 hours up to 8 days, usually in 3–6 days, following the ingestion of the contaminated food. Among them are: dry mouth, difficulties in swallowing and speech, double vision, and difficulty in breathing. The cause of death is a paralysis of the muscles of respiration. Botulism has a high death rate in the United States, in that approximately 65 per cent of afflicted persons die. This high death rate is probably the reason botulism is much feared in spite of the fact that it occurs rarely in this day and age. Complete recovery of the nonfatal cases is very slow and may extend over several months.

The illness is treated by administering an antitoxin specific for the particular type of toxin involved. Despite the availability of antitoxins, botulism therapy is still not satisfactory due to the lag times between the ingestion of the food, the appearance of symptoms, the diagnosis, and the procurement of the specific antitoxin. The general availability of the specific antitoxins is limited. Most hospitals do not stock the antitoxins because of the rarity of botulism incidences.

## INCIDENCE

Before 1925, commercially canned foods in the United States were implicated in 32 cases. Since 1925, the implicated foods have been shown to be home-canned items; commercially canned foods have an excellent record of safety, thanks to research efforts which resulted in safe processing practices adopted by the canning industry. Therefore, it was a shock when in the early 1960's some outbreaks occurred in the United States and were traced to commercially processed foods. These were canned tuna and vacuum-packed smoked fresh water fish (whitefish, chubs, ciscoes), the latter originating from the Great Lakes.

The incidence of botulism in the United States was low from 1938 to 1953 inclusive, an average of less than 7 outbreaks per year being reported. For the period from 1952 to 1960 inclusive, a total of 56 outbreaks were reported. Botulism incidents reported in the United States from 1899 to 1963 are shown in Figure 10. The geographic distribution of verified Type E outbreaks is presented in Table 9.

**Table 9. Geographic Distribution of Verified Type E Botulism Outbreaks[a]**
[Adapted from Dolman (1964)]

| Place | Outbreaks | Cases | Deaths |
|---|---|---|---|
| Japan: Hokkaido | 27 | 218 | 42 |
| Northern Honshu | 19 | 79 | 36 |
| USA: Alaska | 7 | 19 | 6 |
| Other states | 8 | 37 | 15 |
| Canada: British Columbia | 9 | 22 | 12 |
| Labrador | 3 | 10 | 8 |
| USSR | 4 | 5 | 4 |
| Denmark | 3 | 8 | 1 |
| Sweden | 3 | 5 | 1 |
| Norway | 1 | 4 | 1 |
| Totals | 84 | 408 | 126 |

[a] Overall cases fatality rate, 31 per cent.

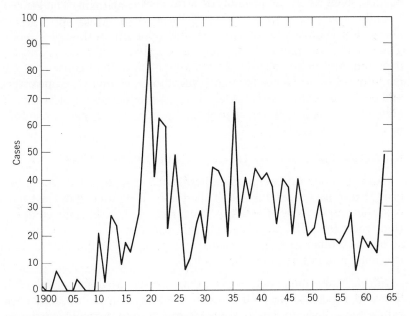

*Fig. 10. Botulism cases in the United States, 1899–1963.* Data from Morbidity and Mortality (1964).

Inadequately processed, usually home-canned, foods such as meats and many kinds of vegetables, especially green beans, sweet corn, beets, asparagus, and spinach, have been frequently associated with outbreaks; tomatoes and fruits have been indicted also.

Since in quantity food service commercially processed foods are usually used, a complete listing of botulism outbreaks in the United States associated with commercial foods is presented in Table 10.

Smoked products, among them smoked fish, sausage, and other products made from meat, have caused botulism when inadequately processed.

Frozen foods have not been indicted in botulism. However, it is known that the spores of *Clostridium botulinum* may survive long storage periods in raw and precooked frozen foods and that during warm holding, after thawing, the spores are able to germinate and form toxins.

The appearance of foods carrying the toxins of *C. botulinum* is not necessarily indicative of the presence and activity of the organism. Frequently the food has been described by the victims as looking normal, even when the proteolytic strains of A and B were involved. Usually, the proteolytic strains of Type A and some of Type B noticeably change the appearance and odor of the invaded foods. The appearance may become more or less slimy and cheesy, and the odor foul and obnoxious. However, when the protein content of the medium is low, as is true for many vegetables, changes in appearance and odor may not be detectable. Also, gas production is not always in evidence. Type E will not visibly change the appearance of the food in which it multiplies.

## FACTORS AFFECTING GROWTH AND PRODUCTION OF TOXINS

Toxin production goes hand in hand with growth. Whatever favors growth also favors production of the toxin. The potency of the toxins has been shown to be affected by the strain of organism, the composition, moisture, pH, oxygen, and salt content of the food, as well as by the temperature and time of food storage. The botulinum toxin is stable in acid but unstable in alkali.

*Food.* Many foods may serve as substrates. Meats, shellfish, fish, low-acid vegetables as well as some medium-acid to low-acid vegetables have been found to support growth and toxin formation of *Clostridium botulinum*.

For Type A the potency of the toxin has been found to differ with

**Table 10. Botulism Outbreaks in the United States Associated with Commercial Foods [Adapted from Osheroff, Slocum, and Decker (1964)]**

| Year | Food | Outbreaks | Cases | Deaths | Type |
|------|------|-----------|-------|--------|------|
| 1906 | Pork and beans | 1 | 3 | 3 | — |
| 1910 | String beans | 1 | 4 | 4 | — |
| 1912 | Clam juice | 1 | 2 | 1 | — |
| 1913 | Clam juice | 1 | 3 | 2 | — |
| 1914 | Clam juice | 1 | 2 | 2 | — |
| 1915 | Tomato catsup | 1 | 2 | 0 | — |
|      | Sausages | 1 | 2 | 2 | — |
| 1918 | Corn | 1 | 1 | 0 | — |
|      | Minced olives | 1 | 2 | 2 | — |
|      | Tuna | 1 | 1 | 1 | — |
| 1919 | Olives | 3 | 28 | 17 | A |
|      | Summer sausage | 1 | 3 | 0 | — |
| 1920 | Ripe olives | 1 | 7 | 7 | A |
|      | Ripe olives | 2 | 2 | 0 | — |
|      | Minced olives | 1 | 5 | 1 | A |
|      | Minced olives | 1 | 1 | 1 | — |
|      | Spinach | 1 | 6 | 3 | A |
|      | Spinach | 1 | 2 | 2 | — |
|      | Ham | 1 | 4 | 4 | — |
|      | Milk | 1 | 4 | 0 | — |
|      | Beets | 1 | 5 | 5 | B |
| 1921 | Spinach | 3 | 32 | 4 | A |
|      | Ripe olives | 1 | 5 | 3 | A |
| 1922 | Spinach | 2 | 11 | 6 | — |
| 1924 | Ripe olives | 2 | 13 | 6 | — |
|      | Ripe olives | 1 | 9 | 2 | A |
| 1925 | Sardines | 1 | 2 | 2 | — |
|      | Sardines | 1 | 2 | 2 | A |
|      | Spinach | 1 | 5 | 1 | B |
|      | Potted meat | 1 | 4 | 4 | B |
| 1929 | Shallots | 1 | 2 | 1 | B |
| 1931 | Antipasto | 1 | 3 | 1 | — |
|      | Milk | 1 | 1 | 0 | A |
|      | Sardines | 1 | 2 | 1 | — |
| 1934 | Sprats | 1 | 3 | 1 | E |
| 1936 | Clams (Japanese canned) | 1 | 4 | 4 | B |
| 1938 | Tuna | 1 | 2 | 2 | — |
| 1941 | Mushroom sauce | 1 | 3 | 1 | E |
| 1951 | Cheese | 1 | 1 | 1 | — |
| 1960 | Smoked ciscoes | 1 | 2 | 2 | E |
| 1963 | Tuna | 1 | 3 | 2 | E |
|      | Smoked whitefish | 1 | 2 | 2 | E |
|      | Smoked whitefish chub | 1 | 17 | 5 | E |
|      | Liver paste | 1 | 2 | 0 | A |
|      | Total | 51 | 219 | 109 | |

the food, the more potent toxin being formed by media containing glucose, casein, and milk. The toxin formed in certain vegetables was found to be more potent than in others, corn and peas being among the vegetables supporting the formation of a very potent toxin.

*Moisture.* A certain amount of moisture has been demonstrated to be required for toxin production of Types A and B. The critical water activity seems to be 0.935. No data are available on the sugar concentration that will inhibit outgrowth of Type E spores.

*Salt and Sugar.* Type E spores are much less salt tolerant than spores of Types A and B (Pederson, 1957; Segner et al., 1964). It is generally concluded that 50% sugar or 10% salt (NaCl) completely inhibits outgrowth of spores Types A and B. However, no definite NaCl concentration can be claimed to suppress growth and toxin production of *C. botulinum;* this concentration is dependent on the nature of the food and on the temperature. More salt is needed when the temperature is favorable to growth and toxin production.

*Oxygen.* *Clostridium botulinum* is an anaerobe which is not poisoned by oxygen and may grow in the presence of oxygen under certain conditions. A reduction in atmospheric pressure of 4–8 per cent has been shown to permit growth. Although the organism can grow and produce toxin in cans, hermetically sealed containers, such as plastic vacuum packs when other environmental conditions are favorable, vacuum packaging per se cannot be blamed as furthering growth and toxin production of the organisms. Yet, when fish contaminated with viable spores of *C. botulinum* Type E is vacuum-packed, and temperature conditions are favorable, and no competition from aerobic organisms interferes, a potential danger from Type E toxin exists. Food not hermetically sealed will allow growth of slime-forming bacteria and molds which tend to suppress *C. botulinum.* Among the bacteria which are able to strongly suppress *C. botulinum* are the lactic acid bacteria.

It has been shown (Kautter, 1964) in laboratory experiments that smoked ciscoes inoculated with Type E spores and held at 30°C (86°F) in packages open to access of air were rendered toxic in about the same time as those held under anaerobic conditions. In vacuum-packaged inoculated fish, toxin production was demonstrated after 5 days storage at 10°C (50°F) with no visible signs of quality reduction; at higher storage temperatures a greater percentage of fish contained toxin. The studies proved that Type E is able to produce toxin in open packages as well as under vacuum. However, vacuum packaging is perhaps more hazardous because molds and contaminating aerobes are suppressed, giving *C. botulinum* longer time and opportunity for toxin formation.

*pH. C. botulinum* favors a pH near neutrality, but spores germinate and toxin may be produced over a considerably wide pH range. The lowest pH at which toxin is produced varies with the type of food and also with the organism. Thus, no definite limits can be given. In general, at a pH of 4.6 the germination of spores, growth, and toxin production of Types A and B has ceased. (Proceedings "Botulism," 1964). Maximum production of toxin occurs between pH 5 and pH 8. For Type E fewer data are available than for A and B. However, it appears from available evidence that a pH of 4.6 will inhibit Type E also (Proceedings "Botulism," 1964).

*Temperature.* The temperature requirements of the various strains vary somewhat. Spores require a somewhat higher temperature for germination than the vegetative cells used for fission. For spore germination, the minimum temperature for Types A and B is somewhat above 50°F and the optimum near 98.6°F. Active growth and toxin formation of the vegetative cells of these types takes place over a similar range of temperature.

As demonstrated by Schmidt et al. (1961), Type E is quite different in that its minimum temperature requirement is 38°F for spore germination and subsequent multiplication and toxin formation. Freezing prevents formation of botulinus toxins but does not kill *C. botulinum* spores.

The spores of *Clostridium botulinum* vary in their resistance to heating. Thermal death is affected by many factors, a discussion of which is beyond the scope of this book; the reader is therefore referred to textbooks on food preservation. Some of the factors are: type and strain of organism, conditions under which the spores were formed, the age of the spores, the kind of food in which the organism is suspended during heating, and the number of spores present. To kill spores of Types A and B several hours of boiling is required; shorter time is necessary at higher temperatures, approximately 10 minutes at 250°F. The National Canners Association and other agencies which set up specifications for the canning industry allow a wide margin of safety in the time–temperature requirements for the killing of *C. botulinum* spores.

The spores of Type E have been shown to be less heat resistant. In smoking of fish, the heat treatment should be aimed at killing all

Type E spores. Type E varies in heat resistance with strain. (Sheneman, 1965).

Spores of *C. botulinum* are very resistant to adverse conditions other than heat and may remain viable for extremely long periods of time.

The toxins are not very resistant to heat, and are readily denatured at temperatures above 176°F. Types A and B are more heat-resistant than Type E. For foods suspected of containing toxins A and B, 15 minutes of boiling is recommended. This treatment provides a margin of safety, since in laboratory experiments shorter times were sufficient to inactivate the toxins. Heat resistance has been shown to vary with the pH of the substrate, resistance decreasing with decreasing pH. For Type E spores, however, shorter times were found to be required for heat inactivation at pH of 7.5 and 3.5 than at an intermediate pH range of 4.6–4.9 (Ohye and Scott, 1957).

Following the Type E botulism episodes of the early 1960's, an emergency measure was recommended for fish taken from suspected waters. An advisory Committee on Botulism Hazard was organized by the Food and Drug Administration. Their suggested measures were: (1) heating smoked fish immediately after packaging to 180°F for 30 minutes as determined in the coldest part, storing it under refrigeration, and labeling it "perishable—keep under refrigeration"; or (2) freezing the smoked fish immediately after packaging and keeping it in the frozen state until sold to the consumer.

The recommendation suggested by the Food and Drug Administration's Advisory Committee has been accepted by the National Fisheries Institute, and smoked fish from the Great Lakes is now stored and distributed in the frozen state.

In quantity food service, precautions to avoid botulism are briefly these: (1) the procurement of a safe food supply; (2) rejection of canned goods exhibiting defects such as swell, rust, leakage; (3) storage of canned goods under conditions recommended for these items, practicing reasonably frequent turnover of canned goods; (4) storage under refrigeration at 37°F of all perishable fish items which have received light heat treatment and are labeled "keep refrigerated"; and (5) the use of appropriate procedures for the storage and thawing of frozen food items.

## Staphylococcus aureus

*Staphylococcus* food poisoning (enterotoxemia) is caused by the toxins of *Staphylococcus aureus*, a yellow facultative aerobic organism. The toxins set off an inflammation of the lining in the stomach and the intestinal tract of the victim. Another, nonpigmented variety, *S. albus*, has only seldom been associated with outbreaks of foodborne gastroenteritis, although it has been shown to be an organism able to produce toxin.

### ORGANISM

As the name *Staphylococcus* indicates, the organism is characterized by a group of cocci combined in grapelike clusters. The cells may also occur in pairs and short chains. The cocci are tiny, less than 1 $\mu$ in diameter.

Many strains of *S. aureus* are known, some being extremely pathogenic. The cultures are usually golden yellow, and nearly always liquify gelatin and ferment lactose and manitol. Many virulent strains coagulate citrated plasma, and the strains associated with food poisoning outbreaks are usually coagulase-positive.

The staphylococci are susceptible to specific bacteriophages. For identification of strains, phage typing is now commonly practiced. Phage typing is a useful tool, because resistance to the lytic action of the phages is a genetically stable character. The typing is extremely useful in tracing down the origin of a strain causing an outbreak of *Staphylococcus* food poisoning, and linking the victims of an outbreak to a particular menu item.

The various *S. aureus* strains elaborate a number of toxins. They are exotoxins, since they are diffusible and are eliminated from the living cell into the substrate. The toxins which are able to produce gastrointestinal illnesses are called enterotoxins. The *Staphylococcus* toxins are soluble and thermostable. Active cell multiplication is a prerequisite for the elaboration of toxins by the cells into the medium, which may be a food.

Proof of the pathogenicity of the toxins has been a stumbling block in the past. Although most, if not all, of the enterotoxic staphylococci were known to produce coagulase, this was not a foolproof test for pathogenicity, since there was the possibility that some strains of coagulase-negative staphylococci might produce enterotoxin. Many investigators therefore relied on testing the pathogenicity on human volunteers or on laboratory animals— especially on monkeys, but also on cats, frogs, mice, guinea pigs, dogs, rats, and rabbits. The tests consist of feeding filtrates of the media on which the isolates were grown to the volunteers or animals and observing the reaction regarding vomiting and diarrhea. Intravenous and intraperitoneal injection tests were also made. The difficulties were manifold; the expense, the slowness of the test, the specificity of human and animal reactions were all points against this method of proving pathogenicity.

In 1947, the Food and Drug Administration Division of Microbiology initiated studies with the aim of developing practical methods for detecting staphylococcal enterotoxin in food, and for demonstrating enterogenicity of *Staphylococcus* strains. The steps involved were: to demonstrate the antigenicity of the staphylococcal enterotoxin; to determine the number of possible types involved; to detect and make available specific antienterotoxins; to develop methods for the production of enterotoxin; and develop methods for the serological detection of enterotoxin in cultures and in food materials. The results of these studies were published by Casman and co-workers (1958, 1960, 1962, 1963). The data proved the antigenicity of the staphylococcal enterotoxin. Using serological typing methods, serological types of heat-resistant enterotoxin were detected one of which was associated with food poisoning. Certain staphylococci were seen to produce an emetic substance which was not heat stable. The Ouchterlony plate gel-diffusion precipitation test (see Pelczar and Reid, 1965, Chapter 25) could be successfully applied for the detection of enterotoxigenicity. This achievement represents a milestone, because it shows a way of detecting enterogenicity in the organism as well as enterotoxins in foods. Quantitative detection of exterotoxin B in food by a gel-diffusion method was reported by Hall et al. (1963).

At present, the staphylococcal enterotoxins are enterotoxin A (formerly "F" or "196E") and enterotoxin B (formerly "E" or "S-6"); others may exist and may have to be added to this listing as time goes on.

Trace amounts can now be detected of enterotoxins A and B in foods incriminated in *Staphylococcus* food-poisoning outbreaks (Casman and Bennett, 1965).

DISTRIBUTION AND SOURCE

The distribution of *S. aureus* is worldwide. Although the organism does not form spores, it is relatively resistant to injurious environmental conditions. In dust, soil, or frozen foods or on cloth, floors, or walls, the cells may survive for a considerable length of time, even months.

The most important source of *S. aureus* is probably the human body. A healthy man harbors the organism on his skin, in his mouth and throat, and in his nasal passages. Skin abrasions, wounds, and cuts are commonly a rich source of the organism. Infected sinuses, pimples, furuncles, and carbuncles abound with *S. aureus*. The human reservoir of the staphylococci will be discussed more fully in Chapter V.

Another important source of *S. aureus* may be the food supply. Other sources of the organism are man's pets, especially cats and dogs.

### SYMPTOMS

The ingestion of toxin-containing food causes the symptoms. The toxins build up in a food when *Staphylococcus aureus* cells are allowed to multiply profusely in it. When the toxin-containing food is ingested, it usually causes acute gastroenteritis in the victim, the severity of the symptoms varying with the susceptibility of the individual, the concentration of the toxin in the food, and the amount consumed.

The symptoms appear on an average of 2–3 hours after ingestion of the toxic food, but the times vary from ½ to 6 hours. The symptoms include salivation, nausea, vomiting, abdominal cramps, diarrhea, headache, muscular cramps, sweating, chills, prostration, weak pulse, and shallow respiration.

The duration of the illness is 24 hours to 2 days; the mortality is extremely low. Medical treatment is usually not indicated, for the illness runs its course. In severe poisoning, saline solutions are administered. The minimum amount of enterotoxin necessary to evoke symptoms in man is not known. Considerable variation in susceptibility has been noted in tests performed with human volunteers and animals.

### INCIDENCE

Staphylococcal intoxication outbreaks occur frequently. Along with salmonellosis and the episodes of unknown cause, this form of foodborne gastroenteritis ranks high. Frequently hundreds of persons are involved in one outbreak. The cause of this form of foodborne illness was not recognized until 1880, when Pasteur detected the organisms in pie.

Since 1930, great strides have been made in understanding the cause of and the circumstances favoring foodborne staphylococcal intoxications. Unfortunately, this knowledge is not put into good practice, as the high incidence of outbreaks proves.

### FOODS IMPLICATED

The foods involved in staphylococcal episodes are of great variety; food items high in protein are most frequently involved. Examples of indicted items are: custards, cream-filled bakery goods, meat sauces, gravies, meats and meat products, meat-filled sandwiches, roast turkey and dressing, chicken salad, milk, cheese, butter, ice cream, fish and fish products, and other dairy products and cream items. Regarding preparation procedures, the items frequently indicted are menu items that have been handled a great deal and, therefore, have had a good chance of becoming contaminated with the bacteria clinging to human hands and unsanitary equipment. Endangered are items cut, sliced, and cubed, then placed in a sauce and not sufficiently reheated; items which are allowed to cool slowly and therefore remain in the danger zone of bacterial growth for long periods of time; and items which are "warmed over" several times without ever getting hot enough for the contaminants to be killed. More will be said about that in later chapters.

The appearance, flavor, or odor of the food items in which *Staphylococcus aureus* multiplies are not noticeably altered. The invaded food does not seem spoiled, although some proteolysis and fermentation may be present.

FACTORS AFFECTING GROWTH AND PRODUCTION OF TOXINS

*Food.* Being a facultative aerobe, *S. aureus* may grow on solid or in liquid foods. It is tolerant of sugar and extremely tolerant to salt. In fact, it has been found to grow in sodium chloride near saturation. It also tolerates nitrites quite well; this is important, since this faculty enables the staphylococci to grow on curing, and cured, meats.

The tolerance of *S. aureus* to sodium chloride has been shown by Parfentjev and Catelli (1964) to be affected by the presence of other substances in the salt solution. The cells multiplied at 98.6°F in tryptose phosphate broth saturated with sodium chloride. In contrast, saturated solutions of this salt in distilled water were injurious to the cells and killed most of them within 1 hour. The addition of just traces of tryptose phosphate broth was observed to have a protective effect.

*pH.* The organism, *S. aureus*, grows in substrates of a wide range of pH, from 2 to 10, a pH near neutral being very favorable.

*Competition from Other Microorganisms.* *S. aureus* has been demonstrated to be sensitive to competitors. For example, repressive effects have been shown to be exerted by psychrophilic saprophytes. These interactions were found to be very complex. They were affected not only by temperature, but also by the composition and pH of the media (Peterson et al., 1964a, b, c).

Due to the activity of competitors, the staphylococci may, under certain circumstances, become discouraged while the food assumes a "spoiled" appearance. Such food would not be served because of its unsightliness (Post et al., 1961). However, to rely upon microbial competitors in the control of *S. aureus* would be folly.

*Temperature.* The temperature range within which *S. aureus* may grow is affected by, among other factors, the strain, the number of cells, and the medium in which the organism is suspended. According to research by Angelotti et al. (1961a), temperatures between 44 and 114°F may be expected to support growth of *S. aureus*. For growth and toxin formation the optimum temperature range is 70 to 98.7°F, but the organism grows profusely with elaboration of toxins within a wide range of temperatures.

Under favorable growth conditions, the toxin becomes evident after 4–6 hours of active multiplication. At lower temperatures, longer time is required. As is true for growth, the production of the toxin is affected by the presence of competitive microorganisms.

*S. aureus* is fairly resistant to heat and is not always killed in the pasteurization of milk. Heat resistance varies with, among other things, the strain and the nature of the medium in which the cells are suspended.

Angelotti et al. (1961b) reported on survival of cells of a heat-resistant strain when these were suspended in custard and ham salad and exposed to temperatures up to 150°F. The authors concluded from their data that heating these perishable foods to 150°F and holding every particle of the food at this temperature for at least 12 minutes rendered the food practically sterile. The same degree of destruction was achieved when the foods were held at 140°F for 78–83 minutes.

The heat stability of the toxins is considerable. This fact is important in food sanitation since routine cooking procedures will not destroy these toxins. Inactivation of the toxins varies with many factors and therefore the data will not be reported here. Also, more research is needed to clarify the thermostability of the various toxins produced by the organism under varying conditions.

Multiplication of the organism is possible under refrigeration, when the cooling process does not proceed fast enough and if the bacteria find the temperatures conducive to multiplication. Storage in a refrigerator for 67 days has been found to keep the toxin intact.

Viable cells of food-poisoning *Staphylococcus* have been found to withstand freezing well; freezing will not even reduce the potency of the toxins.

The control of foodborne illnesses caused by *Staphylococcus aureus* should include: first, sanitary precautions in connection with the food handler, because the human body is the main reservoir of *S. aureus;* second, efficient measures to preclude the multiplication of the organism in the food during its preparation, service, and storage; and third, using heat for the destruction of the contaminants.

## Bacteria Causing Foodborne Infections

Among the bacteria causing foodborne infections are the salmonellae and the fecal streptococci. The salmonellae are an extremely important group of pathogens in this respect.

### Salmonellae

Foodborne acute gastroenteritis in man is caused by many different salmonellae. The organisms, when ingested in large numbers, will cause an infection-type illness.

Salmonellae have been associated with foodborne illnesses for a long time. Recently, evidence has shown that in the past the salmonellae may have been unjustifiably indicted in outbreaks of food illness when *Staphylococcus aureus* was the causative agent. Dack (1956) stated that perhaps no field is more confused than that concerned with the role of *Salmonella* organisms in food poisoning.

The evidence points toward the fact that *Salmonella* food poisoning is an infection and that no significant evidence supports the view that exotoxins play a role.

ORGANISM

The salmonellae are facultative aerobic rods which ferment glucose, usually with gas, and do not form spores. Many serotypes are known. In the United States, the first salmonellae typing center was established in 1934 by the Public Health Service. The serotyping of salmonellae from the animals was later taken over by the Animal Disease Eradication Division of the Agricultural Research Service (USDA) (Moran et al., 1965). Through the work of typing centers great strides have been made in the identification of the many forms of this organism and its many sources. An international Salmonella Center has been established at the State Serum Institute in Copenhagen, Denmark.

Approximately 1100 serotypes are known now, and this number may grow. The differentiation of a particular *Salmonella* is made with the aid of the agglutination test. A description of the serological identification test has been presented by Edwards and Bruner (1942). The members of this group which cause acute gastroenteritis live in the intestinal tract of man and animals. Not included in this group are the salmonellae causing typhoid and paratyphoid fevers.

It has been observed that at times a high incidence of a particular serotype in a food in a given locality was accompanied by a high incidence of the same type in man in that area. In one epidemiological investigation, a foodborne *Salmonella* outbreak in a hospital was traced to lightly cooked egg contaminated with *S. infantis* and from there to a chicken flock and its feed which were contaminated with the same serotype.

The principal serotype of *Salmonella* connected with human salmonellosis is *S. typhimurium*. Sanders et al. (1963) made a report of an 8-month surveillance of human salmonellosis in 22 states in the United States. The percentage of the various serotypes isolated is given in Table 11. It is an interesting fact that by comparison, only 3.6% of all salmonellae isolated were identified as *S. typhosa*.

Table 11. Serotypes of Human Origin Recovered during an 8-Month Surveillance in 22 Participating States in 1962 [Data from Sanders, Friedman, McCall, and Brachman (1963)]

| Serotype | Per cent of all isolations |
|---|---|
| Typhimurium | 42.6 |
| Heidelberg | 7.9 |
| Newport | 6.9 |
| Infantis | 6.1 |
| Enteritidis | 4.0 |

Serotypes most common in man are also common in hogs, dogs, poultry, and animal feed. The nine most prevalent salmonellae serotypes identified from animal sources in the United States, from April 1962 to April 1963, were according to the statistics published by the Public Health Service in October of 1963; *S. typhimurium, heidelberg, anatum, cholera-suis, infantis, montevideo, derby, saint-paul,* and *oranienburg.*

DISTRIBUTION AND SOURCE

The salmonellae are distributed over the world (Proceedings, National Conference on Salmonellosis, 1965). The fact that unusual serotypes have appeared in countries far apart has indicted foods and feeds as vehicles. Within the United States, the salmonellae are distributed by way of foods and feeds also (Bowner, E. J., 1965).

The primary source of *Salmonella* is, before all, the intestinal tract of animals, whether these are acute cases or carriers. A carrier is an individual harboring causative organisms of a particular illness who appears to be well and shows no symptoms or signs of being ill. Man once infected may also act as a reservoir (Proceedings, National Conference on Salmonellosis, 1965). A carrier eliminates these organisms from his body and thus serves as a source of infection for weeks, months, or years. Man's enemies such as rodents, flies, and cockroaches, as well as his pets, such as cats and dogs, seem to be frequent reservoirs of salmonellae. Food animals are very important reservoirs: hogs, chickens, turkeys, ducks and their eggs are all sources of salmonellae; cattle, hogs, and sheep have also been shown to harbor salmonellae.

Poultry feed and dog food have been reported to be heavily contaminated with *Salmonella*.

Salmonellae are discharged into sewage and manure. They have been found in soil contaminated with raw sewage and are known to survive in soil for months. They are associated with sewage-polluted waters.

The reader of the literature dealing with *Salmonella* and the salmonelloses cannot help being appalled by the seemingly endless host cycles which encompass man, food animals, pets, rodents, insects, processed meats and poultry, prepared food items, animal feed, pet food, feces, and manure. The interrelated facets of the problems connected with salmonellosis were discussed at a National Conference on Salmonellosis in 1964, and the records of the conference were published as Proceedings (1965).

SYMPTOMS

The symptoms of salmonellosis resemble those of *Staphylococcus* food poisoning. The onset is not as rapid, due to the fact that there is no toxin present in the food. The illness results from an ingestion of large numbers of bacteria. The incubation time varies from 3 to 72 hours, with an average of 12–24 hours. The incubation time of typical "food-poisoning" salmonellae is shorter than that of the salmonellae species capable of causing typhoid and paratyphoid fevers and that of the pathogens causing bacillary dysentery.

The severity of the disease depends on the strains of *Salmonella* involved, the individual's susceptibility to the organisms, and the total number of cells ingested with the food.

The symptoms include: nausea, vomiting, abdominal pain, diarrhea, headache, chills, marked prostration, watery and foul-smelling stools, muscular weakness, faintness, drowsiness, and thirst; there may be fever and septicemia. Mortality is less than 1%.

The illness usually lasts 2 or 3 days, but it may linger. A small percentage of persons may become carriers; numerous *Salmonella* species have been isolated from the stools of seemingly healthy persons.

INCIDENCE

The salmonellae are frequent causes of foodborne gastroenteritis in the United States (see Table 5). There is reason to suspect that relatively more outbreaks occur in the summer and autumn than in the other months of the year. Salmonellosis seems to be on the increase; the incidence of salmonellosis has risen more than 20-fold since 1946. One reason may lie in the expansion of centralized processing and bulk distribution of processed food items. Another explanation for the larger figures on salmonellosis is that the detection and reporting of salmonellosis have been vastly improved in recent years. In this connection, the reader is reminded that even nowadays only a small percentage of all cases of salmonellosis is reported.

FOODS IMPLICATED

The list of foods and prepared menu items implicated in salmonellosis is a long one and is headed by the proteinaceous menu items. Among the very frequent offenders are poultry and products made from poultry, such as poultry dressing and gravy, chicken and turkey salads; eggs and products made from eggs; meats, especially pork and products made from pork; meat pies, hash, sandwiches made with meat; puddings; cream-filled pastries; custards; cream cakes; meringue pies; and many other items too numerous to mention. The appearance, odor, and flavor of prepared foods contaminated with salmonellae are usually not noticeably altered.

Examples of circumstances frequently associated with *Salmonella* outbreaks are: poor personal hygiene of food handlers; poor supervision; poor general sanitation practices in the preparation, storage, and service of food; food handlers who are carriers; poor maintenance of equipment; presence of rodents, flies, and cockroaches; long holding of food at warm temperatures; slow cooling due to refrigeration of large batches; cutting boards used for raw as well as cooked meats and poultry; and poor cleaning of cutting boards, to name just a few.

### FACTORS AFFECTING GROWTH

*Food.* The great variety of foods that have been involved in outbreaks of salmonellosis speaks for the fact that the causative organisms are able to multiply to large numbers in many commonly served menu items.

*pH.* The organisms grow best in non-acid media and foods. At pH below 5.5 growth is apt to be scant; yet acid foods like tomatoes have been reported to allow growth of *Salmonella*. Segalove and Dack (1944) inoculated cans of asparagus, spinach, string beans, tomato juice, peaches, shrimp, salmon, corn, and peas with a strain of *S. enteritidis* and incubated the samples at two temperatures, 71.6 and 98.6°F. Multiplication took place at the lower temperature in all the foods except peaches, and at the higher temperature in all the foods except peaches and asparagus.

*Temperature.* The salmonellae multiply over a rather wide range of temperature, but there is some variation due to strains. Angelotti et al. (1959, 1961a) studied the time–temperature effects on salmonellae using *S. manhattan, enteritidis, typhimurium, senftenberg, cubana,* and *montevideo* (*typhimurium* and *senftenberg,* heat-resistant strains) suspended in broth. They found that these organisms did not multiply at 41°F; but good growth occurred at 50, 59, and 68°F. Some of the strains were also inoculated into custard, ham salad, and chicken a la king. The lowest temperature at which multiplication was observed was 44°F.

The same authors (1961b) conducted a study on the behavior of salmonellae at warm holding temperatures. The test strains were *S. senftenberg, enteritidis,* and *manhattan.* The foods in which the bacteria were suspended were custard, ham salad, and chicken a la king. It was shown that the salmonellae were able to multiply in certain foods at temperatures as high as 112–114°F. Maximum growth temperatures of 110–115°F were also demonstrated by Elliott and Heiniger (1965) for 34 selected strains of *Salmonella;* among the species represented were *S. typhimurium, senftenberg, derby,* and *anatum.*

Results of these studies have an important bearing on refrigeration and holding of prepared menu items. The implications will be discussed in more detail in Chapter XIII.

The optimum temperature for growth of the salmonellae is about

98°F; at this temperature, the generation time may be expected to be 15 minutes.

Thermal death of the salmonellae depends on many factors, as is true for other microorganisms. Among these are: the heat resistance of the strain; the number of cells in the medium exposed to heating; the type of medium—in particular, the presence of substances protecting the cells from the heat; pH; and temperatures and times used in the heat treatment.

Angelotti et al. (1961b), using a heat-resistant strain of *S. senften-berg* and a non-heat-resistant strain of *S. manhattan*, in the same three foods mentioned above, exposed these salmonellae to temperatures up to 150°F. They found that no instantaneous kill resulted from this exposure. Holding the inoculated foods at 150°F for several minutes resulted in the death of the inoculum. The authors suggest that to effect a 90% reduction in numbers of salmonellae, heating at 150°F for 12 minutes is necessary. The same degree of destruction was achieved by heating at 140°F for 78–83 minutes.

Salmonellae have been shown to survive freezing and freezer storage. The survival of *Salmonella* cells in processing and subsequent storage of foods will be discussed in a later chapter.

Principles of control are generally the same as listed for *Staphylococcus aureus*. In connection with control of the salmonellae it should be remembered that several important reservoirs of this organism must be kept under control, two of the main reservoirs being certain food items of animal origin and the intestinal tract of man.

## Fecal Streptococci

Several fecal streptococci have been indicted in foodborne gastrointestinal illness on circumstantial evidence, in that these streptococci represented the predominant flora of the foods ingested in connection with the outbreaks. No toxins have been associated with the illness-producing capacities of these bacteria.

### ORGANISM

The fecal streptococci are members of the enterococcus group of the lactic streptococci. Several species of *Streptococcus* are of interest as possible causes of foodborne illnesses. They are: *S. faecalis, faecalis* var. *zymogenes, faecalis* var. *liquefaciens, durans,* and *faecium*. These species are generally referred to as the enterococci.

In the past there has been some degree of synonomy regarding the terms fecal streptococci, Lancefield's Group D streptococci, and enterococci. At present, some diversion from this trend is noticeable.

The species *S. faecium* is now regarded by many as a definite entity within the enterococcus group, and *S. durans* is considered a variety of that species. For practical reasons, the term enterococci will be used throughout this discussion. Enterococci were first associated with foodborne gastroenteritis outbreaks by Linden, Turner, and Thom (1926).

Dack (1956) reported on several food-poisoning outbreaks with human volunteers. Using live cultures and also filtrates of the organisms isolated in connection with these outbreaks it was proven that the cultures caused gastroenteritis in the subjects, whereas the filtrates did not.

A number of other bacteriologists have attempted to establish experimentally the enterococci as the cause of gastroenteritic symptoms in man. Using volunteers, food poisoning has been achieved at times. A literature review on the subject is presented by Deibel and Silliker (1963). These authors call attention to the fact that a clear distinction must be drawn between food poisoning attributable to this group and *Streptococcus* disease transmission in which food may play a role as a simple vehicle of transmission.

DISTRIBUTION AND SOURCE

As the name indicates, the enterococci are inhabitants of the intestinal tract. They are harbored by man and animals. When discharged with the feces they may contaminate whatever has contact with the feces, sewage, and manure, such as: meat animals, hide, the abdominal cavity of the freshly slaughtered animal, soil, water, air, and the hands of the food handler. In processing, the meat may become heavily contaminated when sanitary standards in the packing plants are low. Distribution of the enterococci is wide.

SYMPTOMS

The symptoms in persons who ingest food items containing large numbers of the enterococci include nausea, vomiting, colic, and diarrhea. Incubation time may vary from 3 to 18 hours. Symptoms are milder than those caused by *Salmonella* and *Staphylococcus*.

INCIDENCE

Few incidences are reported. Because of their relative mildness the illness may easily escape reporting.

FOODS IMPLICATED

Mentioned have been a variety of items, among them pasteurized canned ham, vienna sausage, beef croquettes, pork sausage, barbecued beef, bologna, turkey dressing, turkey a la king, dried eggs, evaporated milk from rusty and leaky cans, charlotte russe, cheese, chocolate pudding, and whipped cream.

### FACTORS AFFECTING GROWTH

Conditions favoring growth vary somewhat with species and strains.

*Food.* A variety of foods are able to serve as substrates. Enterococci, in general, need complex substrates and grow poorly on many culture media. Their salt tolerance is high, approximately 6.5%, or more, being tolerated. *Streptococcus faecium* grows well on salt-cured hams.

*pH.* The organisms may grow over an extremely wide range of pH. Especially unusual is their capability to grow in alkaline media of pH 9 and higher.

*Temperature.* The organisms are capable of growing over a very wide range of temperature. The widest range is 42–115°F. Angelotti et al. (1963) have studied the time–temperature effects on fecal streptococci in foods at refrigeration temperatures as well as at warm-holding temperatures. Mixtures of enterococcal species were incubated in custard, chicken a la king, and ham salad, at temperatures ranging from 40°F through 128°F. In custard, growth was slight at 42°F, but good growth was observed at 48°F through 115°F. In chicken a la king no growth was noted at 42°F or below, but good growth occurred at the temperature range between 50°F and 115°F. In ham salad, no growth occurred at 48°F and below, at 50°F growth was slight, and excellent growth was observed at 60°F through 115°F.

The enterococci are thermoduric and are able to survive pasteurization of milk. *Streptococcus faecalis* and *S. faecium* have been shown to survive the pasteurization treatment given certain canned hams. In general, processors aim at a terminal internal food temperature of 158°F to preclude the hazard from bacterial spoilage.

Research data collected in laboratory experiments by White (1953) have shown that the heat resistance of *S. faecalis* to exposure at 140°F was considerably influenced by the age of the culture.

Angelotti et al. (unpublished data, 1962b) found *S. faecalis* to become inactivated in custard when held at 150°F for 38 minutes, at 155°F for 14 minutes, or at 160°F for 5 minutes. In chicken a la king the inactivation times were shorter. In the same study, these workers investigated the heat treatment required to kill *S. faecium.*

The average number of minutes required to eliminate the inoculum in chicken a la king was 12 minutes at 160°F and in custard as long as 38 minutes at this same temperature. These data are evidence of the protective action of certain foods, in this case custard.

Surgalla et al. (1944) demonstrated that *S. faecalis* remained viable for at least 30 days at 98.6°F in foods of varying acidity. At below-freezing temperatures the cells remained viable for long periods of time. This property has been claimed to be of some value as a microbiological index of food quality for foods such as water, milk, and frozen foods stored at low temperatures. The role of the enterococci as indicators of food quality will be discussed in a later chapter.

## Miscellaneous Bacteria Associated with Foodborne Gastroenteric Outbreaks

Here are grouped bacteria which have been associated with gastroenteritis in humans, although the cause and effect of relationships of these pathogens require further research.

### Clostridium perfringens (welchii)

This organism has gained in importance as a pathogen capable of causing "food poisoning," first in England, then on the European continent (Germany, Hungary, Poland, Sweden, Denmark), Japan, Canada, and the United States.

The gastrointestinal illness associated with this organism was first described in the late 1890's and again by McClung (1945). However, *Clostridium perfringens* did not attract much attention until recently, when Hobbs et al. (1953) described several outbreaks ascribed to the organism in England.

#### ORGANISM

Forms of *C. perfringens* have been known to be one of the causes of gas gangrene in man, and to cause various intestinal diseases in animals, especially young lambs, pigs, and calves. *C. perfringens* is a gram-positive, anaerobic, spore-forming rod. Sporulation and heat resistance of the spores vary with strains and many other factors. The strains may be differential on the basis of pattern of toxin formation, typical for the various strains. Of several toxigenic strains known at present, Types A and F are most commonly associated with foodborne illness. The antigenic properties of the organism have been studied by Ellner and Bohan (1962) and Klotz (1965).

*Clostridium perfringens* Type A has been reported by English workers to form alpha toxin (lecithinase) but little or no theta toxin (hemolysin), and to produce heat-resistant spores.

The strains isolated in the laboratory of Angelotti and co-workers (1962a) from American foods do not follow the criteria for food-poisoning types as described by the English workers. Angelotti et al. studied 83 strains of *C. perfringens*, 30 from England and the European continent and Asia, and 28 from the United States; all of these had been associated with gastrointestinal illness. Another group of 25 came from other sources. On the basis of the results, these workers concluded that the American food-poisoning strains vary widely in their characteristics. They also stated that it does not seem likely that *C. perfringens* strains causing gastroenteritic outbreaks in the United States are restricted to the criteria for food-poisoning strains set up for England.

Ellner (1961) studied the fate of *C. perfringens* Type A toxin in susceptible small animals. Purified and $C^{14}$-labeled toxin was injected intravenously into mice and rabbits. Disappearance of the toxin from the blood stream, appearance in urine and expired air, and deposition in certain organs were followed. It was shown that toxin disappeared rapidly from the blood and left the body with urine and expired air. Certain organs such as the liver, lungs, kidneys, and spleen took up toxin.

Future research data will help clarify the etiology of the gastro-enteric upsets following the ingestion of the organism. It is a puzzling fact that the rather slow onset of the symptoms suggest an infection, although the symptoms resemble those of an intoxication.

DISTRIBUTION AND SOURCE

The organism is extremely widespread in nature here and abroad. It is a common inhabitant of the intestinal tract of healthy animals and human beings. It occurs in large numbers in the soil, sewage, manure, water, and dust; therefore, many foods, especially meats, reaching the kitchen are likely to be contaminated with *Clostridium perfringens*. In Europe, *C. perfringens* serves as an indicator of fecal pollution.

Strong et al. (1963) studied the incidence of the organism in American foods and reported that the incidence in the foods examined was 6.1% (Table 12).

Canada et al. (1964) recovered *C. perfringens* from 26% of 100 bovine liver samples purchased in retail markets and in 12% of the livers from freshly slaughtered animals. The strains were typed as

Table 12. Incidence of *Clostridium perfringens* in Foods [Adapted from Strong, Canada, and Griffiths (1963)]

| Food group | No. of samples | Samples positive | Range of count cells/g | Incidence, % |
|---|---|---|---|---|
| Commercially prepared frozen foods | 111 | 3 | 10–20 | 2.7 |
| Raw fruits and vegetables | 52 | 2 | 10–140 | 3.8 |
| Spices | 60 | 3 | 10–30 | 5.0 |
| Home-prepared foods | 165 | 3 | 10 | 1.8 |
| Meat, poultry, and fish | 122 | 20 | 10–1180 | 16.4 |

Table 13. Recovery of *Clostridium perfringens* from Processed Meats and Meat Dishes [Adapted from Hall and Angelotti (1965)]

| Type of specimen | No. of specimens examined | No. of specimens positive for *C. perfringens* | Per cent positive for *C. perfringens* |
|---|---|---|---|
| Require full cooking | 38 | 14 | 36.8 |
| Require warming or light cooking | 21 | 4 | 19.0 |
| Require no cooking | 42 | 2 | 4.7 |
| Total | 101 | 20 | 19.8 |

producing toxins, but it was not know whether they were able to cause gastrointestinal disturbances in man.

Hall and Angelotti (1965) studied the incidence of *Clostridium perfringens* in meat and meat products in the Cincinnati area. Some of the items studied were raw, some partially cooked, and some fully processed, requiring no cooking (Table 13). The organism was isolated from 43.1% of 262 specimens, the highest percentage of contamination being found in veal cuts (Table 14), and the lowest in sandwich cuts and spreads.

Only 2 of the 113 isolates produced heat-resistant spores.

SYMPTOMS

The symptoms begin between and 8 and 22, usually 8–15, hours after the ingestion of the contaminated food and may continue for 6–12 hours. They are somewhat similar to those of staphylococcal intoxication, but are milder. Symptoms include nausea, sometimes

**Table 14. Recovery of *Clostridium perfringens* from Raw, Unprocessed Meat [Adapted from Hall and Angelotti (1965)]**

| Type of specimen | No. of specimens examined | No. of specimens positive for *C. perfringens* | Per cent positive for *C. perfringens* |
|---|---|---|---|
| Veal | 17 | 14 | 82 |
| Beef | 50 | 35 | 70 |
| Chicken | 26 | 15 | 58 |
| Lamb | 27 | 14 | 52 |
| Pork | 41 | 15 | 37 |
| Total | 161 | 93 | 58 |

accompanied by vomiting, intestinal cramps, and diarrhea. Fever, chills, and headache are rarely experienced. The illness, with one exception, has not been fatal.

INCIDENCE

In the United States, the incidence of this foodborne illness is relatively low (Table 5). Many states have never reported an outbreak. From England, a fairly high rate of incidents has been reported for a number of years. Reports have also been made from Canada, Europe, and Asia.

FOODS IMPLICATED

In connection with gastrointestinal episodes believed to be caused by *Clostridium perfringens* were listed meats, items in which meat served as an ingredient, and gravy. The organisms may be carried into the kitchen on the hands of the food handlers as well as on many food stuffs. It has also been isolated from other uncooked and cooked food products, such as vegetables, dairy products, eggs, and condiments such as pepper.

An outbreak was reported in 1960 which originated from a turkey dinner served on a train. Approximately one-half of 450 passengers became ill (Hart et al. 1960). In 1962, a large outbreak in which creamed turkey was implicated occurred in a mental institution in California. The circumstances have been described by Kemp et al. (1962). In a recent outbreak in a high school cafeteria, roast beef was the incriminated menu item (Morbidity and Mortality, 1965).

Contamination of food with the pathogen is common, but the counts have, in general, been shown to be low and the spores largely of the non-heat-resistant type; therefore it follows that opportunity is afforded in the kitchen for the organism to build up to dangerously high numbers and that recontamination of cooked foods occurs frequently. Obviously, this has been the case when outbreaks due to *C. perfringens* have occurred. To cause illness, the critical dose is several hundred million organisms, or 5–10 million organisms per gram of food.

## FACTORS AFFECTING GROWTH

*Food.* Meats and menu items made with meat have been shown to support the multiplication of this organism extremely well. Experimental data reported by Smith (1962) showed that *Clostridium perfringens* required 13 or 14 amino acids.

*pH.* Smith (1962) stated that multiplication took place within the pH range 5–8.5, and that it was most rapid within the pH range of 6–7.5.

*Temperature.* Smith (1962) reported the effect of temperature on generation time of *C. perfringens* using five strains, and a temperature range of 5–50°C (41–122°F). None of the strains grew appreciably at 15°C (59°F) and none grew at 5°C (41°F), but they grew well over a wide range of 20–50°C (68–122°F). Under most favorable conditions, the shortest generation time was about 18 minutes. Excellent growth took place at 35°C (95°F).

The ability of the organism to multiply profusely at high temperatures was also reported by Hall and Angelotti (1965), who obtained excellent growth at 35–46°C (95–114.8°F). At the lower temperature, rapid growth was found to be preceded by a 2–4-hour lag period, whereas no lag phase was observed at 46°C (114.8°F). The authors point out the dangers of holding meat items at these higher temperatures for even brief periods of time. Complete inhibition was observed at 49 and 52°C (120.2 and 125.6°F). No multiplication was observed by these workers at a temperature range of 5–15°C (41–59°F).

The thermal resistance of *Clostridium perfringens* varies considerably. Heat-resistant strains are common in England, but in the United States the percentage of such strains seems much lower. Hall and Angelotti (1965) found heat-resistant strains to constitute less than 1% for the Cincinnati area. Thermal resistance varies with the presence or absence of protective substances (Collee et al., 1961), meat being quite protective.

Canada et al. (1964), using four strains of *C. perfringens*, exposed the vegetative cells to temperatures lower than boiling. Essentially, no vegetative cells and few spores survived a heat treatment of 10 minutes at 80°C (176°F). Boiling for 5–10 minutes eliminated most spores of non-heat-resistant strains. However, the spores of heat-resistant strains have been reported to be extremely resistant to heat and to resist boiling for several hours (Hobbs and Wilson, 1959).

In this connection the 1965 outbreak involving roast beef should be mentioned again. According to the report (Morbidity and Mortality, 1965), a bacteriological examination of the roast beef yielded a viable count of 80,000 cells per gram, and numbers seen on a direct microscopic smear proved that the count had previously been much higher. These findings may indicate that the contaminant was present before roasting and survived the heating applied during the roasting process. In 1966 an outbreak ascribed to heat-resistant *C. perfringens* was reported from Wisconsin (Morbidity and Mortality, 1966). In this case gravy was implicated. The organism had multiplied in the gravy at some time during preparation or inadequate refrigeration. Bringing the gravy to a "rolling boil" did not kill the contaminant.

Canada et al. (1964) determined the response of *C. perfringens* spores and vegetative cells to low temperature, using 4 strains. Exposure to freezing at −17.7°C (0°F), and a refrigeration temperature of 7.1°C (45°F), killed a large percentage of the vegetative cells. The spores of *C. perfringens* are resistant to freezing and freezer storage.

The control of this organism in qualtity food service lies mostly in preventing its multiplication by strict time–temperature control.

### Other Bacteria

*Bacillus cereus, Escherichia coli, Proteus mirabilis*, and *Proteus vulgaris* have been indicted occasionally in connection with foodborne gastroenteritis. Because of their uncertain etiology and relative unimportance, they will be discussed only briefly.

#### BACILLUS CEREUS

*Bacillus cereus*, a spore former commonly associated with cereal, grains and flour, has been implicated in several outbreaks of food poisoning in Norway (Dack, 1956) involving many persons.

#### PROTEUS

According to Dack (1956), members of the genus *Proteus* are suspected of having caused food-poisoning outbreaks involving fish, crab, sausage, and baked ham. *Proteus* organisms are common inhabitants of the intestinal tract of man as well as animals. The species suspected of causing foodborne gastroenteritis were *P. vulgaris* and *P. mirabilis*.

### ESCHERICHIA COLI

*Escherichia coli*, a common inhabitant of the intestinal tract of man and warm-blooded animals, is usually regarded as a harmless saprophyte. Specific strains, however, have been associated with infant diarrhea (Riley, 1964). Work with human volunteers has indicated the possible pathogenicity of large numbers of cells ingested (June et al., 1953). The number of outbreaks possibly caused by *E. coli* is unknown, but it may be large. For example, it has been stated (Food Protection Committee, National Academy of Sciences, 1964) that in Illinois during 1962 one small hospital of fewer than 300 beds reported 25% of all outbreaks were caused by enteropathogenic *E. coli*.

### HALOPHILIC BACTERIA

In 1955 an outbreak of gastroenteritis occurred at a hospital in Yokohama, Japan. The persons who became ill had eaten salted cucumbers. Unfamiliar bacteria were recovered at a high ratio on media containing 5% sodium chloride. It was demonstrated that these bacteria produced the typical symptoms in human volunteers. In 1959, another episode was caused by similar organisms, but this time the food implicated was raw fish. At a later date some cooked food items caused outbreaks. The exact identity and the pathogenicity of the organisms are still obscure.

## Fungi

Fungal toxins causing mycotoxicoses may affect both animals and humans. Mycotoxicoses are poisonings caused by fungus contaminated feed or food that manifest themselves in various types in the hosts. A summary of information pertaining to the problem of mycotoxins in foodstuffs was made available recently (Wogan, 1965). Some of these toxins have carcinogenic properties. The poisoning follows ingestion of moldy substrate; actually, the intoxication does not manifest itself in the form of acute intestinal gastroenteritis and therefore does not meet all qualifications of "food poisoning." It was felt that fungal toxins should be mentioned in order to warn that, at present, molds are no longer regarded as a harmless group of microorganisms.

The acute form of mycotoxicosis is characterized by hemorrhages in many tissues. The chronic form also includes changes in the blood and bone marrow, and damage to liver and kidneys is frequent. The molds capable of forming toxins and causing mycotoxicosis in man and animals are distributed over the world. They grow, produce toxins, and multiply on a wide variety of foods over side ranges of temperature and humidity.

### Aspergillus flavus

*Aspergillus flavus* is a mold which is able to produce a group of toxins which have been named aflatoxins, the potential hazard of which is only now beginning to be recognized. Aflatoxins are metabolic products of certain strains of this organism. They represent a group of structurally related derivatives of coumarin.

The toxins affect the liver. The initial problem showed up in England where these toxins were identified as causing a disease in turkeys, ducks, and pheasants that had been fed peanut meal. Young hogs and calves, guinea pigs, and rats—in fact, most domestic animal species—are susceptible to the toxins to some extent.

It has been feared that potential danger from aflatoxins to humans could exist when moldy peanuts were consumed. In the United States careful handling of the peanut crop makes this danger seem remote. However, in countries of humid and warm climates a potential hazard exists when the harvesting and subsequent handling of peanuts is not carried out in a way to preclude conditions favoring the growth of molds.

Research is now underway to clarify the role of these and other mycotoxins, from a public health point of view.

In this country, the Pure Food and Drug law has made moldy foods illegal in interstate commerce since 1906. At present, they fall in the category of adulterated foods, since they contain a filthy, putrid, or decomposed substance, or are otherwise unfit for food. Since the FDA can prove unfitness by demonstrating the presence of mycotoxins in significant concentrations, research on mycotoxins is being pushed ahead. Other research involves tests dealing with fungus–host relationships, breeding for varieties resistant to molds, and developing effective fungicides. Also, attention is being given to the improvement of harvesting methods, storage, processing, and plant sanitation. The food industry is cooperating with government agencies to safeguard the country's food supply against toxins from molds; similar efforts are being made abroad.

### Reporting and Investigation of Outbreaks

Gastroenteric outbreaks caused by food have been reported, on a small scale at first, for over 40 years. The reports were in the beginning limited to milk and were summarized by the Public Health Service. In 1938, waterborne and foodborne outbreaks were added. The decision to expand the reports grew out of concern over outbreaks of typhoid fever and infant diarrhea.

Since 1951, notices of outbreaks traced to milk, food, and water by various states have been collected and published in the Morbidity and Mortality Weekly Reports, which since 1961 have been handled by the Communicable Disease Center, Atlanta, Georgia.

Although in some states reporting of incidents of foodborne illness is now compulsory, this is unfortunately not true for all states. In the states requiring such reporting, the local authorities attend to the investigation, although some of the laboratory work may be performed in special centers within or even outside the state.

*Reports*

Family-limited gastrointestinal episodes are frequently unreported, an exception being suspected or confirmed cases of botulism. For many upsets, a physician is not called in. However, when meals which are served to the public cause illness, the impact may be very dramatic and the authorities are informed.

The initial report may be made through various channels of communication. Some of the basic data asked for are: date, time, and place of the suspected meal; names, addresses, and telephone numbers of at least some of the victims; symptoms of the victims; and the name of the person making the report. If the onset of the symptoms is slow, as is true for infection-type outbreaks, it may be difficult to even pinpoint the food service establishment where the illness-producing food was consumed, let alone the meal or particular item.

Some patients are very slow to report. When the onset of symptoms is brief, however, as in *Staphylococcus* food poisoning, the victims may be still present in the building or compound, such as in a school or industrial park. The principal or management would be the person reporting to the local authorities.

For success in followup and eventual control, reporting to the health authority should be as prompt as possible. The unsatisfactory outcome of many investigations is caused by a delay in reporting which makes it impossible for the epidemiologist or sanitarian to get all the facts he needs to pinpoint the case. A full knowledge of all pertinent facts is immediately helpful in limiting the spread of the outbreak and in treating the victims. In addition, it serves to deepen the understanding of cause and effect which are at play in foodborne outbreaks. At the time of an outbreak food service personnel and the public are probably most receptive to information on the subject of sanitary handling of foods.

*Investigations*

Many outbreaks require the knowledgable services of an entire team: the physician, the epidemiologist, the engineer, the sanitarian, the veterinarian, and the laboratory personnel (McCutchen, 1963). After the initial report has been received, immediate action is paramount to success. The objects of the investigation of foodborne illness are to: (1) determine the responsible meal; (2) determine the responsible item within the meal; (3) determine the nature and source of the contaminants; (4) determine the circumstances leading to contamination of and growth in the food; and (5) establish, in case of infections, proof that the pathogen has infected the patient.

The actual steps to take are: interview the victims, locate and visit the food service establishment suspected of having served the illness-producing food, impound the suspect food, take samples, and determine the causative agent.

Persons who ate the suspected meal, both ill and healthy, are interviewed as to what they ate. Also interviewed are physicians and nurses in care of the ill victims and the food managers and/or employees of the suspected establishment. Samples of suspect food items are collected and transmitted to the laboratory team for analysis.

The food establishment is scrutinized for detailed information on the source of the suspect food, storage condition, length of storage, preparation, holding, and other pertinent information in connection with the history of the suspect meal and its components. The health of the employees and the sanitary conditions of the premises, including washroom facilities, are also surveyed. The cooperation of the food service staff, dietitian, manager, and other employees, is extremely important if the survey is to be successful. All this information is entered on the appropriate forms.

The detailed food report usually includes: a copy of the suspected menu and a list of the ingredients used; preparation and holding conditions; brand and manufacturer and/or packer of ingredients; method of and circumstances pertaining to transportation, especially time; time of arrival and history after arrival; place, conditions, and length of storage; holding time and method of holding between preparation and service; and other information of importance in specific cases.

In the laboratory the food samples are subjected to chemical and microbiological analyses and a report is made on those findings. Specimens may also be obtained from patients and food handlers. The leader of the investigation team, an epidemiologist or sanitarian, interprets the information gained from interviews and laboratory tests as to the cause and source of the agent causing the outbreak.

*Present Status*

The current status of food poisoning has been reviewed by Dack (1960). The deficiencies and difficulties of reporting have been evaluated and possibilities for improvement have been suggested by the Food Protection Committee of the Food and Nutrition Board, National Academy of Sciences, National Research Council (1964).

They point out that the well-known deficiencies of morbidity reporting place great limitations on much interesting information furnished by local and state health departments; that reports give no indication of a significant decline of foodborne illnesses; and that, at the same time, improvement in food sanitation has prevented a marked increase in incidents, in spite of the steady increase in population.

According to this Committee it is not possible to assess the relative frequency of commercially processed and kitchen-prepared foods responsible for outbreaks. It is felt that improvement is needed regarding identification of causative agents approximately one-half of the outbreaks being now in the "etiology unknown" class.

Reporting of foodborne illnesses is poor indeed; two-fifths of the states do not report, another two-fifths report one or two per year, and only one-fifth report properly. The suggestions for improvement given by the above-mentioned Committee include that the reasons for nonreporting be identified and overcome through leadership education.

For effective investigation, improvement and evaluation of laboratory methodology are needed as it pertains to fast and accurate determination of types and levels of bacterial food contaminants important to public health. Many of the methods now used are not specifically adapted to foods and not always best suited to the wide variety of products for which they are used.

In summary these conclusions were drawn by the Committee (1964):

1) There is renewed interest in the microbiological contaminants of food that adversely affect public health, but current efforts are inadequate to cope with the problems arising from rapid changes and new developments in the food supply.

2) Reports of foodborne diseases submitted by the states to the Public Health Service represent only a few of the many outbreaks actually occurring in the United States.

3) More thorough investigation and consistent reporting of foodborne illnesses are needed for the guidance of industry and government in their efforts to protect the public health.

4) Additional technical intelligence about microbial contaminants in foods can be obtained from laboratory examination of products available to the public, as demonstrated by recent surveys indicating the prevalence of food-poisoning organisms in several widely used items.

5) Improved methods for the quantitative detection and rapid identification of microorganisms in foods are needed as a basis for the development of standard procedures.

6) Continuing evaluation of food protection programs and practices is necessary to keep them abreast of technological changes.

7) A broadened national program of research and education is essential to generate the specialized knowledge, skills, and public understanding needed to achieve control of foodborne illnesses.

## References

Angelotti, R., E. Wilson, M. J. Foter, and K. H. Lewis. (1959). "Time–Temperature Effects on Salmonellae and Staphylococci in Foods. I. Behavior in Broth Cultures and Refrigerated Foods." The Robert A. Taft Sanitary Engineering Center Technical Report F 59–2.

Angelotti, R., M. J. Foter, and K. H. Lewis. (1961a). "Time–Temperature Effects on Salmonellae and Staphylococci in Foods. I. Behavior in Refrigerated Foods. II. Behavior at Warm Holding Temperatures." Amer. Jour. Publ. Hlth., 51: 76–83; 83–88.

Angelotti, R., M. J., Foter, and K. H. Lewis. (1961b). "Time–Temperature Effects on Salmonellae and Staphylococci in Foods. III. Thermal death time studies." Appl. Micr., 9(4): 308–315.

Angelotti, R., H. E. Hall, M. J. Foter, and K. H. Lewis. (1962a). "Quantitation of Clostridium perfringens in Foods." Appl. Micr., 10(3): 193–199.

Angelotti, R., Keith H. Lewis, and Milton J. Foter. (1962b). "Time–Temperature Effects On Fecal Streptococci in Foods. Unpublished Paper presented before the Laboratory Section 90th Annual Meeting, Amer. Publ. Health Assoc., Miami, Fla., October.

Angelotti, Robert, Keith H. Lewis, and Milton J. Foter. (1963). "Time–Temperature Effects on Fecal Streptococci in Foods. I. Behavior in Refrigerated Foods and at Warm-holding Temperatures." Jour. Milk & Food Tech., 26(9): 296–301.

Bowmer, E. J. (1965). "Salmonellae in Food—A Review." Jour. Milk & Food Tech., 28 (3): 74–86.

Canada, James C., Dorothy H. Strong, and Lelia G. Scott. (1964). "Response of Clostridium perfringens Spores and Vegetative Cells to Temperature Variation." Appl. Micr., 12(3): 273–276.

Casman, E. P. (1958). "Serologic Studies of Staphylococcal Enterotoxin." Publ. Hlth. Repts., 73: 599–609.

Casman, E. P. (1960). "Further Serological Studies of Staphylococcal Entero-toxin." *Jour. Bact.*, *79:* 849–856.

Casman, E. P. (1962). "The Nature and Detection of Staphylococcal Entero-toxin." *In:* Slanetz, L. W., et al. Microbiological Quality of Foods. Proceedings of a Conference held at Franconia, New Hampshire, August 27–29, 1962. Academic Press, New York. p. 50–54.

Casman, E. P., M. S. Bergdoll, and J. Robinson. (1963). "Designation of Staphylococcal Enterotoxins." *Jour. Bact.*, *85:* 715–716.

Casman, E. P., and R. Bennett. (1965). "Detection of Staphylococcal Entero-toxin in Food." *Appl. Micr.*, *13*(2): 181–189.

Collee, J. G., Jill A. Knowlden, and Betty C. Hobbs. (1961). "Studies on the Growth, Sporulation and Carriage of *Clostridium welchii* with Special Reference to Food Poisoning Strains." *Jour. Appl. Bact.*, *24*(3): 326–339.

Dack, G. M. (1956). *Food Poisoning*. 3rd ed. Univ. Chicago Press, Chicago, Ill.

Dack, G. M. (1960). "Current Status of Therapy in Microbial Food Poisoning." *Jour. Amer. Med. Assoc.*, *172*(9): 929–932.

Dauer, Carl C. (1961). "Summary of Disease Outbreaks and a 10-year Resume." *U.S. Publ. Hlth. Repts.*, *76*(10): 915–922.

Deibel, R. H., and J. H. Silliker. (1963). "Food Poisoning Potential of the Entero-cocci." *Jour. Bact.*, *85:* 827–832.

Dolman, C. E. (1964). "Botulism as a World Problem." *In:* "Botulism." Proceedings of a Symposium. U. S. Department of Health, Education, and Welfare, Public Health Service. Cincinnati, Ohio.

Edwards, P. R., and D. W. Bruner. (1942). "Serological Identification of *Salmonella* Cultures." *Kentucky Agr. Exper. Sta. Circular*, *54:* 1–35.

Eklund, M. W., and F. Paysky. (1965). *"Clostridium botulinum* Type F from Marine Sediments." *Science*, *149* No. 3681: 306. July 16.

Elliott, R. P., and P. K. Heiniger. (1965). "Improved Temperature-gradient Incubation and the Maximal Growth Temperature and Heat Resistance of *Salmonella.*" *Appl. Micr.*, *13*(1): 73–76.

Ellner, P. D. (1961). "Fate of Partially Purified C¹⁴-labeled Toxin of *Clostridium perfringens.*" *Jour. Bact.*, *82*(2): 275–283.

Ellner, P. D., and C. D. Bohan. (1962). "Serology of the Soluble Antigens of *Clostridium perfringens* Types A–F by Agar-Gel Diffusion." *Jour. Bact.*, *83:* 284–296.

Food Protection Committee of The Food and Nutrition Board. (1964). "An Evaluation of Public Health Hazards From Microbiological Contamination of Foods." National Academy of Sciences, National Research Council Publication 1195.

Foster, E. M., J. S. Deffner, T. L. Bott, and E. McCoy. (1965). *"Clostridium botulinum* Food Poisoning." *Jour. Milk & Food Tech.*, *28*(3): 86–91.

Hall, Herbert, R. Angelotti, and K. H. Lewis. (1963). "Quantitative Detection of Staphylococcal Enterotoxin B in Food by Gel-Diffusion Methods." *U.S. Publ. Health Reports*, *78*(12): 1089–1098.

Hall, Herbert, and Robert Angelotti. (1965). *"Clostridium perfringens* in Meat and Meat Products." *Appl Micr.*, *13*(3): 352–357.

Hart, C. H., W. W. Sherwood, and E. Wilson. (1960). "A Food Poisoning Outbreak Aboard a Common Carrier." *Publ. Hlth. Repts.*, *75:* 527–531.

Hobbs, Betty C., M. E. Smith, C. L. Oakley, H. G. Warrack, and J. C. Cruik-shank. (1953). *"Clostridium welchii* Food Poisoning." *Jour. Hyg.*, *51:* 75–101.

Hobbs, B. C., and J. G. Wilson. (1959). "Contamination of Wholesale Meat Supplies with *Salmonella* and Heat Resistant *Clostridium welchii.*" *Monthly Bull. Min. Hlth., Publ. Hlth. Lab. Serv., 18:* 198–206.

June, R. C., W. W. Ferguson, and M. T. Worfel. (1953). "Experiments in feeding adult Volunteers with *Escherichia coli* 55 B₅₁ a Coliform Organism Associated with Infant Diarrhea." *Amer. Jour. Hyg., 57:* 222–236.

Kautter, D. A. (1964). "*Clostridium botulinum* Type E in Smoked Fish." *Jour. Food Sci., 29*(6): 843–849.

Kemp, G. E., R. Proctor, and A. Browne. (1962). "Foodborne Disease in California with Special Reference to *Clostridium perfringens (welchii).*" *Publ. Hlth. Repts., 77:* 910–914.

Klotz, A. W. (1965). "Application of FA Techniques to Detection of *Clostridium perfringens.*" *U.S. Publ. Hlth. Repts., 80*(4): 305–311.

Linden, B. A., W. R. Turner, and C. Thom. (1926). "Food Poisoning from a *Streptococcus* in Cheese." *U.S. Publ. Hlth. Repts., 41*(32): 1647–1652.

McClung, L. S. (1945). "Human Food Poisoning Due to Growth of *Clostridium perfringens (welchii)* in Freshly Cooked Chicken: preliminary note." *Jour. Bact., 50:* 229–231.

McCutchen, J. H. (1963). "Investigation of Foodborne Diseases." *Jour. Envir. Hlth., 25:* 339–346.

Morbidity and Mortality Weekly Reports, U.S. Department of Health, Education and Welfare, *Public Health Service, 13*(1), Jan. 1964.

Morbidity and Mortality Weekly Reports, U.S. Department of Health, Education and Welfare, *Public Health Service, 24*(22): June 5, 1965.

Morbidity and Mortality Weekly Reports, U.S. Department of Health, Education and Welfare, *Public Health Service, 15*(12), Mar. 26, 1966.

Ohye, D. F., and W. J. Scott. (1957). "Studies in the Physiology of *Clostridium botulinum* Type E." *Australian Jour. Biolog. Sci., 10:* 85–94.

Osheroff, B. J., G. G. Slocum, and W. M. Decker. (1964). "Status of Botulism in the United States." *Public Health Reports, 79*(10): 871–878.

Parfentjev, I. A., and Anna R. Catelli. (1964). "Tolerance of *Staphylococcus aureus* to Sodium Chloride." *Jour. Bact., 88*(1): 1–3.

Pederson, H. O. (1957). "The Survival of *Clostridium botulinum* in Curing Brines." Symposium on Food Microbiology, 283.

Peterson, A. C., J. J. Black, and M. F. Gunderson. (1964a). "Staphylococci in Competition. III. Influence of pH and Salt of Staphylococcal Growth in Mixed Populations." (1964b) IV. Effect of Starch and Kind and Concentration of Sugar on Staphylococcal Growth in Mixed Populations." (1964c) V. Effect of Eggs, Eggs Plus Carbohydrates and Lipids on Staphylococcal Growth." *Appl. Micr., 12*(1): 70–76; 77–82; 83–86.

Post, F. J., A. H. Bliss, and W. B. O'Keefe. (1961). "Studies on the Ecology of Selected Food Poisoning Organisms in Foods. I. Growth of *Staphylococcus aureus* in Cream and a Cream Product." *Jour. Food Sci., 26*(4): 436–441.

Proceedings of a Symposium, "Botulism." (1964). U.S. Department of Health, Education and Welfare, Public Health Service, Publication No. 999-FP-1, Cincinnati, Ohio.

Proceedings, National Conference on Salmonellosis, March, 1964. (1965). U.S. Department of Health, Education and Welfare, Public Health Service, Publication No. 1262.

Riley, H. D. "Enteropathogenic *E. coli* Gastroenteritis." (1964). *Chem. Pediatrics,* *3:* 93.

Sanders, Eugene, Eli A. Friedman, Charles E. McCall, and Philip S. Brachman. (1963). "Surveillance of Human Salmonellosis." *U.S. Publ. Hlth. Repts.,* *78*(12): 1080–1083.

Schmidt, C. F., R. V. Lechowich, and J. F. Folinazzo. (1961). "Growth and Toxin Production By Type E *Clostridium botulinum* Below 40°F." *Jour. Food Sci.,* *26:* 626–630.

Segalove, M., and G. M. Dack. (1944). "Growth of a Strain of *Salmonella enteritidis* Experimentally Inoculated Into Canned Foods." *Food Res.,* *9:* 1–5.

Segner, W. P., C. F. Schmidt, and J. K. Baltz. (1964). "The Effect of Sodium Chloride and pH on the Outgrowth of Spores of Type E *Clostridium botulinum* at Optimal and Suboptimal Temperatures." *Bact. Proc. Amer. Soc. Microbiol.,* 1964. p. 3.

Sheneman, J. M. (1964). "Prevention of Type E *Clostridium botulinum* Toxin Formation in Smoked Whitefish Chubs with Tylosin Lactate." *Jour. Food Sci.,* *30*(2): 337–343.

Smith, Louis, DS. (1962). "*Clostridium perfringens* Food Poisoning." *In:* Slanetz, L. W., et al. Microbiological Quality of Foods. Proceedings of a Conference held at Franconia, New Hampshire, August 27–29, 1962. Academic Press, New York, pp. 77–83.

Strong, Dorothy H., James C. Canada, and Bertie B. Griffiths. (1963). "Incidence of *Clostridium perfringens* in American Foods." *Appl. Micr.,* *11*(1): 42–44.

Surgalla, M., M. Segalove, and G. Dack. (1944). "Growth of Food-poisoning Strain of Alpha-type *Streptococcus* Experimentally Inoculated into Canned Foods." *Food Res.,* *9:* 112–114.

White, Helen R. (1953). "The Heat Resistance of *Streptococcus faecalis.*" *Jour. Gen. Micr.,* *8:* 27–37.

Wogan, Gerald W. (ed.), *Mycotoxins in Foodstuffs.* MIT Press, Cambridge, Mass. 1965.

## Additional Readings

Anonymous. "Moldy Peanuts and Liver Cancers." *Jour. Amer. Med. Assoc.,* *184:* 57. April–June, 1963.

Anonymous. "Botulism Outbreaks From Smoked White Fish." Government Action. *Food Tech.,* *18*(1): 71–74. 1964.

Bergdoll, M. S. "Chemistry and Detection of Staphylococcal Enterotoxin." Proceedings of the 14th Research Conference Sponsored by the Research Council of AMIF. *Amer. Meat Inst. Found. Circular No. 70:* 47–53. July, 1962.

Canada, James C., and Dorothy H. Strong. "*Clostridium perfringens* in Bovine Livers." *Jour. Food Sci.,* *29*(6): 862–864. 1964.

Chang, S. B., M. M. Abdel Kader, E. Wick, and C. N. Wogan. "Aflatoxin B2 Chemical Identity and Biological Activity." *Science,* *142:* 1191–1192. 1963.

Dack, G. M. "Problems in Foodborne Diseases." *In:* Slanetz, L. W., et al. Microbiological Quality of Foods. Proceedings of a Conference held at Franconia, New Hampshire, August 27–29, 1962. Academic Press, New York. p. 41–49.

Dolman, C. E., and H. Iida. "Type E Botulism: Its epidemiology, prevention and specific treatment." *Canad. Jour. Publ. Hlth.*, *54:* 293-308. 1963.

Esselen, William and Arthur Levine. *Food Poisoning: Its Nature, History and Causation.* 4th ed. Hill, London, 1959.

Feig, M. "The Investigation of Foodborne Disease Outbreaks of Acute Gastroenteritis." *Amer. Jour. Publ. Hlth.*, *42:* 1535-1541. 1952.

Forgacs, J., and W. T. Carll. "Mycotoxicoses." *Advances Vet. Sci.*, *7:* 273-382. 1962.

Frazier, William C. *Food Microbiology.* McGraw-Hill Book Co. New York. 1958.

Graikoski, J. T., and L. L. Kempe. "Factors Affecting the Toxin Production by *Clostridium botulinum* Type E." *Bacter. Proc.*, *8: 8.* Abstract No. A29.

Hall, H. E., D. F. Brown, and R. Angelotti. "The Recovery of Enterococci From Food Using KF *Streptococcus* media." *Jour. Food Sci.*, *28*(5): 566-571. 1963.

Hall, H. E., Robert Angelotti, Keith H. Lewis, and Milton J. Foter. "Characteristics of *Clostridium perfringens* Strains Associated With Food and Foodborne Disease." *Jour. Bact.*, *85:* 1094-1103. 1963.

Hobbs, B. "Staphylococcal and *Clostridium welchii* Food Poisoning." *Royal Soc. Prom. Hlth. Jour.*, *80:* 267-272. 1960.

Hoyashi, K., Y. Kugeta, M. Towana, and Y. Hiroshi. "A Mass Food Poisoning Affair Caused by *Clostridium welchii* Hobbs, Type 2" *Endemic Disease Bull.*, Nagasaki University, *3:* 1-9. 1961.

International Association of Milk and Food Sanitarians. "Procedure for Investigation of Foodborne Disease Outbreaks." Internat. Assoc. Milk & Food Sanitarians, Shelbyville, Indiana. 1957.

Johnston, Ralph W., John Feldman, and Rosemary Sullivan. "Botulism From Canned Tuna Fish." *U.S. Publ. Hlth. Repts.*, *78*(7): 561-564. 1963.

Kaufmann, O. W., and A. B. Brilland. "Development of *Clostridium botulinum* in Experimentally Inoculated Sterile Skim Milk Held at Low Temperatures." *Amer. Jour. Publ. Hlth.*, *54:* 1514-1521. 1964.

Kawataba, T., and G. Sakaguchi. "Halophilic Bacteria As a Cause of Food Poisoning." *In:* Slanetz, L. W., et al. Microbiological Quality of Foods. Proceedings of a Conference held at Franconia, New Hampshire, August 27-29, 1962. Academic Press, New York, p. 63-70.

Lewis, Keith H., and Kenneth Cassel (ed.). "Botulism." Proceedings of a Symposium. U.S. Department of Health, Education and Welfare, Public Health Service, Environmental Health Series, Food Protection. December 1964.

Meisel, H. P., P. Toembowlen, and B. Pogorzka. "Über *Perfringens Clostridien* als Bestandteil der normalen fäkalen Bakterienflora beim Menschen." *Pathol. Micr.*, *24:* 307-316. 1961.

Meyer, K. F., and B. Eddie. "Fifty Years of Botulism in the United States and Canada." George Williams Hooper Foundation, Univ. California, San Francisco, July 1950.

Moran, A. B., C. D. Van Houweling, and E. M. Ellis. "The Results of Typing Salmonella from Animal Sources in the United States," *In:* Proceedings, Nat. Conf. on Salmonellosis. March 11-13, 1964. Commun. Disease Center, Atlanta, Ga., p. 33-37. PHS. Publ. 1262. 1965.

Morbidity and Mortality Weekly Reports, U.S. Department of Health, Education and Welfare; *Public Health Service, 12*(47), Dec. 2, 1963.

Morrison, S. M., J. F. Fair, and K. K. Kennedy. "*Staphylococcus aureus* in domestic animals." *Publ. Hlth. Repts.*, *76:* 673-677. 1961

Morrison, R. B. "The Coagulase Test in the Identification of Pathogenic Staphylococci." *Jour. Appl. Bact.*, *25*(3): 432–435. 1962.

Munch-Petersen, E. "Staphylococci in Food and Food Intoxications. A Review and An Appraisal of Phage-typing Results." *Jour. Food Sci.*, *28:* 692–710. 1963.

Niven, C. F., Jr., "Microbial Indexes of Food Quality: fecal streptococci." *In:* Slanetz, L. W., et al. Microbiological Quality of Foods. Proceedings of a Conference Held at Franconia, New Hampshire, August 27–29, 1962. Academic Press, New York. p. 119–131.

Osheroff, B. J., G. G. Slocum, and W. M. Decker. "Status of Botulism in the United States." *Publ. Hlth. Repts.*, *79*(10): 871–878. 1964.

Parker, M. T. "Phage-typing and the Epidemiology of *Staphylococcus aureus* Infection." *Jour. Appl. Bact.*, *25*(3): 389–402. 1962.

Pelczar, Jr., M. J., and R. D. Reid. *Microbiology.* 2nd ed. McGraw-Hill Book Co., New York. 1965.

Ravenholt, Reimert T., Robert C. Eelkeman, Marie Mulhern, and Ray B. Watkins. "Staphylococcal Infection in Meat Animals and Meat Workers." *U.S. Publ. Hlth. Repts.*, *76:* 879–888. Oct. 1961.

Reed, James R. "A Review of Botulism in The United States." *Jour. Envir. Hlth.*, *27*(3): 632–642. 1964.

Sterne, M., and G. H. Warrack. "The Types of *Clostridium perfringens.*" *Jour. Path. Bact.*, *88:* 279–283. 1964.

Sugiyama, H., M. S. Bergdoll, and G. M. Dack. "*In vitro* Studies on Staphylococcal Enterotoxin Production." *Jour. Bact.*, *80:* 265–270. 1960.

Tanner, Fred W. and Louise P. Tanner. *Foodborne Infections and Intoxications.* 2nd. ed. Garrard Press, Champaign, Ill. 1953.

Taylor, J. "Coliform Bacteria in Relation to Foodborne Disease." *Jour. Appl. Bact.*, *18:* 596–605. 1955.

Thatcher, F. S., and J. Robinson. "Food Poisoning: An analysis of staphylococcal toxins." *Jour. Appl. Bact.*, *25*(3): 378–388. 1962.

CHAPTER **V**

# RESERVOIRS OF MICROORGANISMS CAUSING FOODBORNE GASTROENTERIC OUTBREAKS: MAN, ANIMALS, ENVIRONMENT

Many reservoirs of the bacteria which cause foodborne gastroenteric illnesses could be listed. Some important ones are man and the animals he keeps, sewage, manure, soil, water, air, rodents, insects, and the food supply. Water and soil frequently acquire pathogens from sewage (human source) and manure (animal source); in turn, the food supply may acquire pathogens from all the above-named sources. Thus, man and animals emerge as the fundamental sources of the organisms which are responsible for foodborne gastrointestinal illnesses.

## Man

Of special interest to the food service manager is the inherent danger from the bacterial flora of the healthy person and carrier. Persons suffering from obvious communicable diseases are not as likely to prepare food for the public as is the carrier. A carrier is a person who harbors and disseminates the disease-producing microbes without having the symptoms of the disease. He may have recovered from the disease or he may never have been ill at all. He is immune to the organisms which he harbors in his system.

### Skin

The human skin is never free of bacteria; even clean skin carries some organisms. But when skin is not clean, an impressive number and variety of microorganisms are present, including bacteria, molds, yeasts, and protozoa. Since man uses his hands for many different purposes he touches a great many things, acquiring the microbial population from almost everything he contacts. This population of microorganisms is apt to include pathogens capable of causing various foodborne gastroenteritis.

The bacteria clinging to the skin may multiply there, especially near the sebacious glands. Although thorough washing removes many bacteria from the skin, some microorganisms are apt to remain.

The common flora of the human skin includes representatives of the genus *Staphylococcus*, one being the nonpathogenic *S. epidermidis*. *S. aureus*, however, includes strains that are able to multiply in food and form toxins which, when such food is ingested, causes the dreaded intoxications or food poisonings.

It has been estimated that at least one-half of the normal, healthy population harbors virulent, or potentially virulent, staphylococci. Staphylococci are generally found in connection with pimples, acne, skin wounds, and other inflamed skin conditions. Some pyogenic strains of *S. aureus* may cause skin infections of various kinds. The resistance of the body to staphylococci varies with the virulence of the organisms and the resistance of the invaded tissues.

Furunculosis is a type of infection that follows a cut or simple abrasion. Carbuncles are a more severe skin disorder which follows the invasion of the staphylococci into the deeper tissues. While the furuncle is characterized by a single superficial abscess, the carbuncle involves a large area of deeper tissues characterized by the formation of several "heads" containing pus and staphylococci. Impetigo contagiosa is a contagious skin infection characterized by small pustules which occur on the face but may also spread to other parts of the body. Paronychia is an infection of the nail bed of either fingers or toes. Scratching of infected skin transfers the staphylococci to the hands, especially the nails.

From the foregoing discussion it is obvious that in food service, the person afflicted with pyogenic infections of the skin is a menace; unfortunately, the person who is so afflicted is usually not ill enough to stay away from work. Furthermore, since the infections are largely localized on the exposed body parts, the fingers, hands, arms, and face, an infected food handler is in a particularly excellent position to spread these organisms around, contaminating the food and equipment he touches and sowing the seeds of food poisoning in the food preparation area.

## Mouth, Nose, Throat, Eyes, and Ears

The areas of the mouth, nose, and throat of a healthy human abound with microorganisms of various kinds. The environment is moist and warm, and acceptable nutrients are available to the bacteria in the form of remnants from food consumed by the human.

Among the numerous kinds of microorganisms represented, one is of outstanding significance here, namely *Staphylococcus aureus,* which lodges in the respiratory passages of many healthy individuals. Virulent strains of the organism are associated with ailments such as sinusitis and the common cold. Persons recovering from these ailments may remain carriers for extended periods. *S. aureus* is also frequently associated with infections of the eyes and ears.

Persons suffering from infections of the respiratory tract, eyes, and ears, or who are carriers while or after recovering from these diseases, must be suspected of being a rich source of virulent staphylococci and should be prevented from handling food.

## Intestinal Tract

The composition of the intestinal flora of the healthy human body may vary with certain external factors. The first part of the small intestine has, like the stomach, no natural microbial flora. In the jejunum and ileum, microorganisms begin to appear. It is in the lower end of the small intestine that a variety of bacteria are found in large numbers. The major representatives are the coliforms, *Escherichia coli* and *Aerobacter aerogenes.* Bacteria important in connection with foodborne illnesses are *Clostridium perfringens,* fecal streptococci (enterococci), salmonellae, and occasionally staphylococci. The salmonellae are particularly plentiful in the intestinal tracts of persons recovering from salmonelloses.

It is important for food service management to realize that some of the pathogens for which food is a vehicle of transmission may remain in the human carrier for prolonged periods of time, as in the case of typhoid fever, the dysenteries, the salmonelloses, and hepatitis. In typhoid fever, convalescent carriers usually discharge the bacteria for 8–10 weeks following recovery, but some patients become chronic or permanent carriers for the rest of their lives. Following salmonellosis victims may remain carriers for several weeks; *S. derby* has been found to persist for months in the victims' intestinal system (Sanders and Friedman, 1965).

Patients who have recovered from bacillary dysentery or shigellosis are carriers for a while, but no chronic carriers result from this infection. Patients who have recovered from amoebic dysentery may become chronic carriers for the rest of their lives. The hepatitis virus has been found to remain with patients from one to five years.

It is readily understandable that the principles of control include these important items: (1) Exclusion of carriers from the area of food preparation and service; (2) education of food service workers in the importance of sanitary habits; and (3) unrelenting supervision.

## Animals

### Livestock

*Staphylococcus aureus* is an inhabitant of the nose, mouth, throat, and skin of farm animals. However, Morrison et al. (1961), who reviewed the literature on the subject and studied the incidence of staphylococci in cattle and horses, concluded that the majority of the forms are coagulase-negative and therefore not likely to be potentially virulent.

Fecal streptococci, *Clostridium perfringens*, and coliforms are natural inhabitants of the intestinal tract of livestock.

Salmonellae have been shown to be frequent inhabitants of farm animals, including horses, cattle, and hogs (Moran, 1961; Galton, 1963). These animals may become carriers. The increase in salmonellosis was discussed by Galton (1963), who stated that during the 14 years 1934–1947, only 0.7% of the cultures isolated from livestock were from cattle whereas during the years 1957–1961, the percentage had risen to 7. During this same period an increase was noted in cultures from fowl.

According to a report by Galton (1963) of a survey made in Florida, hogs harbor salmonellae very frequently. It has been shown that the organisms spread when the animals are crowded together in barns during the months when pasturing is not possible. Crowding during shipment to the abattoirs and in the corrals near abattoirs has shown to increase salmonellae incidence up to tenfold what it is in farm animals.

Galton and Hardy (1953) found in a study made in Florida that the relative prevalence of most common *Salmonella* types isolated from man, swine, and dogs was similar. This seems to indicate that infections were either spread from one host to the other, or that these salmonellae came originally from the same source.

### Poultry

Poultry may become an important reservoir of *Staphylococcus aureus* when the skin of the live bird has been injured and the bruises have become infected with staphylococci. Hamdy and Barton (1965) demonstrated that multiplication of *S. aureus* is related to the severity of the bruise.

Poultry is the greatest single animal reservoir of *Salmonella*, including strains pathogenic to man. A high proportion, approximately one-half, of the *Salmonella*-caused gastroenteric outbreaks in man are traced to poultry and poultry products.

It seems that poultry has an unusual susceptibility to salmonellae. One of the species, *S. pullorum*, seriously affects baby chicks and poults, causing many fatalities. The organism invades practically all of the internal organs. In the United States the poultry-raising industry has made a supreme effort to eradicate *S. pullorum* from flocks and has been quite successful by testing birds for carriers, eliminating carriers, hatching eggs from sources known to be free of the disease, and maintaining high sanitary standards in the plants. *S. pullorum* does not seem to be pathogenic to man. However, it has been demonstrated in some instances that the ingestion of massive doses of the organism caused gastrointestinal disorders in the volunteers participating in the experiments.

Other species and strains of *Salmonella* harbored by poultry, among these *S. typhimurium*, are quite pathogenic to man. Poultry, especially turkeys, are known to become carriers of these organisms. The adult carriers usually look healthy and escape culling for disease. Therefore, they represent a constant source of infection to other birds and a source of contamination to eggs (Quist, 1963). When the birds are processed into meat, the flesh is likely to become contaminated with salmonellae originating from the intestinal tract.

The shells of eggs become a source of *Salmonella* and may contaminate the contents when the shell and membranes are injured, or when the shell is deliberately opened in the egg-processing plant.

Control measures include, for all livestock and poultry, the elimination of carriers of *Salmonella*, high sanitary standards in the care of farm animals and poultry flocks, and the use of feedstuffs known to be free from *Salmonella* (Morehouse and Wedman, 1961).

*Pets*

Morrison et al. (1961) studied *Staphylococcus aureus* in dogs and cats. They found that carrier rates of coagulase-positive, antibiotic-resistant staphylococci on the skin and nose were high in the canine and feline species. The authors concluded that domestic animals may serve as sources of pathogenic staphylococci.

These companions of man are known to harbor many serotypes of

*Salmonella* (Mackel et al., 1952). In one study involving greyhounds in Florida, Stucker et al. (1952) were able to relate the extent of incidences to the sanitation in the kennels. Even family dogs have been shown to be extensively infected with salmonellae. *Salmonella* incidences in dogs have been related to intake of *Salmonella*-contaminated, underprocessed dog food (Galton et al., 1955).

*Salmonella* from turtles has also been reported to cause foodborne gastroenteric outbreaks (Morbidity and Mortality, 1964). Case histories showed that the contaminated agent was the turtles' water, which was discarded into the kitchen sink. Although the chances are remote that food prepared in public eating places becomes contaminated from such a source, opportunities might be afforded when food is prepared in the family kitchen for community meal service, or when children handling pets are taking part in meal preparation, as may happen in a camp situation.

Pets do not belong in an area where food is prepared, served, and stored. Persons who have handled pets should change clothing and wash up thoroughly before handling food. Although these hygienic practices are obligatory for personnel employed by food service establishments, they are not always enforced and they are not likely to be always followed when food is prepared in the home for community food service.

The control of salmonellae in pet food is another means of reducing the incidence of salmonelloses in pets and indirectly in man.

## Rodents

Rats and mice may contaminate food during harvest, in transport, in storage, and in the food preparation area. These animals carry disease-producing organisms on their feet and/or in their intestinal tracts. Rats, in particular have a habit of feeding in places of filth, like garbage dumps and sewers.

These rodents are known to harbor salmonellae of serotypes frequently associated with foodborne infections in man, such as *Salmonella typhimurium, enteritidis*, and *newport*.

Poultry men in this country are plagued by rats and suffer great losses from their activity caused not only by loss of feed eaten by the rats, but also by the disease which rats pass on to poultry. Rats infect, by their droppings, poultry feed and eggs with *Salmonella*. Rats are largely nocturnal animals and are among the most prolific of mammals. Their appetite for food is tremendous. The control of rats is most essential but, unfortunately, is more difficult than the control of mice. Rats are very suspicious animals and evade trapping.

Rats and mice must be kept out of places where food animals, feed, and food are housed. They should be exterminated from appropriate access places where they like to feed, like garbage cans; these places should be protected. Rodents must be kept out of the areas where food is stored, prepared, and served.

*Insects*

FLIES

The fly most frequently associated with man is the housefly, *Musa domestica*. This species is the predominant one found in food establishments. During warm weather, two or more housefly generations per month may be produced. The female lays large numbers of eggs each time and populations increase at a tremendous rate. In the winter the housefly seeks protected areas. In temperate climatic zones, the fly passes the winter months by a combination of adult hibernation and semicontinuous breeding.

Animal manure, human feces, sewage, and garbage are favored breeding places of flies. Open garbage cans and dumps are, therefore, a menace to sanitation.

Flies frequently carry disease-causing organisms in their mouth parts, intestinal tract, and on their leg hairs and feet. Since flies feed on feces, animal manure, and human filth, all of which may contain intestinal pathogens of human and animal origin, they are an important reservoir of microorganisms causing many foodborne illnesses; among these are the salmonelloses, typhoid and paratyphoid fevers, and dysenteries. Flies are attracted to many foods. Carbohydrates are needed as well as proteins, the latter being required for production of eggs. Flies are constantly moving about, taking nourishment here and there. Since they are attracted to feces as well as to food, they are a menace to food sanitation: as the fly feeds on the materials on which it alights, it periodically regurgitates liquid from the crop. This liquid may contain pathogens picked up from fecal material on which the animal fed previously. Therefore, it is extremely important that the food supply be protected from flies at all times.

COCKROACHES

Cockroaches are one of the most common and troublesome pests in food establishments. There are several kinds, the American, German, Brown-Banded, and Oriental being the most frequent ones.

Cockroaches are nocturnal in habit and scurry away to hide when disturbed. They may leave a musty odor on objects on which they rest for a while; another sign of their presence is a stain which they leave with their rather liquid feces. When dry, droppings resemble mouse pellets, but they are distinguished by lengthwise ridges.

Cockroaches are able to contaminate more food than they are able to eat. They are particularly fond of starchy foods, cheese, and beer; but they will also feed on dead animals, leather, wallpaper, and the like. They contaminate food, equipment, and utensils by carrying filthy material that may contain pathogens on their legs and bodies. Also, while feeding on food, cockroaches may regurgitate filthy material previously eaten which may be laden with bacteria capable of causing foodborne illnesses.

ANTS AND SILVERFISH

Ants are frequent pests in some food establishments, including camps. Ants may carry disease organisms around and thus may contaminate the food. Their life cycle consists of eggs, larvae, pupae, and adults.

Silverfish are related to the centipedes. They like warmth and are often found to infest warm places, such as in the neighborhood of bakery ovens where they feed on crumbs. Silverfish like starchy foods.

In summary, foods must be protected from insects at all times. To achieve this, basic sanitation must be constantly applied because it deprives the insects of food and shelter. For chemical control, the services of professional exterminators should be sought. However, only permanent methods such as pestproofing and sanitation can achieve long-time control (Johnson, 1960).

## Environment

### Sewage

COMPOSITION

Sewage consists of fecal matter of human origin, much diluted with water, and other wastes such as laundry water, bathwater, and residues resulting from comminuted household garbage, mostly vegetable matter and similar wastes. Sewage is approximately 99% water and has pH near neutral.

FLORA

The flora of sewage includes aerobes, strict anaerobes, and facultative anaerobes. The bacteria include forms that stem from soil and the intestinal tract of humans. Examples of bacteria are fecal streptococci, *Clostridium perfringens*, *Salmonella*, *Shigella*, micrococci,

Pseudomonadaceae, and Lactobacillaceae. Also present may be viruses, yeasts, molds, algalike forms, and slime-forming organisms often called "sewage fungi." These organisms aid in one way or another to decompose the organic matter in sewage.

Sewage is thus a potential source of human pathogens, especially those of intestinal origin. Sewage plays a most important role in the contamination of water and food.

## CONTAMINATION OF WATER AND FOOD

The chances for contamination are manifold. Excellent opportunity is afforded when sewage is used to fertilize fields in which vegetable crops are raised. In this country, the use of raw sewage for the purpose of fertilization of truck crops is not practiced.

When sewage is allowed to flow into rivers, lakes, and seas, it contributes its flora, including pathogens, to the fish, shellfish, and other potential foods native to these waters. Sewage also creates a nuisance: when raw domestic sewage is not properly treated by oxidation and is allowed to flow directly into natural waters such as ponds, lakes, and streams, the microorganisms furnished by the raw sewage soon deplete these waters of oxygen and other hydrogen acceptors. In consequence, anaerobic processes develop, creating foul-smelling products and making conditions for natural biologic life of these waters very unfavorable. A most undesirable situation is thus created. Besides these waters not being usable for drinking or recreational purposes, they have spoiled much of the surrounding areas because of their distasteful odor.

Drinking water may become contaminated with sewage in various ways. In some rural and suburban areas the water supply is not as strictly and permanently controlled as in most cities. Also, in dwellings that have their own water source as well as sewage disposal tanks, cross-connection sometimes occurs.

## TREATMENT

In most communities, raw sewage is rendered safer by these steps: (1) collection in septic tanks or central sewage disposal plants; (2) separation of the organic materials by gravity as the sewage is held for several hours; (3) digestion of the sludge through mostly anaerobic microorganisms; (4) processing of the sludge to a powder which serves as a fertilizer; (5) treating the supernatant fluid part by aeration and oxidation with the aid of aerobic bacteria; (6) filtering the residual oxidized fluid; and (7), as a possible final step, chlorination of the fluid. The major steps in sewage treatment have been illustrated by Pelczar and Reid (1965).

Control measures should be directed at preventing the contact of sewage with food and water.

Perfectly pure and wholesome food and water may be recontaminated on the premises of a food service establishment through faulty plumbing and leaky sewer connections.

## Soil

The soil abounds with microorganisms, abundant in kind as well as in number. The microorganisms from soil affect the microbial flora of air, water, plants, and animals. In turn, soil may become contaminated by sewage and manure.

All microorganisms of importance in connection with foodborne illness may come from soil. Of bacteria causing foodborne illnesses, *Clostridium botulinum* and *perfringens* are natural inhabitants of soil and may survive there for very long periods of time.

Soil may enter the areas of food preparation and storage in many ways: with the food and its wrappings, on the employees' shoes, and in the air. Most "dust" is actually soil.

## Water

In the United States sanitation of drinking water is well controlled, in general, by agencies concerned with public health. In fact, the present generation must find it rather difficult to visualize the seriousness of a situation when a public water supply becomes contaminated. Waterborne outbreaks of typhoid and paratyphoid fevers have almost disappeared from the records.

### FLORA

Water found in nature is seldom sterile. Water coming down as rain or snow picks up contaminants from the air, and as it contacts the ground picks up contaminants from the soil and other surfaces. Thus, surface waters of streams, lakes, and seas contain these microorganisms also. As water penetrates the ground the soil has a filtering effect, and many of the contaminants which move downward with the water are removed. The deeper the water goes, the cleaner it becomes, although seldom is water rendered sterile by this kind of filtration.

Surface waters usually contain more organic matter than deep waters and thus support microbial life better. Near cities, surface waters are frequently contaminated with sewage, and in the country with sewage as well as manure.

Most microorganisms including the pathogens do not multiply profusely in pure water. They may sustain life for a while there, then die. Spores, however, may survive for months or years in water.

Although natural waters have a capacity to assimilate as well as transport waste, increase in wastes from the population and industrial plants is making it increasingly important that ways other than simple dilution be found to dispose of these wastes. The water of some streams and rivers is already now being used over several times, especially at periods of low flow.

Man should not rely upon self-purification of streams for pure supply of water. The popular belief that streams clarify themselves within a distance of 20 miles from the source of pollution has numerous loopholes. Purification is strongly affected by rate of flow; in fast-flowing streams the dilution of organic matter and of microorganisms is much more efficient than in slow-flowing ones. In ponds and reservoirs, water becomes purified by sedimentation. It has been stated that up to 90% of the bacteria can be removed in this manner.

Although industrial wastes seriously reduce the quality of our water supply, the main source of pollution of public health significance is sewage. Fecal coliforms, fecal staphylococci, enterococci, salmonellae, and clostridia are even discharged from healthy persons, and, of course, from carriers, and are transferred with sewage into the water. As was pointed out above, persons who suffer from acute cases of intestinal diseases contribute tremendous numbers of virulent pathogens into sewage. Serious and widespread epidemics of communicable diseases have resulted from fouled water supplies. Today, waterborne epidemics of typhoid and dysentery are rare in the United States but are still found in other parts of the world.

Pathogenic bacteria and viruses do not multiply in water. To be a hazard, a water supply must be either freshly contaminated or possess a continuous source of contaminants.

TREATMENT

To safeguard the water supply it is essential that the disposal of sewage be strictly controlled. Improper disposal of sewage is, in particular, a menace to private water supply systems which may escape the constant scrutiny to which the public water supply is subjected. The treatment of sewage was discussed above. In the United States the water supply is generally of excellent quality, thanks to strict sanitary supervision and treatment.

Requirements for a public water supply are listed by Weiser (1962) as the following:

(1) that it shall contain no organisms which cause disease
(2) that it be sparkling clear and colorless
(3) that it be good tasting, free from odors and preferably cool
(4) that it be neither scale-forming nor corrosive
(5) that it be reasonably soft
(6) that it be free from objectionable gas, such as hydrogen sulfide, and objectionable minerals, such as iron and manganese
(7) that it be plentiful and low in cost.

The test for freedom from pathogens is the presumptive test for coliform bacteria which comprise two species, *Escherichia coli* and *Aerobacter aerogenes*. The former is an intestinal organism, the latter is found more frequently in soils and on plant surfaces.

In the test for presence of these indicators, dilutions of the water are cultured in fermentation tubes of lactose broth at a temperature of 98.6°F. If acid and gas are produced, it is assumed that coliforms are present, and more detailed tests are performed.

Almost all our drinking water undergoes treatment before it is released to the public. Although water may purify itself under certain conditions, this purification is rather inefficient and cannot be relied on for a supply of safe water. In the United States, aeration, coagulation, filtration, and chemical treatment are used. Aeration helps to purify the water from dissolved gases and to oxidize iron as well as organic material; coagulation is induced by the addition of coagulants such as aluminum sulfate resulting in precipitation of organic material and bacteria, and settling and subsequent removal of the larger clumps. The process of filtration removes approximately 99% of the bacteria and other microorganisms of public health significance. The slow sand filter and the rapid sand filter are two types of filters used in this procedure. The slow filter has an approximate yield of 3 million gallons of filtered water per acre per day. The fast yields approximately 130 million gallons per acre per day.

The chemical treatments serve to adjust the hardness of the water and to control the bacterial population. Chlorine has characteristics which make it desirable as a chemical agent in the treatment of water; it is highly bactericidal and not expensive. Viruses and the protozoa *Entamoeba histolytica* resist chlorination.

Failure to chlorinate water recently led to a serious and extensive outbreak of gastroenteritis caused by *Salmonella typhimurium* in

Riverside, California (Morbidity and Mortality, 1965). The community water supply consisted of deep wells inside and outside the city. The water had always been pure and had never been chlorinated. Regular testing for the presence of *Escherichia coli* did not reveal high counts, even during the time of the *Salmonella* outbreak.

Water used in the processing and preparation of food should be of drinking quality. Water is used in food as an ingredient and as a cleaning agent for ingredients and equipment. Water must, therefore, be free from pathogens.

When a food establishment does not receive a piped-in supply of pure water, it may have to transport water from an approved outside supply in approved containers. In an emergency, boiling may be used to destroy pathogens present in water. Certain chemicals of bactericidal effect may be used for small quantities of water, if the directions are followed meticulously. Treatment of large amounts is to be entrusted to a trained person.

Ice manufactured from contaminated water, and ice manufactured, stored, or shipped under unsanitary conditions, may contaminate food and drink in which it is used.

## Air

Air does not contain a natural flora of microorganisms, but dust particles or moisture droplets present in air may pick up microorganisms. Therefore, air may serve as a reservoir of contaminants. If forced air is used on foods, contamination of food from air is greater than in still air.

The kinds and numbers of microorganisms present in air are so varied that enumeration is beyond the scope of this book. The numbers and kinds of microorganisms depend on many factors, among them location and season. Rain and snow remove organisms from the air. On mountain tops the air is generally low in microbial counts.

### AIR IN FOOD PREPARATION AREA

The kinds of microorganisms found in the air in a given area depend on many factors. Droplets of moisture from persons talking, coughing, and sneezing may contribute microorganisms to the air. Soil clinging to shoes and other clothing and soil adhering to materials brought into a room are examples of the sources of microorganisms that may be transmitted through air. Diseases which are typically transmitted through air are the common cold and some other respiratory illnesses spread by droplets discharged by the affected person.

It is known that bacteria may be spread through coughs and sneezes to considerable distances, up to 15 feet.

The number of microorganisms present in a given air space depends on many factors, among them presence of dust and droplets of moisture and air movement brought about by ventilation breezes or persons moving about.

The bacterial content of air can be diluted by simply opening a window and letting in fresh air. However, admitting dusty air would not achieve much or may make matters worse. Air conditioning can be used to control the bacteriological quality of air in a food service establishment. Removal of microorganisms from air can be achieved by methods such as filtration, heat, electrostatic precipitation, and treatment by chemicals. Filtration involves the passing of air through filters, such as asbestos, activated carbon, fiber glass, and cotton. Chemicals used for reducing the microbial load of air include di- or triethylene glycol, propylene glycol, formaldehyde, o-p-benzyl phenols, and hypochlorites.

Ultraviolet rays are also used to reduce the bacterial load of air. Rays of wavelengths 136–3900 angstroms are germicidal, those between 2500 and 2800 being particularly effective. Each kind of microorganism has a specific resistance to these rays. It may take several times as much exposure to kill vegetative cells of one kind of bacteria as of another. Spores are more resistant to the killing effect than vegetative cells.

Ultraviolet rays are used very little in food service but are employed to some extent in the food-processing industry. Examples of successful uses are listed by Frazier (1958) as: treatment of water for beverages; aging of meat; treatment of knives for slicing bread; treatment of bread and cakes; sanitizing of eating utensils; storage and packaging of cheese; and treatment of air for or in storage and processing rooms.

## References

Frazier, William C. (1958). *Food Microbiology*. McGraw-Hill Book Co., New York.
Galton, M. M. (1963). "Salmonellosis In Livestock." *In:* Epidemiology of Salmonellosis. *U.S. Publ. Hlth. Repts.*, 78(12): 1066–1070.
Galton, M. M., and A. V. Hardy. (1953). "The Distribution Of *Salmonella* Infections In Florida During The Past Decade." *The Publ. Hlth. Labor.*, 11: 88–93.
Galton, M. M., M. Harless, and A. V. Hardy. (1955). "Salmonella Isolations From Dehydrated Dog Meals." *Jour. Amer. Vet. Med. Assoc.*, 126: 57–58.

Hamdy, M. K., and Barton, N. D. (1965). "Fate of *Staphylococcus aureus* in Bruised Tissue." *Appl. Micr.*, *13*(1): 13–21.

Johnson, W. H. (1960). "Sanitation In The Control of Insects and Rodents of Public Health Importance." Public Health Service, Publication No. 772. Part IV.

Mackel, D. C., M. M. Galton, H. Gray, and A. V. Hardy. (1952). "Salmonellosis In Dogs. IV. Prevalence In Normal Dogs and Their Contacts." *Jour. Infect. Diseases*, *91:* 15–18.

Moran, A. B. (1961). "Occurrence and Distribution of Salmonella in Animals in the United States." *In:* Proceedings, 65th Annual Meeting, U.S. Livestock Sanitary Association, Minneapolis, Minnesota. October. p. 441–448.

Morbidity and Mortality Weekly Reports, U.S. Department of Health, Education and Welfare. "Salmonellosis." *Public Health Service*, *13*(21); *21*(33), 1964.

Morbidity and Mortality Weekly Reports, U.S. Department of Health, Education and Welfare, *Public Health Service*, 14(22): June 5; 14(23): June 12, 1965.

Morehouse, L. G., and E. E. Wedman. (1961). "*Salmonella* and Other Disease-Producing Organisms in Animal By-Products." A Survey. *Jour. Amer. Vet. Med. Assoc.*, *139:* 989–995.

Morrison, S. M., J. F. Fair, and K. K. Kennedy. (1961). "*Staphylococcus aureus* in domestic animals." *U.S. Publ. Hlth. Repts.*, *76:* 673–677.

Pelczar, M. J., Jr., and R. D. Reid. *Microbiology*, 2nd ed. McGraw-Hill, New York, 1965.

Quist, Kenneth D. (1963). "Salmonellosis in Poultry." *In:* Epidemiology of Salmonellosis. *U.S. Publ. Hlth. Repts.*, *78*(12): 1071–1073.

Sanders, E., and E. A. Friedman. (1965). "Epidemiological Investigation of the Outbreak." *In:* Proceedings of National Conference on Salmonellosis, March 11–13, p. 111–116. U.S. Public Health Service Publication No. 1262.

Stucker, C., M. M. Galton, J. Cowdery, and A. V. Hardy. (1952). "*Salmonella* in Dogs. II. Prevalence and Distribution in Greyhounds in Florida." *Jour. Infect. Diseases*, *91:* 6–11.

Weiser, Harry H. (1962). *Practical Food Microbiology and Technology*. Avi Publishing Co., Westport, Conn.

## Additional Readings

Auld, D. V. "Problems of the Physical Environment." *U.S. Publ. Hlth. Repts.*, *76:* 633–639. 1961.

Berger, B. B. "Public Health Considerations in Municipal Water Use." *Southwest Water Works Jour.*, 42: 20–30. April 1960.

Burdon, K. L., and Robert P. Williams. *Microbiology*. 5th ed. MacMillan Co., New York. 1964.

Burton, A. "Salmonellosis in Animals." *Veterinary Record*, *70:* 1044–1050. 1958.

Bjornson, B. F., and C. V. Wright. "Control of Domestic Rats and Mice." Training Guide—Rodent Control Series. *U.S. Publ. Hlth. Service*, PHS Publication No. 563. 1960.

Edwards, P. K., A. C. McWhorter, and M. A. Fife. "The Occurrence of Bacteria of The Arizona Group in Man." *Canad. Jour. Micr.*, *2:* 281–287. 1956.

Eichenwald, H. F., and J. W. Mosley. "Viral Hepatitis, Clinical and Public

Health Aspects." *U.S. Publ. Hlth. Service,* Publication No. 435. Reprinted 1960.

Elek, S. D. *Staphylococcus pyogenes and its Relation to Disease.* E. & E. Livingstone, Edinburgh. 1962.

Fair, G. M., J. C. Geyer, and J. C. Morris. *Water Supply and Waste Water Disposal.* John Wiley & Sons, New York. 1954.

Hamilton, W. J. "Rats and Their Control." *Cornell Extension Bulletin,* 353. May 1950.

Hollis, M. D., and G. E. McCallum. "Dilution is No Longer The Solution For Pollution." *Wastes Engineering, 30:* 578–581, 638. October 1959.

Horwood, M. P., and V. A. Minch. "The Numbers and Types of Bacteria Found on the Hands of Food Handlers." *Food Res., 16:* 133–136. 1951.

Kabler, P. W. "Purification and Sanitary Control of Water (potable and waste.)" *Ann. Rev. Micr., 16:* 127–140. 1962.

Mair, N. S., and A. E. Ross. "Survival of *Salmonella typhimurium* in the Soil." *Monthly Bull. Ministry of Hlth., 19:* 39–41. 1960.

Mudd, S. "The *Staphylococcus* Problem." *Sci. Amer., 200*(1): 41–45. 1959.

Pike, E. B. "The Classification of Staphylococci and Micrococci From the Human Mouth." *Jour. Appl. Bact., 25*(3): 448–455. 1962.

Ruddock, J. C. "Cockroach Control." *Sanitarian's Jour. Envir. Hlth., 25*(6): 417–420. 1963.

Sarles, William B., William C. Frazier, Joe Wilson, and Stanley G. Knight. *Microbiology.* 2nd ed. Harper and Brothers, New York. 1956.

Scott, H. G. "Household and Stored-Food Insects of Public Health Importance." *U.S. Publ. Hlth. Service,* PHS Publication No. 772. 1962.

Scott, H. G., and Kent S. Littig. "Flies of Public Health Importance and Their Control." *U.S. Publ. Hlth. Service,* PHS Publication No. 772, 1962.

*Standard Methods For The Examination of Water and Waste Water.* 11th ed. American Public Health Association, New York. 1960.

Steel, E. W. *Water Supply and Sewerage.* 4th ed. McGraw-Hill Book Co., New York. 1960.

U.S. Department of Commerce. "Water Use In The United States, 1900–1980." U.S. Government Printing Office, Washington, D.C. 1960.

Williams, R. E. O. "Healthy Carriage of *Staphylococcus aureus:* its Prevalence and Importance." *Bact. Review, 27:* 56–71. 1963.

Wright, C. V. "New Standards of Chemical Quality For Drinking Water." *U.S. Publ. Hlth. Repts., 77*(7): 628–632.

# CHAPTER VI

# RESERVOIRS OF MICROORGANISMS CAUSING FOODBORNE GASTROENTERIC OUTBREAKS: FOOD SUPPLY

## PART I. FOOD SUPPLY OF ANIMAL ORIGIN

Included in this group are milk and other dairy products, meats, poultry, eggs, fish, and shellfish.

## Milk and Other Dairy Products

### Fluid Milk and Cream

These foods are highly perishable, yet in United States milk and cream are seldom associated with foodborne illnesses under the present conditions of milk production. The market milk produced in this country is, generally, of excellent quality. This is due to elimination of disease from dairy herds, sanitary milk production, pasteurization, and care in transportation and delivery to the consumer. The situation is not as favorable in many other countries.

CONTAMINANTS

At the time milk leaves the udder of the healthy cow it contains few bacteria; these stem from milk ducts and cistern. During the milking process bacteria are usually added from various sources. In hand milking the sources are air, the hair of the animal, manure, the milker, equipment such as pails, flies, feed, and many others.

When milking is performed by machine, most of these environmental factors are of less importance. However, the milking equipment may serve as an important source of contamination if it is not

111

carefully cleaned and sanitized. Water has been known to have been a source of contamination of milk, and so has the person handling the cows, the milking equipment, or the milk.

Among the contaminants which come from the intestinal origin of the cow are the salmonellae and the fecal streptococci (enterococci). Staphylococci may be contributed from the udder, skin, and respiratory tract.

Contaminants known to have come from the handler include many forms, among these *Staphylococcus aureus* and various intestinal pathogens of man, including representatives of *Salmonella*. The contaminants originating from flies and barn dust are varied. Among the contaminants from equipment are staphylococci, micrococci, and other heat-resistant organisms which tend to build up on dairy equipment (Sharpe et al., 1962).

When milk cows suffer from certain diseases, microorganisms injurious to public health may be released into the milk. Mastitis is a common disorder of the udder. Microorganisms associated with this disease include *S. aureus*, micrococci, and streptococci.

After the milk has been drawn it is rapidly cooled to below 50°F to prevent contaminants from multiplying. Further processing is given the milk at the creamery.

## PASTEURIZATION

To eliminate pathogens from milk and cream, the process of pasteurization is applied. This involves application of heat below the boiling point, since the physical and culinary quality of these important foods must be kept intact.

Pasteurization procedures have been devised to eliminate, before all, important pathogens and at the same time to kill the majority of other microorganisms in the raw milk. Milk may be treated either at a relatively low temperature for an extended period of time or at a higher temperature for a brief period. The slow, or holding, treatment is a process of heating every particle of milk, or milk products, to at least 145°F,* and holding at such temperature continuously for at least 30 minutes. The short-time high-temperature, or flash, method, requires that the product be heated to at least 161°F and held at that temperature continuously for at least 15 seconds. Nowadays, a terminal temperature of 170°F is commonly used. Approved

---

* The requirement of heating at 143°F for 30 minutes had to be changed to 145°F for 30 minutes because it was discovered after the code was established that *Coxiella burnetii*, the causative agent of Q fever, survived the heat treatment at lower temperature.

and properly operated equipment is required for both methods. After heating, the products are quickly cooled to 50°F or lower.

Some important pathogens which should be destroyed by pasteurization include *Mycobacterium tuberculosis* causing tuberculosis; *Brucella* species causing brucellosis; and *Streptococcus* species and *Micrococcus pyogenes*, which are involved in causing chronic mastitis, as well as other organisms associated with acute mastitis including *Staphylococcus aureus*, *Clostridium perfringens*, and *Streptococcus pyogenes*. Pasteurization also kills yeasts, molds, and bacteria which grow readily at low temperatures. Thus, pasteurized milk should keep well under refrigeration and usually does.

The number of bacteria remaining in pasteurized milk varies mostly with the number of heat-resistant bacteria present. The percentage of survivors varies from 1 to 10%. The kinds of bacteria likely to survive are the "thermodurics" which include spore formers, lactobacilli, *S. thermophilus*, and *S. faecalis*, micrococci, heat-resistant strains of *Escherichia coli*, and a variety of thermophilic bacteria. The presence of thermophiles, heat-loving forms whose optimum growth temperatures are above 113°F, reflects poor sanitation in the processing plant. However, some thermophiles are difficult to eliminate; some forms are even capable of multiplication at the temperatures applied in the holding method of pasteurization. In the properly pasteurized product, the heat-resistant survivors do not exceed small numbers.

Cream for butter-making and ice cream mixes is given a more severe heat treatment than milk, and cream to be used as coffee cream, whipped cream, and the like. Cream is more protective to microorganisms than milk, and ice cream mixes are more protective than cream.

Foltz et al. (1960) studied the incidence of potentially pathogenic staphylococci in fluid milk and other fluid dairy products such as coffee cream, whipping cream, half and half, buttermilk, and chocolate milk for retail outlets throughout Kansas. Potentially virulent coagulase-positive strains of staphylococci were isolated from 3.4% of the samples (Table 15). A test for presence of toxins was not made. The authors suggest that dairy plant workers might have been the reservoir of the contaminants.

It should be remembered that the pasteurized product devoid of its natural flora is a more agreeable medium to *S. aureus* than the raw product because of the antagonistic effects which the natural flora exerts. An interesting example of antagonistic contaminants interfering with growth of *S. aureus* was given by Post et al. (1961),

Table 15. Isolations of Staphylococci from Dairy Products in Consumer Marketing Channels [Adapted from Foltz, Mickelsen, Martin, and Hunter (1960)]

| Product | No. samples examined | Samples containing staphylococci[a] | | Samples containing Staph. epid.[b] | | Samples containing Staph. aureus | | Samples containing both Staph. epid. and Staph. aureus | | Samples containing coagulase-positive staph. | No. of coagulase-positive cultures isolated |
|---|---|---|---|---|---|---|---|---|---|---|---|
| | | No. | % | No. | % | No. | % | No. | % | | |
| Past. milk | 86 | 23 | 26.7 | 17 | 19.8 | 12 | 14.0 | 6 | 7.0 | 1 | 1 |
| Low fat | 28 | 12 | 42.9 | 10 | 35.7 | 3 | 10.7 | 1 | 3.6 | 0 | 0 |
| Choc. milk | 10 | 1 | 10.0 | 1 | 10.0 | 0 | 0 | 0 | 0 | 0 | 0 |
| Buttermilk | 15 | 3 | 20.0 | 1 | 6.7 | 2 | 13.3 | 0 | 0 | 1 | 4 |
| Half & half | 35 | 10 | 28.6 | 5 | 14.3 | 6 | 17.1 | 1 | 2.9 | 3 | 15 |
| Coffee cream | 6 | 2 | 33.3 | 1 | 16.7 | 2 | 33.3 | 1 | 16.7 | 0 | 0 |
| Whipping cream | 27 | 11 | 40.7 | 10 | 37.0 | 2 | 7.4 | 1 | 3.7 | 2 | 5 |

a Staphylococci differentiated from micrococci on the basis of anaerobic growth in glucose medium.
b Staphylococcus epidermidis differentiated from Staphylococcus aureus on the basis of mannitol fermentation.

who studied growth of this organism in cream and cream products. The authors sought an explanation for the fact that although these potentially perishable products were carried for hours in warm trucks in Southern California, they were not known to have caused illnesses.

For years the dairy industry has endeavored to prevent the dissemination of pathogens through milk and to make safety of the milk supply a prime consideration (Smith, 1961). The health of dairy herds is generally good and elimination of pathogens by pasteurization is compulsory in most localities. Efforts are made to prevent contamination of pasteurized milk from the human reservoir by eliminating as far as possible direct contact between the employee of the dairy plant and the pasteurized product, to control flies and rodents, to maintain the equipment in sanitary condition, and to keep sanitary standards high at all times.

In spite of precautions and generally high standards of sanitation found in the United States, some outbreaks of foodborne gastroenteritis are occasionally caused by milk and other dairy products. The incidence is very low. Causative organisms have included *Staphylococcus aureus*, salmonellae, enterococci, and *Clostridium perfringens*.

ANTIBIOTICS AND RADIONUCLIDES

Contamination of milk with antibiotics may occur when milk cows are treated for an udder disease such as mastitis. In 1954 the Food and Drug Administration initiated surveys to determine the level of antibiotic contamination of milk, and the results of these surveys have shown the importance of this problem, especially in regard to penicillin. Penicillin is not only the antibiotic most widely used, it is also one to which man can build up an allergy. As a consequence of these surveys, dairy farmers have been alerted to the problems and warned to discard milk produced within 72 hours following treatment with antibiotics. Also, testing methods for the presence of antibiotics are constantly improved.

Milk is easily contaminated with radionuclides from atomic fallout (Campbell et al., 1961). Methods are under investigation for the elimination of radionuclides from milk (Murthy et al., 1961).

STORAGE

Properly pasteurized milk which has not been recontaminated and is held at appropriate temperatures will not readily spoil and will keep up to two weeks or more. A bacteriological problem in the storage of pasteurized milk is caused by the psychrotropic and psychrophilic forms (Thomas and Druce, 1963); the coliforms are also known to cause spoilage of cold-stored milk.

In general, the dairy industry of the United States has developed standards for dairy products to a high degree of efficacy, and quality standards have been furthered on local, state, and federal levels.

At the local level, the county or municipality entrusts the health departments with this responsibility. On the state level, the departments of health or agriculture are entrusted. On interstate carriers, the supervision of the milk supply is under the U. S. Public Health Service Ordinance and Code published in 1924, amplified in 1927, and constantly revised to keep up with current developments. The code has been adopted widely by cities and counties and serves as a guide for the milk laws of many states. The code is concerned with all the aspects of safe production, processing, transporting, and handling of milk.

## Evaporated Milk

This canned product is prepared from milk which conforms to established high standards. Before condensing, the milk is pasteurized usually at temperatures near boiling for a short time. The milk is then subjected to evaporation, homogenization, and cooling processes, and is eventually canned at temperatures designed to obtain the required viscosity and to destroy enzymes and bacteria.

Bacteriological defects of evaporated milk occur occasionally, the main reason being leaky cans. A variety of contaminants may enter a leaky can and quickly spoil the contents; if the entering contaminants are pathogens, the consequences may be serious. Another reason for spoilage is insufficient heat treatment during the canning process, thermophilic and thermoduric organisms being associated with these defects. Sometimes underprocessed milk has a coagulated appearance, several spore formers being associated such as *Bacillus subtilis*, *B. coagulans*, and *B. cereus*.

If leaky and bulging cans are discarded, the storage time is brief, and opened cans are kept under sanitary conditions and refrigerated, no trouble should result from evaporated milk.

## Condensed Milk

If sugar is added to evaporated milk, which is usually done at the end of the condensing process, and the mixture is cooled, condensed milk results. The average amount of sugar in the finished product is 40–45%; sucrose or a combination of sucrose with some dextrose is used. Packaging is done in hermetically sealed cans using a separate sanitary room, and no further heat treatment is applied. Bacteriological defects depend a great deal on plant sanitation. In spite of extensive precautions, microorganisms such as yeasts, molds, micrococci, coliforms, and spore-forming aerobes can become contaminants of condensed milk. The yeasts which are quite tolerant of sugar may cause gas which leads to bursting of the cans' seams. No organisms of public health significance are associated with these bacteriological defects.

## Dried Milk

MANUFACTURE

Whole milk and skim milk are dried, the latter being of greater importance in quantity food service. Other milk products which are dried include cream, buttermilk, whey, malted milk, and ice cream mixes (Coulter et al., 1951). To prepare dried skim milk (nonfat milk solids, or NFMS) either the spray or the roller process can be used. In connection with the bacteriological quality of the powders, the temperatures used in the drying process are of interest. The clarified homogenized liquid is preheated, the terminal temperatures ranging from 145 to 200°F; the length of exposure depends on the temperature employed. Thermoduric bacteria may survive this treatment.

The temperatures during the drying process vary with the method. In the spray process the milk is briefly subjected to dry air at temperatures ranging from 250 to 400°F. In the roller process, without vacuum, temperatures up to 270°F are employed for a short period of time; under vacuum, lower temperatures up to 170°F can be used.

During the concentration of the milk to a high solid content, surviving thermodurics, especially the streptococci, may multiply if the temperature remains at 100–120°F for a sufficiently long time. This has been found to occur in exceptional cases.

CONTAMINANTS

Among the factors affecting the bacterial flora of the finished powder are: kind and number of bacteria originally present in the raw milk; plant sanitation; preheating temperatures; and the drying process used. It is difficult for a plant practicing poor sanitation to obtain a low-count powder, because of heat-resistant bacteria which build up in the plant.

The flora of dried milk may include: (1) thermoduric micrococci that are usually associated with dairy supplies and equipment; (2)

thermoduric streptococci, mainly strains of *S. thermophilus, faecalis, bovis, faecalis* var. *liquefaciens,* and *durans,* proliferation of which is favored by sanitary conditions in the plant; (3) thermoduric species of *Corynebacteria* which stem from the milk; (4) bacterial spores, mostly the aerobic kinds such as *Bacillus subtilis;* and (5) miscellaneous contaminants, among which *Escherichia coli* is the most important, since it indicates poor sanitation, and contaminants from the human reservoir—the employee in the processing plant.

Laboratory studies on milk powders have shown that although drying destroys the majority of organisms, some nonthermoduric types survive unless very high heat is used. Thus, drying cannot be relied upon to destroy all bacteria under all conditions. Recontamination of the finished product is also possible. These facts are important to remember when dried milk is reconstituted because it is at that time that moisture will be restored and the powder again becomes a highly perishable item.

McDivitt et al. (1964) made a field study on the manufacture of nonfat dry milk in two plants. Similar equipment was used in these plants, but modifications in processing procedures were possible in that the operation varied regarding temperatures used and regarding the coordination of the steps used in processing. The raw milk supply varied in quality and volume.

The main difference in the plants was the handling of the concentrated product previous to the actual drying. The results from analyses made at different stages of processing led the authors to the conclusion that efficient equipment and well-controlled practices are prerequisites to a safe quality product, and that low bacterial counts of a milk powder could be misleading as a sole indicator of safety.

It might be appropriate to mention at this point that dangers from toxins exist when staphylococci are allowed to build up to high numbers before the milk is subjected to the drying process. Since heat-stable toxins will resist inactivation by heat, the dried product may contain these toxins. This has been dramatically demonstrated by a series of food-poisoning outbreaks in Puerto Rico in 1956 (Armijo et al., 1957), the first such cases reported in the United States. Sixteen schools were involved; 775 of 4094 children became violently ill but recovered within 24 hours. Through the cooperation of human volunteers the toxic batches were identified and were traced to certain manufacturing plants (in the continental U.S.) where sanitary standards were found to be low.

The bacterial population of milk powder declines gradually during storage, but spores will survive for long periods of time. In general, dried milk has an excellent record for freedom from pathogenic bacteria.

RECONSTITUTED MILK

When powder has been reconstituted with water and become a fluid, it has all the prerequisites of a highly perishable food item and must be handled accordingly. Milk reconstituted from powder will contain the bacterial population of the powder plus the contaminants added by handling. In general, good quality powder reconstituted with potable water, using clean equipment, by a food handler employing high standards of hygiene, should be a satisfactory product. Reconstituted milk should be kept under refrigeration unless used immediately following reconstitution. It is important for the kitchen supervisor to educate employees regarding the perishability of this item.

## Ice Cream

Ice cream mixes are given more rigorous heat treatments than those used for milk. Pasteurization temperatures are 155°F for 30 minutes or 175°F for 25 seconds. With a well-controlled sanitation program, counts should be low.

The types of organisms that have been found in ice cream are of a wide variety, and include streptococci, micrococci, spore formers, coliforms, and *Pseudomonas*.

Other sources of these contaminants can be cream and other milk derivatives. Sugar, stabilizers, flavoring, and coloring are unimportant sources. One important reservoir of contaminants is the employee in the ice cream plant since he may contribute bacteria of public health significance. The list of pathogens which have been isolated from ice cream includes salmonellae and staphylococci. *Mycobacterium* and *Brucella* have been recovered occasionally. These pathogenic contaminants have been seen to survive for considerable periods of time.

Control measures include the use of high quality supplies, excellent sanitation during preparation of the product, and protection from recontamination. High sanitary standards of the industry and strict control of the agencies entrusted with food protection are powerful tools in making ice cream produced in the United States the safe and delightful dessert it is.

## Butter

In general, the conditions prevailing in butter are not conducive to bacterial growth, although molds may grow on butter. The moisture content of butter is low and is restricted to droplets. Since most butter is salted, the water present in butter is apt to be of high salt concentration.

Survival of bacteria has been observed occasionally in butter, however. The organisms studied varied regarding length of survival time from a few weeks to several months. The source of contaminants is usually the cream. *Staphylococcus aureus* and salmonellae have been found to survive in butter, but in practice butter has never been indicated in food poisoning outbreaks.

### Cheese

There are many different kinds of cheeses and the reader is referred to books on dairy microbiology for information on the bacterial flora of cheeses.

Bacteria of importance to public health have been found in cheese; and cheeses have occasionally been indicted in outbreaks of foodborne illnesses.

Use of unpasteurized milk and recontamination of pasteurized milk have been two of the reasons for the presence of pathogens in cheese. Another cause has been direct contamination of the finished product. Because of the long holding periods which many cheeses undergo and because of wide shipping distances, the original source of the pathogens is usually difficult to determine.

Among the contaminants of public health significance reported are coagulase-positive staphylococci. Donnelly et al. (1962) investigated the occurrence of these organisms in cheddar cheese. Samples from several lots of cheese incriminated in foodborne gastroenteritis, and 343 samples of cheese procured over a period of 3 years in retail markets, were analyzed for the presence of these bacteria. Of the 13 food-poisoning samples, 11 contained coagulase-positive staphylococci; the contamination ranged from low to very high. The market cheeses labeled "pasteurized" were contaminated 20% of the time, some bacteria being capable of causing food poisoning. Of the cheeses which were not labeled "pasteurized," a similar percentage was contaminated with *Staphylococcus aureus*. The incidence of potentially pathogenic staphylococci in cheese has been discussed by Mickelsen et al. (1961).

Thatcher et al. (1956), studying the incidence of coagulase-positive staphylococci in cheeses in Canada, obtained such organisms from 45% of 106 samples of cheese made with unpasteurized milk, and from 13% of 83 samples labeled as processed from pasteurized milk.

The presence of these contaminants in the cheeses made from

unpasteurized milk is not surprising in view of the fact that *Staphylococcus aureus* is among the causative organisms of mastitis so prevalent in milk cows. But their presence in the cheeses made from pasteurized milk is baffling, since the organisms should be eliminated in common pasteurization treatment. Insufficient pasteurization may be one explanation, and recontamination from various sources may be another. Laboratory studies by Takahashi and Johns (1959) showed that *S. aureus* grew poorly in cheddar cheese during the cheese-making process, most of the cells being concentrated in the curd.

Survival of pathogens in cheese may last for a long time (Nevot et al., 1963). Survival of *Salmonella typhosa* in cheese has been shown to be affected by temperature, the length of survival being favored by refrigerator temperatures. This organism, as well as *Mycobacterium tuberculosis* and *S. aureus*, may remain viable in cheddar cheese for several months. Either pasteurization or curing may be prescribed by law. For example, in the state of New York the following regulation is in effect:

No person manufacturing cheese or cheese curd or handling cheese or cheese curd as a wholesaler, assembler or broker in the state of New York and no person obtaining cheese from outside the state shall release any cheese or cheese curd to the retail trade or to consumers unless such cheese or cheese curd has been pasteurized or has been made from whole milk, skim milk, or cream which has been pasteurized in accordance with rules and regulations promulgated by the commissioner after inquiry and public hearing; except that cheese cured for sixty days or longer after manufacture may be made from unpasteurized milk. [State of New York, Department of Agriculture and Markets, §67b]

## Meat and Meat Products

Animals on farms are, as a rule, healthier than when crowded in abattoirs, since healthy animals become infected during transit to markets and in the pens. Cross infection may take place from diseased animals or carriers to the healthy specimens during this period. By direct contact or through manure the bacteria become disseminated. For example, fecal specimens taken from animals at the farm showed that a small percentage of the animals harbored salmonellae. Specimens taken from animals penned at the packing plant indicated that the incidence had increased tenfold. Infection of meat animals prior to slaughter may even cause certain bacteria to penetrate into the muscle fiber although the tissues of normal and healthy meat animals do not harbor them. This may be true for salmonellae, streptococci, *Brucella*, and *Mycobacterium tuberculosis*.

*Processing of Fresh Meat*

Thanks to a very effective inspection service in the United States, diseased animals are excluded from processing for human consumption; 83% of the meat animals slaughtered commercially are government inspected.

The flesh of healthy living meat animals is practically sterile. Microorganisms have been isolated occasionally from flesh and more readily from lymph nodes and bone marrow (Lepovetsky et al., 1953).

When the animal is killed the walls of the intestines and other mucose tissues lose resistance to bacterial penetration; intestinal bacteria are known to have contaminated sterile tissues by this way of penetration.

The main and massive contamination of meats occurs, however, after the animal carcass has been opened. The sources of the contaminants of public health significance are the animal itself, the handler, the abattoir, and the surroundings.

The following factors are known to affect the chance for, and degree of, contamination of the carcass:

(1)  Bacterial flora of the animal, including the bacterial load in the gut
(2)  State of fatigue and excitement
(3)  Method of slaughter and degree of bleeding
(4)  Injury during dehairing
(5)  Rate of cooling the carcass
(6)  Degree of sanitation in operations during killing and opening of carcass, contact of meat with fecal matter, hide, hoofs, hair; sanitation of knives; sanitation of scalding and skinning operations
(7)  Sanitation in operations during cutting of meat, possible contacts with diseased meats and other contaminated surfaces
(8)  General sanitary state of plant as a whole; freedom from rodents and insects; effectiveness of cleaning operations
(9)  Health, working habits, and personal hygiene of workers
(10) Competency of supervision.

The bacterial flora of the animal gut may affect the flora of the meat in that when the animal is killed and the intestinal walls lose their resistance, the pathogens may penetrate the walls and may be subsequently carried around through blood and lymph vessels and connective tissue interspaces. The excited or fatigued condition of the animal prevents the pH of the tissues to go down as it should; the glycogen being used up in fatigue. With a smaller glycogen reserve, less lactic acid is produced in the tissues. Normally the pH would fall from near neutral to approximately pH 5.7. Failure of drop in pH will also result when incomplete bleeding is practiced.

Injury during dehairing may carry microorganisms into the flesh of the animal. The hide of the animal is apt to be contaminated with many species of bacteria, among them *Staphylococcus aureus*, *Salmonella* species, *Clostridium perfringens*, and fecal streptococci.

The rate of cooling the carcass has an effect also. When the animal is cooled rapidly the rate at which the microorganisms invade the tissue is reduced.

The effect of sanitary operations during the entire process is so obvious that a detailed discussion would seem unnecessary, if it were not for the fact that surveys of bacterial contamination of market meat have shown a great need of improvement of sanitation in the packing plants, involving every step of the operation.

CONTAMINANTS

Although the organisms causing foodborne disease are of greatest interest here, it should be pointed out that there are many kinds of microorganisms found on meat. These include molds, yeasts, and bacteria of the genera *Achromobacter*, *Clostridium*, *Escherichia*, *Flavobacterium*, *Pseudomonas*, *Micrococcus*, *Salmonella*, *Sarcina*, *Staphylococcus*, *Streptococcus*, *Lactobacillus*, *Streptomyces*, *Leuconostoc*, and *Proteus*.

The contaminants which are potential hazards in connection with foodborne gastroenteric episodes are of greatest concern to those entrusted with quantity food production and service.

Many studies have been made of total counts of bacteria found on market meats, usually from retail stores including large supermarkets and small neighborhood stores. In general, the smaller the stores, the higher the counts. Meat that has been federally inspected and passed tends to have lower counts than non-inspected meats. Very high counts are invariably found in hamburger. Even if "scraps," a rich source of contaminants, are excluded and pure meat is ground, the large surface and available air in ground meats favor bacterial growth.

Total bacterial counts reported in the literature vary so much that no attempt is made here to present the voluminous literature on the subject. Bacterial counts of meats other than ground meats may vary from 100 per gram to 1 million per gram and of ground meat up to 100 million per gram. High total counts do not prove the presence of pathogens, but they indicate that the meat was either of poor sanitary quality to begin with or has been exposed to conditions favoring bacterial proliferation.

## STAPHYLOCOCCUS AUREUS

The incidence of this organism in market meats has been studied by Jay (1961a,b; 1962), who was particularly interested in those meats which are commonly cooked to uncertain and varying degrees of doneness such as hamburger, beef steaks, and liver. The investigations were concerned with the number of coagulase-positive *S. aureus* in various meat cuts. The meat markets were located in the Baton Rouge, Louisiana area. Twenty-eight stores and markets, representing 10% of all such stores in that area, were sampled. Of these 28 outlets, 16 yielded coagulase-positive strains of *S. aureus* in hamburger, 11 on round steak, 15 on beef liver, and 14 on pork chops. Prepackaged meat obtained from large chain stores contained relatively fewer coagulase-positive organisms; the author suggests that this may be due to several reasons which could involve the prepackaging per se as well as the fact that the chain stores kept available fresher meats.

The same author, surveying retail grocery stores and markets, found that 38.7% of 174 samples obtained from 27 stores yielded coagulase-positive *S. aureus*. The meats from which this contaminant was recovered most frequently were, in order of frequency: chicken, pork, liver, fish, spiced ham, round beef steak, hamburger, beef liver, pork chops, veal steak, and lamb chops.

Contamination of the meat from human sources is a great problem in meat-packing plants and retail stores, and so is the reverse situation: contamination of humans with staphylococci originating from the animal source. A very interesting study by Ravenholt et al. (1961), involving meat workers in the Seattle, Washington area, has pointed to the importance of this type of cross-contamination.

## SALMONELLAE

The results of several studies have shed light on the incidence of *Salmonella* in market meats. In general, pork cuts and products made from pork have shown the highest incidence.

According to Felsenfeld et al. (1950), the incidence of *Salmonella* in uninspected pork was higher (27%) than in inspected pork (14%). These figures are somewhat higher than recoveries reported elsewhere. Cherry et al. (1943) found an incidence of 6% and Wilson et al. (1961) reported 4%. However, some very high recovery rates were found by Galton et al. (1954) for fresh pork sausage; these rates averaged from 8% in samples from national distributors to as high as 58% from local sources (Table 16). The same authors reported that up to 37% of fresh pork sausage sampled from retail markets in Florida was contaminated with *Salmonella*.

**Table 16.** *Salmonella* **Isolations from Fresh and Smoked Pork Sausage [Adapted from Galton, Lowrey, and Hardy (1954)]**

| Source | Producer no. | Fresh sausage | | | Smoked sausage | | |
|---|---|---|---|---|---|---|---|
| | | Samples cultured | Positive | | Samples cultured | Positive | |
| | | | Number | Per cent | | Number | Per cent |
| Local abattoirs | 1 | 10 | 9 | 90.0 | 11 | 3 | 27 |
| | 2 | 10 | 7 | 70.0 | 0 | | |
| | 3 | 10 | 5 | 50.0 | 0 | | |
| | 4 | 10 | 2 | 20.0 | 11 | 6 | 54 |
| | Total | 40 | 23 | 57.5 | 22 | 9 | 40.9 |
| Local markets | 5 | 5 | 4 | 80.0 | 0 | | |
| | 6 | 3 | 2 | 66.6 | 0 | | |
| | 7 | 11 | 3 | 27.2 | 10 | 0 | |
| | 8 | 10 | 2 | 20.0 | 11 | 1 | 9 |
| | 9 | 10 | 1 | 10.0 | 0 | | |
| | 10 | 9 | 0 | | 6 | 3 | 50 |
| | Total | 48 | 12 | 25.0 | 27 | 4 | 14.4 |
| Regional abattoirs | 11 | 5 | 3 | 60.0 | 0 | | |
| | 12 | 10 | 3 | 30.0 | 0 | | |
| | 13 | 11 | 2 | 18.1 | 8 | 0 | |
| | 14 | 13 | 2 | 15.3 | 11 | 1 | 9 |
| | 15 | 11 | 0 | | 10 | 2 | 20 |
| | Total | 50 | 10 | 20.0 | 29 | 3 | 10.3 |
| National distributors | 16 | 9 | 2 | 22.2 | 9 | 0 | |
| | 17 | 10 | 2 | 20.0 | 0 | | |
| | 18 | 10 | 1 | 10.0 | 0 | | |
| | 19 | 10 | 1 | 10.0 | 10 | 0 | |
| | 20 | 10 | 0 | | 10 | 0 | |
| | 21 | 10 | 0 | | 0 | | |
| | 22 | 9 | 0 | | 10 | 0 | |
| | 23 | 11 | 0 | | 10 | 0 | |
| | Total | 79 | 6 | 7.5 | 49 | 0 | |
| Grand totals | | 217 | 51 | 23.0 | 127 | 16 | 12.5 |

Wilson et al. (1961) found that the types of pork products from which salmonellae were most frequently isolated were, besides sausage, the assorted cheap parts such as feet, tails, neckbones, chitterlings, and stomach (Table 17).

Table 17. Prevalence of Salmonellae in Various Pork Products [Adapted from Wilson, Paffenbarger, Foter, and Lewis (1961)]

| Product | Ratio[a] | % Positive |
|---------|----------|------------|
| Cheap parts[b] | 5/24 | 21 |
| Sausage[c] | 5/47 | 11 |
| Kidney | 2/28 | 7 |
| Liver | 2/34 | 6 |
| Sausage[d] | 1/21 | 5 |
| Steak, cubed | 2/42 | 5 |

[a] Specimens containing salmonellae to total specimens tested.
[b] Including feet, tails, neck bones, stomach, and chitterlings.
[c] Market-prepared bulk.
[d] Packer-prepared bulk.

Regarding salmonellae in beef cuts, Wilson et al. (1961) found incidences highest in ground beef. They observed little seasonal variation in the recovery of salmonellae, and in their samples, which were purchased from 96 retail markets in Cincinnati; no difference seemed to exist regarding the incidence of salmonellae between meats supplied from local and regional meat processors.

CLOSTRIDIUM PERFRINGENS (WELCHII)

*C. perfringens*, an extremely ubiquitous organism, is a common contaminant of meat, especially so in Britain, according to Hobbs and Wilson (1959). Strong et al. (1963) analyzed American foods for the presence of this organism in Wisconsin and included various meats in their study. Samples positive for this organism were found on most meats. Of 26 beef cuts 2 were contaminated; of 23 pork cuts, 1; of 5 lamb cuts, 2; of 3 veal cuts, 0; of 28 spiced meats, 5; of 14 organ meats, 6; and of 9 ground meats, 4.

Canada and Strong (1964) reported that 26% of 100 bovine liver samples purchased from retail markets within the Madison, Wisconsin area were positive for *C. perfringens* Type A. An examination of liver and bile samples from newly slaughtered cattle revealed the presence of the organism in 12% of the livers, but in none of the bile samples.

Hall and Angelotti (1965) studied the incidence of *Clostridium perfringens* in meats and meat products in the Cincinnati area and found that a high proportion (43.1%) of raw and processed meats were contaminated with the organism (see Table 14). The highest incidence was in raw veal, the lowest (4.7%) in processed sandwich meat and spreads. Of the 101 processed meats and meat products, 19.8% were contaminated with *C. perfringens* (Tables 13 and 18). They found that pork sausage and mettwurst were most frequently contaminated (47.6%) and that contamination was infrequent in ham and bacon (11.1%). In general, in the meat items that require warming, or are usually lightly cooked, contamination was found to be low.

Table 18. Recovery of *Clostridium perfringens* from Processed Meats and Meat Dishes [Adapted from Hall and Angelotti (1965)]

| Type of specimen | Number of specimens examined | Number of specimens positive for *C. perfringens* | Per cent positive for *C. perfringens* |
|---|---|---|---|
| Require full cooking | 38 | 14 | 36.8 |
| Require warming or light cooking | 21 | 4 | 19.0 |
| Require no cooking | 42 | 2 | 4.7 |
| Total | 101 | 20 | 19.8 |

FECAL STREPTOCOCCI

The fecal streptococci, or enterococci, are also common contaminants of meats. They are a special problem in pasteurized hams, and will therefore be discussed under "Heat-Processed Meats."

## Heat-Processed Meats

CANNED MEATS

Included in this category are the canned products which have had rigorous heat treatment and are considered sterile for all intents and purposes, since pathogens are eliminated. This category contains the smaller hams. Today large hams are usually pasteurized to avoid overcooking.

Canning of meat is difficult because of poor heat penetration. Temperatures and times sufficient to kill *Clostridium botulinum* spores are used in commercial canning operations. However, some thermophilic organisms may escape death. Canned meats, like other canned goods, must be stored at cool temperatures. At temperatures over 113°F danger of deterioration from thermophilic bacteria arises. Frequent turnover and cool storage of canned meats is indicated in a food service operation.

Canned meat shipped interstate must be inspected and passed by the Federal government. The packing and processing of canned meat has to be inspected for required sanitary standards.

### CURED AND SMOKED MEATS

The curing process is applied to much pork and some beef. Although years ago the curing process was designed to preserve meats with salt, or salt and sugar, without refrigeration, this is no longer the process. At present, most cured meats are also smoked. The curing agents permitted include salt (NaCl), sugar, vinegar, sodium nitrite, and sodium nitrate. The reader is referred to books on food preservation for detail information on curing. The curing brines are not devoid of halophilic contaminants, the micrococci being frequently among these. *Staphylococcus aureus*, being salt tolerant, has also been known to survive curing of meats.

Eddy and Ingram (1962) studied the occurrence and growth of staphylococci on bacon. These workers reported that *Staphylococcus aureus* could survive in curing brine, although only small numbers were found in "normal" or in vacuum-packed bacon. The organisms grew well on bacon stored anaerobically at 77°F. There was little growth below 50°F.

Another organism of public health significance which is quite salt tolerant is *Streptococcus faecalis*. Resistance to both salt and heat enables this organism to be among the flora of cured and smoked meat products.

At present, many cured meats are smoked and thus dried to some extent. In present-day methods of smoking, the heat treatment is light. The combined effects of curing, heating, and drying, as well as the action of chemicals from the smoke aid in preservation. Research results have shown that these treatments do not guarantee complete sterilization and that microorganisms capable of spoilage as well as pathogens may remain viable. This is also true for products which are smoked without previous curing (see Table 18). Sources of contaminants of public health significance have been shown to be the meat itself; spices; personnel; and contaminated, poorly maintained processing equipment.

Mildly cured and smoked meats and meat products must be kept under refrigeration at all times.

## PASTEURIZED HAMS

Since these meats have received a mild heat treatment, they are not sterile. Large (over 2 lb) pieces, picnic hams, or regular hams, are frequently packaged in cans and so marketed. These hams are, unfortunately, sometimes treated like the canned and sterilized product and held at room temperature. This mishandling has caused serious trouble.

Packaged cooked hams are identified by varying terminology. According to the USDA Manual of Meat Inspection Procedures (1965),

Use of the terms "Cooked," "Fully Cooked," "Thoroughly Cooked," "Ready-to-Eat," or "Ready-to-Serve" on heated and smoked pork product is acceptable only when the processing results in the product exhibiting the usual characteristics of a fully cooked article, such as partial separation of the meat from the bone, easy separation of the tissues, and a cooked color, flavor, and texture throughout the product. This usually requires a minimum internal temperature of 148°F. Proposals for the use of these terms should be accompanied with the full description of the process and internal temperature attained when the marking material is submitted for approval.

Packaged hams which are given a relatively light heat treatment are of interest in connection with possible survival of pathogens. Hams processed as nonsterile and labeled "perishable, keep under refrigeration" are known to contain spores and heat-resistant cocci.

The fate of *Staphylococcus aureus* during the processing of hams was studied by Silliker et al. (1962). Twenty-two of 53 strains of the organism were killed, in excess of 99% kill of cells, after a 10-minute exposure to 137°F. Thirty-one strains were more resistant and were destroyed after 1 hour exposure to 137°F.

The bacterial flora of packaged perishable hams before and after heating to 150°F was studied by Brown et al. (1960). They found that the average total count of 210,000 per gram of meat was reduced to 451 per gram by the heat treatment given the hams. Survivors were cocci, bacilli, and clostridia. The heat-resistant cocci were able to multiply slowly at refrigerator temperatures. The authors also studied the heat resistance of some of the surviving cocci, comparing them with fecal streptococci, among them *Streptococcus faecium* and *durans*. One of the surviving cocci was comparable in resistance to the heat-resistant streptococci.

Thermal death studies (unpublished data) were made by Angelotti et al. (1962), who found that *Streptococcus faecalis* became inactivated when exposed to 150°F for 40 minutes, 155°F for 14 minutes, or 160°F for 5 minutes. It may therefore be concluded that, although Angelotti's studies were not made on canned hams, the possibility of streptococcal survival is not precluded when hams are heated up to 150°F without additional holding at that temperature. There is no doubt that fecal streptococci are extremely important contaminants of pasteurized meat products. They are heat resistant, may multiply under anaerobic conditions and grow at a pH under 5, are salt tolerant, and are able to multiply at very low and very high temperatures. To check multiplication of survivors, canned hams that are labeled "keep under refrigeration" must be kept cold at all times.

*Frozen Meats*

Freezing is frequently used to safeguard the keeping quality of meat during transit. The freezing process may kill approximately one-half of the contaminants. Further decrease in bacterial numbers may be expected during subsequent freezer storage. Bacteria subjected to freezing in or on meat seem to be more resistant to salt and heat than cells not so treated. Frozen meat is not sterile.

*Precautions*

Boned meat and other products which have been handled a great deal have been shown to contain microorganisms capable of causing foodborne illness, such as *Staphylococcus aureus*, the salmonellae, and *Clostridium perfringens*. Particularly high *Salmonella* counts have been found in frozen comminuted or minced meat. The underlying reasons seem to be that, first, scraps and trimmings are often used in these products, and second, the process of mincing tends to distribute the contaminants throughout the meat, and provides surfaces and oxygen.

The quality of market meat is regulated under the Meat Inspection Act. This act applies only to meat shipped in interstate commerce. Many states have passed similar laws and at present approximately 80% of the meat consumed is federally inspected.

Curing and smoking should conform with government meat inspection regulations and thus meet the requirements for the quality and safety of these products.

Poultry and Poultry Products

Poultry is very high on the list as an offender in food-poisoning outbreaks. There is general agreement among the authorities that poultry is an important reservoir of organisms causing foodborne disease, especially salmonellae.

Poultry meat is ideally suited as a culture medium for bacteria, including those causing foodborne illnesses. It is rich in nitrogenous substances, carbohydrates, and other growth factors. It is high in moisture and the pH is favorable to bacterial multiplication. The pH of the white meat is somewhat lower than that of the dark.

The skin of poultry abounds with bacteria. To the natural flora are added contaminants from feathers, which in turn are apt to be contaminated with bacteria from manure, especially when the poultry are kept in dusty and unsanitary quarters.

Bruises in poultry are condemned by federal meat and poultry inspectors. A microbiological examination of poultry bruises conducted by McCarthy et al. (1963) revealed that 61–74% of the tissues harbored aerobic as well as anaerobic bacteria. Age of bruise, sanitation of batteries, temperature, moisture, and severity of the bruise were all factors affecting the microbial content and the growth of the microbes in the bruises. Among the organisms recovered from experimentally inflicted bruises staphylococci were prominent. Approximately one-half of these were *Staphylococcus aureus* and *epidermidis*. It was shown that fecal matter and poultry feed were important sources of the predominant contaminants of the bruises.

Hamdy et al. (1964) reported that the source of the staphylococci was often normal tissue, air sac, and skin; also feed, gut, and droppings. They found that the extent of staphylococcal multiplication was related to the severity of the bruise.

The intestinal tract of healthy poultry is likely to contain, before all, numerous species of *Salmonella, Staphylococcus*, and fecal streptococci with *Clostridium perfringens* being found in smaller numbers. Some members of the *Salmonella* group which are at home in the intestinal tract of poultry are capable of causing infections in man too, provided the number of cells ingested is sufficiently large.

*Processing of Fresh Poultry*

For a sizable poultry processing plant to operate efficiently a great number of live animals must be housed prior to killing and processing. This increases the likelihood of spreading pathogens such as salmonellae among them, unless great care is taken to exercise meticulous sanitation of the batteries. Government inspection is carried out by the Poultry Products Inspection Division, Agricultural Marketing Service, USDA to eliminate obviously sick birds, but carriers remain a problem.

The steps in processing will be briefly discussed since they are important for an understanding of contamination of poultry meat.

Step 1: *Killing* and *bleeding*. The methods used affect quality and flavor of the meat.

Step 2: *Plucking*. Dry-plucking is more apt to leave the skin intact than wet plucking, and this method is less likely to cause decomposition. However, in this method pin feathers are apt to remain. The method used most frequently at present is a semiscald method which consists of immersion or spraying of the carcasses at 128–132°F for 30 seconds. If the water is replenished frequently, it is not an important source of spreading contaminants. If precautions are taken to maintain the required temperatures, a mild pasteurization effect is achieved without adding microorganisms. Bacterial counts have been shown to average 250,000 cells per gram of skin and to be very low under the skin.

Step 3: *Removal of pin feathers*, if necessary. Final finishing requires human hands to pick out pin feathers. Rough picking will break the skin.

Step 4: *Singeing* is performed to remove fine feathers. Some bacteria may possibly be killed then and there.

Step 5: *Washing* is a very important step. This process serves to remove dirt, debris, and surface bacteria. Actual scrubbing is done with some machines. Scrubbing removes bacteria more efficiently than spraying alone. After Step 5, the chickens have arrived at the "New York dressed" state. They may now be treated in one of several ways: (*a*) sold as is; or (*b*) frozen, then sold; or (*c*) eviscerated at once; or (*d*) frozen, then eviscerated at special plants.

Step 6: *Evisceration*. Birds may be eviscerated warm, an easy procedure; or cooled before evisceration, either chilled on racks to get rid of animal heat (this is a slow cooling process); or chilled on slush ice (this is a poor sanitary procedure whereby contacts can be made from contaminated to clean birds).

Step 7: *Washing following evisceration*. These washing operations, usually by spray, are very important since by now the intestinal tract has been handled and bacteria have been released.

Step 8: *Inspection* for blemishes.

## CONTAMINANTS

Gunderson et al. (1954) have made a careful study of poultry flora during the processing operations from freshly killed warm-eviscerated birds and found the average counts to be 4812 per square centimeter of skin. From freshly killed, chilled, iced, cold-eviscerated birds the average counts were 60,625 per square centimeter of skin and from frozen, defrosted, or cold-eviscerated birds, the average counts were 37,233. The reason for the high counts was that the bacteria spread from heavily contaminated birds to clean ones. Total viable bacterial counts of birds arriving at evisceration line averaged over 26,000 per square centimeter of skin. The authors reported that the washing, and to a slight extent the singeing, resulted in marked reduction in bacterial numbers of all types on the skin and the cavity surfaces of the carcasses passing through evisceration. All other procedures, particularly those involving handling or damage to intestines, resulted in additions. A total of over 2000 cultures were studied. Numerous strains of *Salmonella* were isolated from the evisceration line and associated procedures; other contaminants were *Klebsiella*, *Vibrio*, *Alcaligenes*, *Proteus*, and coliforms. *Staphylococcus aureus* was evidently contributed by the human source, since strains of this organism were isolated, at the end of the line, from the packaged product.

A special study was made on the role of the plant worker and the equipment. It was demonstrated that the workers' hands passed the contaminants from bird to bird. This was true in spite of the fact that they frequently rinsed hands in fresh running water, because there simply was no time available for a thorough washing with soap.

Equipment was found to be contaminated with representatives of the intestinal flora of the chickens.

Sadler et al. (1961) made a survey over 20 months, inspecting eight large processing plants in California. Random sampling was employed; *Salmonella* was usually associated with diseased birds. Species of *Salmonella* were isolated from the intestinal tracts of infected birds on 43% of the sampling days for turkeys; 19% for chicken fryers; and 12% for hens. It was found that 22% of the chicken flocks sampled carried infected birds, 37% of the turkey flocks, 18% of the fryer flocks, and 3% of the chicken-hen flocks.

In cases of the fryer chickens, the presence of *Salmonella* was usually associated with disease processes. In turkeys this was not the case, however, since they appeared healthy; they were carriers.

Felsenfeld et al. (1950) found that of 372 U.S. inspected and passed poultry and 748 uninspected specimens, 0.9% and 10.8% respectively, yielded *Salmonella*. Galton et al. (1955) found 2–3% were positive for *Salmonella*.

Wilson et al. (1961) found *Salmonella* in approximately one-sixth of 525 raw poultry specimens. These authors reported that poultry specimens taken in the Cincinnati area from locally processed plants had a *Salmonella* incidence twice as high as specimens from regional sources. The incidence from regional sources was 13% and from local sources 24%.

The parts having the highest ratio of *Salmonella*-positive to total specimens were the so-called inexpensive cuts, the giblets and wings. The prevalence of salmonellae in the various poultry parts is shown in Table 19.

Table 19. **Prevalence of Salmonellae in Various Poultry Products [Adapted from Wilson, Paffenbarger, Foter, and Lewis (1961)]**

| Product | Ratio[a] | % Positive |
|---------|----------|------------|
| Chicken giblets | 22/93 | 24 |
| Chicken wings | 15/73 | 21 |
| Chicken breast | 15/93 | 16 |
| Chicken leg and thigh | 19/144 | 13 |
| Chicken back | 12/94 | 13 |

[a] Specimens containing salmonellae to total specimens tested.

Tailyour and Avery (1960) reported on the result of a survey of turkey viscera for salmonellae which was conducted in British Columbia. One per cent of the birds processed over a 3-week period at one killing plant under federal veterinary inspection were tested. Of these less than 1% were found to harbor *Salmonella*. Thatcher et al. (1961), also in Canada, isolated salmonellae from 15% of chicken samples collected in the retail market. Coagulase-positive staphylococci were also present, but in low numbers. Most of the bacteria were found to lodge on the surfaces of the skin, the body cavity, and on cut surfaces of the flesh.

Wilson et al. (1961) obtained turkey specimens from 77 households during the Thanksgiving–Christmas holiday seasons of 1958 and 1959. Portions of raw meat were removed from 90 turkeys; 8% of these yielded salmonellae.

Several workers have reported the presence of *Clostridium perfringens* from market poultry in the United States and Great Britain. Strong et al. (1963) analyzed a variety of foods available to the consumer. The highest recovery rate (16.4%) was from meat, poultry, and fish. Hall and Angelotti (1965) reported that 58% of poultry samples collected from markets in the Cincinnati area were positive for *C. perfringens*.

ANTIBIOTICS

Poultry may be treated with chlortetracycline or oxytetracycline to discourage bacterial growth. The allowed level in the flesh is 7 ppm. To achieve this level, 10 ppm is added to the chilling water following evisceration. A patented term for this treatment is "acronization."

Thatcher and Loit (1961) found that the ratio of *Salmonella* strains recovered from retail chickens treated with CTC to untreated chickens was 1:14. The effect of antibiotics varies with the strain of the organism. The bacteria may develop strains resistant to the antibiotics.

Spoilage bacteria resistant to the antibiotic, especially *Pseudomonas*, may build up in great numbers in the processing plant and on the poultry. Therefore, the use of antibiotics has its serious limitations.

*Refrigerated Poultry*

When poultry is refrigerated, psychrophilic bacteria will gradually crowd out other bacteria. Nagel and Simpson (1960) determined the types of bacteria associated with the spoilage of chilled poultry. Cultures were isolated from chilled, cut-up fryers which had been allowed to remain chilled at 40°F for 7 days. One hundred and three cultures were isolated. Of these, 81 were of the genus *Pseudomonas*; next in line of frequency were *Achromobacter* and *Alcaligenes*. These psychrophilic bacteria are apt to outnumber others in prolonged cold storage.

Walker and Ayres (1956) reported that storage of poultry at 4.4°C (39.2°F) in polyethylene bags generally resulted in spoilage in 4–6 days. The spoilage was associated with organisms with characteristics of the *Pseudomonas-Achromobacter* group.

*Frozen Poultry*

Much poultry is merchandized in the frozen state because of the keeping quality of the frozen item. Frozen poultry is not sterile and may contain microorganisms capable of causing foodborne illnesses. The staphylococci and fecal streptococci especially are quite resistant to freezing and freezer storage, but even the salmonellae have been shown to survive freezing preservation for over a year. Frozen poultry, after it has become warmed up to an extent making bacterial multiplication possible is as perishable as the fresh product.

Inspection for wholesomeness by Federal inspectors is required of all poultry shipped in interstate commerce. It is important for the food service manager to be well acquainted with local regulations governing poultry in the area in which he purchases the poultry for his establishment.

## Eggs

### Shell Eggs

The majority of the hens' eggs are sterile inside. If the ovary is infected with bacterial pathogens, the egg may become infected before it is laid. An example of such a pathogen is *Salmonella pullorum*, which used to be a common inhabitant of chicken flocks but has now been largely eradicated. The organism is not pathogenic to man unless massive doses are ingested. Another *Salmonella* which has been associated with hens' eggs is *S. gallinarum*, which has not been proven to be pathogenic to man either.

The egg is formed as follows: the yolk is developed in the ovary; it passes through the oviduct, and albumen or egg white is added; when the egg arrives in the uterus the final shell is added. Following this, the egg is moved toward the cloaca. Before it is passed out, the shell is coated with a waxlike substance, the cuticle or so-called "bloom." The shell represents the container, so to speak, for the liquid portion of the egg. On the inside of the shell is a membrane consisting of two layers, the outer and inner membranes. The egg white is composed of several layers, thin, thick, and again thin. The yolk is separated from the whites by the viteline membrane.

#### CONTAMINANTS

Outside, eggs are not sterile. When the egg passes through the cloaca of the hen, it may become contaminated immediately. Since poultry frequently carry salmonellae in their intestines, these contaminants may, and usually do, become part of the bacterial flora of the egg shell. Other sources of contamination include the nest, the hens' feathers and feet, the hands of the person handling the eggs, and previously used, soiled containers. The fecal matter of the hen is a very important source of *Salmonella enteritidis* and *typhimurium* and other enteric organisms including fecal streptococci. Poultry are very resistant to the salmonellae and may carry them in their intestinal tracts without showing signs of illness. Research has shown that chicken feed, especially fish meal, may be heavily contaminated with salmonellae. As long as this is true, it is almost impossible to eliminate *Salmonella* from poultry and the eggs they produce.

Rats and mice, which are common pests in poultry plants, are also important sources of salmonellae, and if present, contribute to the contamination of the hens' living quarters, the feed, nests, and eggs.

Contaminants are constantly added as the eggs are handled for marketing. Washing water has been indicted as an important source of contamination. Bacteria that have been associated with eggs are, besides salmonellae and fecal streptococci: *Achromobacter, Alcaligenes, Flavobacterium, Serratia, Bacillus, Proteus, Pseudomonas, Micrococcus* and *Escherichia*.

Lifshitz et al. (1965) made a study to determine whether or not the exterior structures, namely, cuticle, shell, and membranes, are able to support the growth of two common egg-spoiling bacteria species and of a pathogen, *Salmonella paratyphi*. They reported that these structures supported extensive growth of the three species tested.

PENETRATION

The shell and the outer and inner membranes aid in resisting bacterial penetration. Lifshitz et al. (1964) studied penetration of *Pseudomonas fluorescens* into the egg. Three sets of egg shell models were used to measure the resistance time of penetration. Of three exterior structures resisting penetration—shell, outer membrane, and inner membrane—the inner membrane ranked first, the shell second, and the outer membrane third.

In a subsequent study (1965) these authors investigated penetration through the shell by three organisms: *Pseudomonas fluorescens, Alcaligenes bookeri*, and *Salmonella paratyphi*. *Ps. fluorescens* was the first organism recovered from inside the model, after 5 days of incubation. It was found that *A. bookeri* required 17 days to penetrate 4 of 6 models, and *S. paratyphi* required 23 days. Bacterial spores were not able to penetrate. Stokes et al. (1956) also demonstrated that Salmonellae are able to penetrate the shell.

Certain environmental conditions may affect ease of penetration. When moisture is present and when the temperature is favorably high, penetration may occur. Under commercial egg production an effort is made to strictly control these conditions as much as feasible, using principles of scientific management.

When the shell has been penetrated, the two membranes which separate the shell from the egg white form barriers, the inner membrane being very effective. This membrane is rich in lysozyme which is inhibitory to gram-negative bacteria. However, penetration of the membranes may eventually take place. At refrigeration temperatures, penetration is retarded.

Duck eggs are usually produced under "natural" conditions. Being water birds, ducks are prone to lay eggs in wet places which may be heavily contaminated. When the eggs are gathered and handled the moisture aids in the bacterial penetration. Duck eggs contaminated with *Salmonella* have been frequently indicted as a cause of salmonellosis in man.

## TREATMENT

Various methods are constantly explored, and some are commercially used, to remove the contamination from the shell of the egg or to discourage bacterial penetration. Among these are sandblasting, washing with water, washing with solutions of various sanitizers, use of heat, and use of cold. A combination of some methods of cleaning and disinfecting the shell, followed by storage at low temperatures, is the most common method of preserving the quality of freshly laid eggs.

To make the washing process effective, a sanitizer should be present. The research result of Lifshitz et al. (1965) imply that eradication of the bacteria, not of dirt alone, is essential, since bacteria may in the absence of dirt use the components of the shell as nourishment and multiply.

When washing eggs, the wash water must be kept within a temperature range of 120–130°F. If the wash water is cooler than the egg, the bacteria will be drawn into the egg; water over 130°F may partially coagulate the egg white. The sanitizer-detergent should be left on the shells to protect against growth of bacteria. The eggs must be dried immediately after washing.

An additional precaution sometimes used to keep the shell surface dry is coating the eggs to be stored with a mineral oil which is colorless and odorless. This treatment is also an aid in retaining other quality characteristics of the egg such as preserving the natural moisture content and slowing down physical and chemical changes within the egg. This treatment can have little, if any, effect on the activity of microorganisms already present in the egg before it is treated.

## MULTIPLICATION

The albumen is not a favorable medium for bacterial multiplication. This is partly due to its alkaline pH and also to inhibiting substances, a powerful inhibitor being lysozyme. Conalbumin is also inhibitory, and so is avidin. The microorganisms which succeed in penetrating into the yolk, however, find a medium extremely favorable for their multiplication.

In summary, freshly laid intact eggs coming from healthy flocks free from *Salmonella pullorum* and produced under sanitary conditions may well be considered as sterile inside. However, the possibility exists that bacteria, among these salmonellae pathogenic to man, may be present if bacterial penetration through the shell has taken place. Ample opportunity is afforded when the shell is cracked and the membranes injured. For example, shell eggs have been indicted by circumstantial evidence to have caused gastroenteritis in hospital patients as was described in a report on a series of incidences traced to *S. derby* by Sanders et al. (1963). Raw or undercooked eggs originating from cracked specimens were implicated as the common source vehicle of infection which involved many hospitals in 13 states; extensive secondary spread followed. A discussion of the various aspects of this somewhat controversial topic is presented in the Proceedings (1965) of the National Conference on Salmonellosis held in 1964 at the Communicable Disease Center, Atlanta, Georgia.

STORAGE

Only specimens free from visible internal defects are stored. Selection is made by the method of "candling," a process by which the egg is subjected to light and examined. For best results, storage conditions are carefully controlled regarding temperature and relative humidity. For commercial storage, 6 months or more, temperatures of 29–31°F and a relative humidity of 80–85% are recommended. The air is constantly moved to avoid possible condensation of moisture on the shells which would favor the penetration of microorganisms.

Gas storage involves the use of carbon dioxide. Recommendations for concentrations vary widely. Concentrations sufficiently high to delay microbial activity are apt to unfavorably affect some other quality characteristics of the egg. Ozone has also been used for gas storage of eggs.

Thermostabilization of eggs involves heating them in the shell; either hot water or hot oil is used. Temperatures are just sufficient to pasteurize the shell. Immersion of eggs in a hot detergent-sanitizer solution is another method.

A new approach to prolonging the keeping quality of eggs was taken recently. Kosikowsky and dePaolis (1964) experimented with treating packaged eggs under high (750 mm) vacuum. The packaging material was cellophane-polyethylene film. The eggs were stored at 5°C (41°F) at relative humidity of 85–90% and at room temperature 16–30°C (61–86°F) at relative humidity ranging from 65 to 80%. Microbial analysis of the egg contents revealed that the eggs stored for 120 days at 5°C (41°F) were of excellent quality. Control eggs, stored unpackaged, were spoiled, and so were controls sealed under atmospheric conditions in film pouches of low oxygen permeability. No mold or yeast was present in eggs stored under vacuum and bacterial counts were low.

## Frozen and Dried Eggs

At present, approximately 7% of the total egg production in the United States goes into either frozen or dried eggs; three times as many eggs are frozen as are dried.

Frozen and dried eggs are available as whole eggs, whites, and yolks. High quality processed eggs of low bacterial count are available on specification for preparing lightly heated items such as scrambled eggs and French toast.

The main bacteriological problem in the freezing and drying of eggs is securing raw material worthy of processing. The contaminating bacteria are most usually the kinds that cause spoilage of eggs at low temperatures such as representatives of the genera *Alcaligenes*, *Pseudomonas*, *Proteus*, and *Flavobacterium*. However, *Salmonella* may be present also, and occasionally hemolytic bacteria.

Constant vigilance is necessary to insure that specimens containing bacteria will not be incorporated thereby contaminating an entire batch. Parts of contaminated shell must be kept out. An extremely important precaution is to exercise excellent general plant sanitation. Unless the highest standards prevail as to selection of sound material, healthy and clean personnel, and frequent cleaning of equipment, the finished product may not be acceptable bacteriologically. Another reason for high counts may be excessive multiplication of contaminants occurring prior to processing, caused by delays along the processing line.

PASTEURIZATION

Pasteurizing the egg magma prior to freezing and drying will reduce the bacterial load substantially. The aim is to rid the product of the majority of contaminants, without coagulating the egg.

Among the factors affecting survival are the time–temperature relationships of the pasteurization process, type of organism involved, cell load, and pH of medium.

A new regulation requires that all egg products be pasteurized beginning 1966. Regulations are administered by the Consumer and Marketing Administration, USDA.

A new development has taken place in regard to pasteurization of egg white. Previously, liquid egg white could not be adequately pasteurized because the temperatures required to kill the pathogens proved damaging to the physical properties of the proteins. The new process involves adjustment of the pH from 9 to 6.8 and the addition of a suitable metal salt for the purpose of stabilizing the heat-susceptible proteins. The stabilized whites may then be pasteurized by the method now used for whole egg: heating to 140–143°F for 3.5–4 minutes.

The process was reported by Lineweaver and Cunningham (1964) at the 24th Annual Meeting of the Institute of Food Technology (program paper 151). When the pH of the whites is lowered to a level of 6.6–7.0, the heat stability of ovalbumin, lysozyme, and ovomucoid is increased and viscosity changes during heating are avoided. The protein conalbumin is stabilized by the addition of aluminum salts or iron salts. The metallic ions combine with the protein to form a complex which is more heat resistant than the free protein. An explanation for the fact that whole egg is more heat stable than white is that the pH is lower and the iron present in the yolk reacts with the conalbumin.

## FROZEN EGGS

During freezing and freezer storage the bacterial population gradually diminishes. The greatest decrease, about 50%, occurs during the first two weeks, but greater reductions have been reported. Slow freezing has a greater killing effect than fast freezing.

It is important to remember that although freezing and freezer-storing eggs will reduce the number of bacterial contaminants, some bacteria will survive and will be ready to multiply in the thawed product. Frozen eggs must be kept frozen until just prior to being used. The method of thawing is important. If the frozen egg is thawed at a high temperature or if the thawed product is held at temperatures favorable for bacterial growth, the survivors may multiply to dangerously high numbers. When defrosting takes place under refrigeration, the process may take days in eggs packaged in large bulk, but is a bacteriologically safe method.

## DRIED EGGS

To achieve a stable product, the glucose content in yolks and whole eggs is usually reduced before drying by enzyme treatment or by fermentation. Egg whites may be hydrolyzed by treating with trypsin under heat (140°F) or they may be yeast fermented before they are dried. Beginning in 1966, all egg products to be dried must be pasteurized.

Most of the egg dried in this country is processed in the spray dryer. The magma is sprayed into a dry, heated (340°F) air current. The aim is to withdraw moisture and to leave only 1% in the product. As is true for frozen eggs, the number of microorganisms may vary considerably except when the product has been pasteurized previous to drying. The drying process itself may reduce the bacterial load to a fraction (1/10 to 1/1000) of the original load, but the number of survivors may still be large unless the initial load is quite low.

A variety of bacteria have been reported to survive, among them pathogens such as heat-resistant salmonellae and fecal streptococci. Micrococci and spore formers have been recovered also.

No multiplication of survivors can take place in the egg powder because of its low moisture content.

Stuart et al. (1945) reported a decrease in the total number of bacteria in whole egg solids during storage. When the egg solids were stored for 46 days at 86°F (30°C) a decrease to approximately one-tenth of the initial count was noted.

Survival in storage of salmonellae in pasteurized whole egg solids of pH 5.5 has been studied by Byrne and Rayman (*In:* U.S. Quartermaster Food and Container Institute For the Armed Forces, 1954). The egg was first pasteurized for 1.5–2 minutes at 140°F (60°C), then stored in cans for 342–416 days at warehouse temperatures. Six out of 30 cans contained viable salmonellae; the counts were 10–475 cells per 100 g of egg solids.

When dried egg is incorporated in mixes the microbial quality of the egg used determines the quality of the mixes. Thatcher and Montford (1962) examined egg products, and foods containing them, in Canada. They warn that inclusion of unpasteurized egg products in mixes renders these unsafe. These workers isolated 14 different *Salmonella* serotypes from 119 egg-containing cake mixes of which 51.2% contained *Salmonella*. They also warn that unpasteurized egg may serve as a source of salmonellae in other non-heat-processed foods such as specific dessert pie fillings. Thorough heating is a safeguard for all products prepared from dried egg or from mixes containing dried egg. A number of "convenience" mixes containing egg were listed by Thatcher (1965) in Canada as having been analyzed and found positive for Salmonella: cake mixes and frostings, pancake and waffle mixes, meringue powders, whip-powder mix, batter mix, piecrust mix, cookie mixes, biscuit mix, gingerbread mix, doughnut mix, sponge pudding mix, coconut dessert mix, and several other mixes. The situation is now remedied; since June 1, 1962, a Canadian government regulation has required that Salmonella-free dried egg must be used in mixes.

RECONSTITUTED EGG

Powdered egg when reconstituted with water assumes the properties of fluid egg, including its vulnerability to bacterial activity. Reconstituted egg should therefore be carefully protected from recontamination and held at temperatures preventing microbial multiplication. It is amazing to observe how carefully shell eggs are routinely treated with regard to refrigeration, while reconstituted egg is found standing for hours in kitchen and bakeshops where the chances for contamination and multiplication are dangerously great.

The production of the highly perishable commodity, eggs, must be guided by stringent principles of sanitation, beginning at the hen house and ending at delivery to the consumer. The consumer, in this case the manager of a food service establishment, must again apply highest standards of sanitation at every step of storage, preparation and service. Cracked eggs should not be used.

It is extremely important that the dried and frozen egg purchased originates from processing plants which employ the highest standards of sanitation so as to ensure low bacterial counts including salmonellae and other enteric pathogens.

Government-inspected egg products carry the official inspection mark which indicates that the items have been produced according to strict sanitary standards under continuous inspection.

## Fish and Shellfish

Fish and shellfish are extremely susceptible to microbial spoilage. They carry a varied bacterial flora, most of it harmless; however, organisms of public health significance may be present.

Much fresh fish and shellfish is immediately absorbed by the local markets but transportation from one locality to another requires icing. Fish eviscerated under hygienic conditions and well iced will tolerate icing for a couple of days without apparent loss in quality. Much fish is frozen and marketed in that state.

### Contaminants

The slime covering fish and shellfish may contain bacteria of the genera *Pseudomonas, Achromobacter, Micrococcus, Flavobacterium,*

*Corynebacterium, Sarcina,* and *Serratia,* all of which are found in water. If the water from which the fish and shellfish originate contains raw sewage, human pathogens are likely to be among the microbial flora associated with the fish and shellfish. An inhabitant of some waters, fresh and salt water, is *Clostridium botulinum* Type E.

In the intestinal tract of fish are found representatives of *Achromobacter, Bacillus, Clostridium, Escherichia,* and *Flavobacterium.* These intestinal bacteria may become quite prevalent as contaminants of opened fish. This is the reason why fish "in the round" have been claimed to keep fresh somewhat better than opened fish, at least for a while.

Shellfish such as oysters, clams, and mussels pass large amounts of water through their bodies. In general, the majority of the bacteria found in and on unprocessed shellfish consists of the water bacteria mentioned above.

Pathogens which may be contained in the water of their origin, and are important from the viewpoint of public health, include bacteria and viruses.

*Clostridium botulinum* spores, Type E, are inhabitants of many waters where fish are caught. They have been found to be associated with tuna prior to canning, but proper canning methods will kill them. The slow heat penetration into fish, especially oily fish, presents a problem. However, the information on heat transfer into these products is available to the food technologist and care is taken to obtain a safe canned product. The recent incident of botulism from tuna was caused by faulty seams of cans. The incidents involving toxin Type E in vacuum-packed whitefish chubs point out the danger that toxin may be formed under certain conditions involving light heat processing followed by mishandling and storage at temperatures at and above 38°F.

*Salmonella typhosa* may cause a serious problem in shellfish when these are harvested from polluted waters. The dangers are particularly serious in oysters and other marine foods which are often eaten raw or only slightly heated, as in stews and soups. Typhoid bacteria survive in shell oysters and shucked oysters for months.

*Salmonella schottmuelleri* has been found to remain viable in shell oysters and soft clams sufficiently long to be a potential hazard to the consumer.

Staphylococci are not members of the typical flora of fresh fish but coagulase-positive forms have been isolated from fillets and other fish cuts. Evidently, these contaminants were added in the cutting operation, their source being the food handler.

Hepatitis virus may be present in sewage-polluted waters and is known to have contaminated seafood.

Oysters and clams, which prefer to live in sheltered bays, are liable to grow in waters which become easily contaminated from fresh water runoffs and even sewage. Places where shellfish grow have plankton, microscopic animals and plant life, which serve as food to shellfish.

In the past, some serious outbreaks of typhoid fever were traced to shellfish from sewage-infested waters. Following this, health departments and the shellfish industry asked the Public Health Service for aid in the sanitary control of the shellfish industry. Effective sanitary supervision was initiated in all shellfish-producing states in 1925. The Public Health Service undertakes research, develops standards, and evaluates the cooperating states' sanitary shellfish program, and carries out training programs. These activities will be discussed further in a later chapter. Sanitation in seafood production and distribution has been discussed by Liston (1965). Thanks to the rigid sanitary requirements now practiced, the program is very effective in preventing the spread of pathogens which may be carried by seafood.

Since fresh fish and shellfish are highly perishable they are consumed or processed as fast as possible. The catch is often processed on the boat; or it is packed in ice, or frozen, prior to transit to the processing plant or market.

## Processed Fish and Shellfish

### CANNED

Many kinds of canned fish and other seafood are available. As is true for other canned products, canned seafood is devoid of disease-producing organisms but may harbor some thermophilic types which will not cause problems unless the cans are stored at high temperatures.

Incidences of food poisoning from commercially canned fish and other seafood have not been on record for many years until a recent episode involving botulism from canned tuna which was probably caused by recontamination in the can due to faulty seals.

Oysters do not lend themselves to the high heat treatment of canning, except when smoked. Crabmeat may be pasteurized and must be kept refrigerated during transport and marketing.

SALTED, DRIED, SMOKED

Salting, marinating, and smoking fish will dry the tissues to some extent. A combination of salting and smoking is frequently used. The heat treatment applied in smoking is nowadays only light. The effect of drying may be intensified by using flowing air. Smoking may be done at fairly low temperatures or at temperatures as high as 200°F. Wood smoke contains certain chemicals which seem to act to some extent as a preservative. Formaldehyde is considered to be one of the more effective compounds; others are aldehydes, alcohols, phenolic compounds, organic acids, and ketones. The germicidal effect of smoking is not completely understood. The volatile compounds omitted differ in their bacteriostatic and bactericidal effects and seem to be most effective against vegetative cells. Spores exhibit more resistance to action of these agents. "Liquid smoke," a solution of chemical similar to those occurring in smoke of burning wood, has little if any bactericidal value, but it enhances flavor.

Appleman et al. (1964), in a study made in Scotland, found coagulase-positive staphylococci in over 60% of the samples they analyzed. The degree of heat treatment would determine survival of this contaminant as well as of *Clostridium botulinum* Type E.

The possibility that insufficient smoking followed by anaerobic packaging might prove a dangerous combination was much discussed when several episodes of Type E botulism occurred in 1963. The outbreaks were caused by smoked whitefish chubs from the Great Lakes (Morbidity and Mortality, 1963). As a result of these incidents, smoked fish products made from the Great Lakes regions henceforth will be stored and distributed as a frozen food, at least for a while. This decision has been made jointly by the National Fisheries Institute and the Food and Drug Administration. This toxin is not known to develop at temperatures below the freezing point, according to the Food and Drug Administration. Since very low temperatures may adversely alter the quality of some smoked fish products, it is not necessary or advisable that these products be kept as low as other frozen foods, but to assure a safe product the fish is to be held at all times in the frozen state. These regulations may be temporary until practices for long-range application have been studied and can be recommended. The treatment is applied only to smoked fish, not the fresh, canned, frozen, or pickled items.

FROZEN

Raw fish is seldom frozen whole, but rather as fillets and steaks. Raw shrimp, scallops, clams, oysters, and lobster tails are frequently marketed frozen. Shrimp, crab meat, and lobster meat are also marketed in the cooked and frozen state.

The freezing kills part, but certainly not all, of the contaminants. Upon thawing, if time–temperature conditions permit, the survivors will resume multiplication.

COOKED FISH AND SHELLFISH

Items which are frequently marketed in the cooked stage include crab, shrimp, and lobster. The process of cooking renders them almost sterile. Unfortunately, however, recontamination with staphylococci and salmonellae is not uncommon (Silverman et al. 1961; Nickerson et al. 1962). In fact, the percentage of samples contaminated with *Staphylococcus aureus* was reported to be extremely high, up to 75%, in some instances.

An extensive study was made by Raj and Liston (1963) on the effect of processing on bacteria of public health significance in frozen seafoods. These authors found that frozen raw seafoods, including fish and oysters, when entering the processing plant carried rather low levels of bacteria of public health significance. The initial cutting operation of the frozen fish caused a tenfold increase in counts. The staphylococci count in the samples increased from 7% to 64%; among these staphylococci were coagulase-positive strains.

Battering and breading operations added more significant contaminants, among them hemolytic streptococci, coagulase-positive staphylococci, enterococci, coliforms, and miscellaneous anaerobes; batter was shown to be an excellent medium for multiplication of contaminants. In 73% of the battered samples, staphylococci were found. The precook operation, done in oil, reduced the counts of some forms, namely, hemolytic streptococci and the coliforms. However, this heat treatment hardly affected the staphylococci, enterococci, and anaerobes.

Research results of other workers have also pointed to the dangers of introducing great numbers of bacteria, including pathogenic contaminants, with the breading operation, especially when it is performed by hand. Contaminants of significance include coagulase-positive staphylococci, salmonellae, shigellae, and enterococci. In a study by Appleman et al. (1964), coagulase-positive staphylococci were isolated in a high percentage of unfrozen crabcakes. Frozen crabcakes were not as high in viable staphylococci.

The importance of sanitary standards is evident from data by Slocum (1960) presented in Table 20.

Table 20. Effect of Sanitary Handling on Total Counts of Fish Sticks before Final Cooking on Bacterial Counts per Gram of Substrate (Fish, Batter, or Both) [Adapted from Slocum (1960)]

|  | Plant A, poor sanitation | Plant B, above average sanitation |
| --- | --- | --- |
| Raw fish | 560,000 | 65,000 |
| Batter | 12,000,000[a] | 210,000[b] |
| Fish and batter | 2,000,000 | 260,000 |

[a] Batter used for 10 hours.
[b] Batter used for 30 minutes.

The same author stressed the point that efficient terminal heat treatment killed a large proportion of the contaminants. The danger of recontamination of cooked items is present wherever food is prepared, including quantity food service. The application of the principle of efficient terminal heat treatment deserves more attention than it now gets in many establishments where food is prepared and served to the public.

In 1956 the Agricultural Marketing Act was extended, and under this act the standards for quality were developed, including fish. The administration is the responsibility of the Bureau of Commercial Fisheries, U. S. Fish and Wildlife Service, Department of the Interior.

Shellfish are under the jurisdiction of the U. S. Public Health Service, and this jurisdiction extends to catching, processing, and marketing. The product must come from beds which are certified to be pure.

Only fish and shellfish from uncontaminated waters should be purchased. Local health authorities are helpful when it comes to choosing vendors for fish and shellfish.

To safeguard high quality fresh fish and shellfish, they should be stored for the shortest periods possible. Frozen products should be kept frozen, and precautions taken during thawing to prevent the items from warming up to temperatures supporting bacterial multiplication.

## References

**Milk and Other Dairy Products**
Armijo, R., D. A. Henderson, R. Timothee, and H. B. Robinson. (1957). "Food

Poisoning Outbreaks with Spray-dried Milk—An Epidemiologic Study."
*Amer. Jour. Publ. Hlth.*, *47*: 1093–1100.

Campbell, J. E., G. K. Murthy, C. P. Straub, K. H. Lewis, and J. G. Terrill.
(1961). "Radionuclides in Milk." *Agr. and Food Chem.*, *9*(2): 117–122.

Coulter, S. T., R. Jenness, and W. F. Geddes. (1951). "Physical and Chemical
Aspects of the Production, Storage and Utility of Dry Milk Products."
*Advances Food Res.*, *3*: 45–118.

Donnelly, C. B., L. A. Black, and K. H. Lewis. (1962). "The Occurrence of
Coagulase-positive Staphylococci in Cheddar Cheese." A Preliminary Report,
Society of The American Bacteriologists. Bacteriological Proceedings, 62nd
Annual Meeting, p. 23.

Foltz, V. D., R. Mickelsen, W. N. Martin, and C. A. Hunter. (1960). "The
Incidence of Potentially Pathogenic Staphylococci in Dairy Products At
The Consumer Level. I. Fluid Milk and Fluid Milk By-products." *Jour. Milk
& Food Tech.*, *23*(9): 280–284.

McDivitt, Maxine E., P. P. Huppler, and A. M. Swanson. (1964). "Bacteriological Changes During the Manufacture of Non-Fat Dry Milk." *Jour. Dairy Sci.*,
47: 936–941.

Mickelsen, R., V. D. Foltz, W. H. Martin, and C. A. Hunter. (1961). "The Incidence of Potentially Pathogenic Staphylococci in Dairy Products at the
Consumer Level. II. Cheese." *Jour. Milk & Food Tech.*, *24*(11): 342–345.

Murthy, G. K., E. B. Masurovsky, J. E. Campbell, and L. F. Edmondson. (1961).
"A Method for Removing Cationic Radionuclides From Milk." *Jour. Dairy
Sci.*, *44*(12): 2158–2170.

Nevot, A., G. Mocquot, P. Lafont, and M. Plommet. (1963). "Studies on The
Survival of Pathogenic Bacteria In Ripened Soft Cheese." *Dairy Sci. Abst.*, *25*:
1170.

Post, F. J., A. H. Bliss, and W. B. O'Keefe. (1961). "Studies on the Ecology of
Selected Food Poisoning Organisms in Food. I. Growth of *Staphylococcus
aureus* in Cream and Cream Products." *Jour. Food Sci.*, *26*(4): 436–441.

Sharpe, M. E., F. K. Neave, and B. Reiter. (1962). "Staphylococci and Micrococci
Associated With Dairying." *Jour. Appl. Bact.*, *25*(3): 403–415.

Smith, J. (1961). "Reviews of the Progress of Dairy Science." Section F. Milkborne Disease (review). *Jour. Dairy Res.*, *28*(1): 87–107.

State of New York, Department of Agriculture and Markets. (1962). "Agriculture
and Markets Laws." Article 4, Relating to Dairy Products.

Takahashi, I., and C. K. Johns. (1959). "*Staphylococcus aureus* in Cheddar Cheese."
*Jour. Dairy Sci.*, *42*(6): 1032–1037.

Thatcher, F. S., W. Simon, and C. Walters. (1956). "Extraneous Matter and
Bacteria of Public Health Significance in Cheese." *Canad. Jour. Publ. Hlth.*,
*47*: 234–243.

Thomas, S. B., and R. G. Druce. (1963). "Types of Psychrophilic Bacteria in
Milk." *Dairy Eng.*, *80*: 378–381.

**Meat and Meat Products**

Angelotti, R., Keith H. Lewis, and Milton J. Foter (1962). "Time–Temperature
Effects on Fecal Streptococi in Foods. Unpublished paper presented before the
Laboratory Section, 90th Annual Meeting, Amer. Public Health Assoc.,
Miami, Fla. October.

Brown, W. L., C. A. Vinton, and C. E. Gross. (1960). "Heat Resistance and

Growth Characteristics of Microorganisms Isolated from Semi-perishable Canned Hams." *Food Res., 25*(3): 345–350.

Canada, James C., and D. H. Strong. (1964). "*Clostridium perfringens* in Bovine Livers." *Jour. Food Sci., 29*(6): 862–864.

Cherry, W. B., M. Scherago, and R. H. Weaver. (1943). "The Occurrence of *Salmonella* in Retail Meat Products." *Amer. Jour. Hygiene, 37:* 211–215.

Eddy, B. P., and M. Ingram. (1962). "The Occurrence and Growth of Staphylococci on Packed Bacon, With Special Reference to *Staphylococcus aureus.*" *Jour. Appl. Bact., 25*(2): 237–247.

Felsenfeld, O., V. M. Young, and T. Yoshimura. (1950). "A Survey of *Salmonella* organism in Market Meat, Eggs, and Milk." *Jour. Amer. Vet. Assoc., 116*(874): 17–21.

Galton, M. M., W. D. Lowrey, and A. V. Hardy. (1954). "*Salmonella* in Fresh and Smoked Pork Sausage." *Jour. Infectious Diseases, 95:* 232–235.

Hall, Herbert, and Robert Angelotti. (1965). "*Clostridium perfringens* in Meat and Meat Products." *Appl. Micr., 13*(3): 352–357.

Hobbs, Betty C., and J. G. Wilson. (1959). "Contamination of Wholesale Meat Supplies with *Salmonella* and Heat-Resistant *Clostridium welchii.*" *Monthly Bull. Ministry of Hlth. Publ. Hlth. Labor. Ser., 18:* 198–206.

Jay, James M. (1961a). "Incidence and Properties of Coagulase-positive Staphylococci in Certain Market Meats as Determined on Three Selective Media." *Appl. Micr., 9*(3): 228–232.

Jay, James M. (1961b). "Some Characteristics of Coagulase-positive Staphylococci from Market Meats Relative to their Origins into the Meats." *Jour. Food Sci., 26*(6): 631–634.

Jay, James M. (1962). "Further Studies on Staphylococci in Meats. III. Occurrence and Characteristics of Coagulase-positive Strains From a Variety of Non-Frozen Market Cuts." *Appl. Micr., 10*(3): 247–251.

Lepovetsky, B. C., H. H. Weiser, and F. E. Deatherage. (1953). "A Microbiological Study of Lymph Nodes, Bone Marrow and Muscle Tissue Obtained From Slaughtered Cattle." *Appl. Micr., 1*(1): 57–59.

Ravenholt, R. T., R. C. Eelkema, M. Mulhern, and R. B. Watkins. (1961). "Staphylococcal Infection in Meat Animals and Meat Workers." *U.S. Publ. Hlth. Repts., 76*(10): 879–888.

Silliker, J. H., C. E. Jensen, M. M. Voegeli, and N. W. Chmura. (1962). "Studies on the Fate of Staphylococci During the Processing of Hams." *Jour. Food. Sci., 27*(1): 50–56.

Strong, Dorothy H., J. C. Canada, and B. B. Griffith. (1963). "Incidence of *Clostridium perfringens* in American Foods." *Appl. Micr., 11*(1): 42–44.

United States Department of Agriculture. (1965). Manual of Meat Inspection Procedures of the USDA. December.

Wilson, E., R. S. Paffenbarger, Jr., M. J. Foter, and K. H. Lewis. (1961). "Prevalence of Salmonellae in Meat and Poultry Products." *Jour. Infectious Diseases, 109:* 166–171.

**Poultry and Poultry Products**

Felsenfeld, O., V. M. Young, and T. Yoshimura. (1950). "A Survey of Salmonella organisms in Market Meat, Eggs and Milk." *Jour. Amer. Vet. Assoc., 116*(874): 17–21.

Galton, M. M., D. C. Mackel, A. L. Lewis, W. C. Haire, and A. V. Hardy. (1955).

REFERENCES 151

"Salmonellosis in Poultry and Poultry Processing Plants in Florida." *Amer. Jour. Vet. Res., 16:* 132–137.

Gunderson, M. F., H. W. McFadden, and T. S. Kyle. (1954). *The Bacteriology of Commercial Poultry Processing.* Burgess Publishing Co., Minneapolis, Minn.

Hall, Herbert, and Robert Angelotti. (1965). *"Clostridium perfringens* in Meat and Meat Products." *Appl. Micr., 13*(3): 352–357.

Hamdy, M. K., N. D. Burton, and W. E. Brown. (1964). "Source and Portal Entry of Bacteria Found in Bruised Poultry Tissue." *Appl. Micr., 12*(6): 464–469.

McCarthy, Patricia A., William Brown, and Mostafa K. Hamdy. (1963). "Microbiological Studies of Bruised Tissues." *Jour. Food Sci., 28*(3): 245–253.

Nagel, Charles, and Kenneth Simpson. (1960). "Microorganisms Associated with Spoilage of Refrigerated Poultry." *Food Tech., 14*(1): 21–23.

Sadler, W. W., R. Yamamoto, H. E. Adler, and G. F. Stewart. (1961). "Survey of Market Poultry for *Salmonella* Infection." *Appl. Micr., 9*(1): 72–76.

Strong, D. H., J. C. Canada, and B. B. Griffith. (1963). "Incidence of *Clostridium perfringens* in American Foods." *Appl. Micr., 11*(1): 42–44.

Tailyour, J. M., and R. J. Avery. (1960). "A Survey of Turkey Viscera for Salmonellae." *Canad. Jour. Publ. Hlth., 51:* 75–77.

Thatcher, F. S., and A Loit. (1961). "Comparative Microflora of Chlortetracycline-treated and Non-treated Poultry With Special Reference to Public Health Aspects." *Appl. Micr., 9*(1): 39–45.

Walker, H. W., and J. C. Ayres. (1956). "Incidence and Kinds of Microorganisms Associated with Commercially Dressed Poultry." *Appl. Micr., 4*(6): 345–349.

Wilson, Elizabeth, R. S. Paffenbarger, Jr., Milton Foter, and Keith Lewis. (1961). "Prevalence of Salmonellae in Meat and Poultry Products." *Jour. Infectious Diseases, 109*(2): 166–171.

**Eggs**

Kosikowsky, Frank V., and P. dePaolis. (1964). "The Keeping Quality of Eggs Packaged Under High Vacuum." *Poultry Sci., 43*(5): 1334.

Lifshitz, A., R. C. Baker, and H. B. Naylor. (1964). "The Relative Importance of Chicken Egg Exterior Structures in Resisting Bacterial Penetration." *Jour. Food Sci., 29* (1): 94–99.

Lifshitz, A., R. C. Baker, and H. B. Naylor. (1965). "The Exterior Structures of the Egg as Nutrients for Bacteria." *Jour. Food Sci., 30*(3): 516–519.

Lineweaver, H., and F. E. Cunningham. "Heat Stability of Egg White and Egg White Proteins." Program paper No. 151, Presented at the 24th Annual Meeting of the Institute of Food Technologists, Washington, D.C. 1964.

Proceedings, National Conference on Salmonellosis, March 11–13, 1964. Communicable Disease Center, Atlanta, Georgia. p. 111–151. 1965.

Sanders, E., F. J. Sweeney, E. A. Friedman, J. R. Boring, E. L. Randall, and L. D. Polk. (1963). "An Outbreak of Hospital-associated Infections Due to *Salmonella derby.*" *Jour. Amer. Med. Assoc., 186:* 984–986.

Stokes, J. L., W. W. Osborne, and H. G. Bayne (1956). "Penetration and Growth of Salmonella in Shell Eggs." *Food Res., 21:* 510–518.

Stuart, L. S., H. E. Goresline, H. F. Smart, and V. T. Dawson. (1945). "Effect of Storage Temperature on Bacteria in Egg Powder." *Food Indust., 17:* 1174–1175, 1266–1274.

Thatcher, Fred S. (1965), "Large Populations at Risk." *In:* Proceedings, Nat.

Conf. on Salmonellosis. March 11–13, 1964, Commun. Disease Center, Atlanta, Ga., p. 56–62.

Thatcher, F. S., and J. Montford. (1962). "Egg Products As A Source of Salmonellae in Processed Foods." *Canad. Jour. Publ. Hlth.*, *53:* 61–69.

U.S. Quartermaster Food and Container Institute For The Armed Forces. Martin S. Peterson and Harry E. Goresline (ed.) "Stability of Dehydrated Eggs." 1954.

### Fish and Shellfish

Appleman, M. D., N. Bain, and J. M. Shewan. (1964). "A Study of Some Organisms of Public Health Significance From Fish and Fishery Products." *Jour. Appl. Bact.*, *27*(1): 69–77.

Liston, J. (1965). Sanitation in Seafood Production and Distribution. *Jour. Milk & Food Tech.*, *28:* 152–158.

Morbidity and Mortality Weekly Reports, U.S. Department of Health, Education and Welfare, *Public Health Service*, *12*(45): 378. 1963.

Nickerson, J. T. R., G. J. Silverman, M. Solberg, D. W. Duncan, and M. M. Joselow. (1962). "Microbial Analysis of Commerical Frozen Fish Sticks." *Jour. Milk & Food Tech.*, *25*(2): 45–47.

Raj, H., and J. Liston. (1963). "Effect of Processing on Public Health Bacteria in Frozen Seafoods." *Food Tech.*, *17*(10): 83–89.

Silverman, G. J., J. T. R. Nickerson, D. W. Duncan, N. S. Davis, J. S. Schachter, and M. M. Joselow. (1961). "Microbial Analysis of Frozen Raw and Cooked Shrimp. I. General Results." *Food Tech.*, *15*(11): 455–458.

Slocum, G. G. (1960). "Microbiological Limits For Frozen Precooked Foods." *In:* Conference on Frozen Food Quality. U.S. Department of Agriculture, Western Utilization Research and Development Division, Albany, Calif. ARS–74–21. p. 70–73.

## Additional Readings

American Meat Institute Foundation. "The Science of Meat and Meat Products." W. H. Freeman and Co., San Francisco and London. 1960.

American Public Health Association. "Standard Methods For The Microbiological Examination of Foods." American Public Health Assoc., Inc. New York. 1958.

Anonymous. *"Salmonella derby* Gastroenteritis." Epidemiologic Note. *Publ. Hlth. Repts.*, *78:* 855. 1963.

Ayers, J. C., and B. Taylor. "Effect of Temperature on Microbial Proliferation in Shell Eggs." *Appl. Micr.*, *4*(6): 355–359. 1956.

Baumann, D. P., and G. W. Reinbold. "Enumeration of Psychrophilic Microorganisms." A Review. *Jour. Milk & Food Tech.*, *26*(3): 81–86. 1963.

Browne, A. S. "The Public Health Significance of *Salmonella* on Poultry and Poultry Products." Ph.D. thesis, University of California, Berkeley, Calif.

Cavett, J. J. "The Microbiology of Vacuum Packed Sliced Bacon." *Jour. Appl. Bact.*, *25:* 282–289. 1962.

Clise, J. "Control of Salmonellae in Shell Eggs." Assoc. of Food and Drug Officials of the United States. *Quarterly Bulletin*, *29*(1): 21–28. 1965.

Dixon, J. M. S., and F. E. Pooley. "Salmonellae in a Poultry Processing Plant." *Monthly Bull. Ministry of Hlth., Publ. Hlth. Labor. Ser.*, *20*(2): 30–33. 1961.

Foltz, V. D., and R. Mickelsen. "Sanitary Studies on Malted Milk Shakes." *Jour. Milk & Food Tech.*, *27*(5): 139–141. 1964.

Foster, E. M., F. E. Nelson, M. L. Speck, R. N. Doetsch, and J. C. Olson, Jr. *Dairy Microbiology.* Prentice-Hall, Englewood Cliffs, N. J. 1957.

Frazier, William C. *Food Microbiology.* McGraw-Hill Book Co., New York. 1958.

Hammer, Bernard W., and Frederick J. Babel. *Dairy Bacteriology.* 4th ed. John Wiley & Sons, New York. 1957.

Hinshaw, W. R., and E. M. McNeil. "Salmonella Infection As a Food Industry Problem." *Advances in Food Res.*, *3:* 209–240. Academic Press, New York. 1951.

Hobbs, Betty C. "Public Health Significance of Salmonella Carriers in Live Stock and Birds." *Jour. Appl. Bact.*, *24*(3): 340–352. 1961.

Ingram, M., and B. C. Hobbs. "The Bacteriology of 'Pasteurized' Canned Hams." *J. R. Sanit.*, *74:* 1151. 1954.

Ingram, M. "Microbiological Principles in Prepackaging Meats." *Jour. Appl. Bact.*, *25*(2): 259–281. 1962.

Jensen, L. B. *The Microbiology of Meat.* 3rd ed. Garrard Press, Champaign, Ill. 1954.

Jensen, E. T. "Shellfish and Public Health." *Jour. Milk & Food Tech.*, *19*(9): 281–283. 1956.

Jensen, Eugene T. "Shellfish Sanitation in the Control of Hepatitis." *Amer. Jour. Publ. Hlth. and The Nation's Hlth.*, *52* (10): 1743–1748. 1962.

Lahiry, N. L., M. M. Moojani, and B. R. Baliga. "Factors Influencing the Keeping Quality of Fresh Water Fish in Ice." *Food Tech.*, *17*(9): 123–125. 1963.

McCoy, E. "Staphylococcal Problems in the Dairy Industry." *Milk Products Jour.*, *50:* 14–16. 1959.

McCullough, Norman B. "Foods in the Epidemiology of Salmonellosis." *Jour. Amer. Dietet. Assoc.*, *34*(3): 254–257. 1958.

Milk Sanitation Administration. U.S. Department of Health, Education and Welfare, U.S. Public Health Service, PHS Publication 728. 1959.

Morehouse, L. G., and E. E. Wedman. "Salmonella and Other Disease-Producing Organisms in Animal By-Products." A survey. *Jour. Amer. Vet. Med. Assoc.*, *139*(9): 989–995. 1961.

Newell, K. W. "The Investigation and Control of Salmonellosis." *World Health Organization Bulletin, 21:* 279–297. 1959.

Osborne, W. W., R. P. Straka, and H. Lineweaver. "Heat Resistance of Strains of Salmonella in Liquid Whole Eggs, Egg Yolk and Egg White." *Food Res.*, *19:* 451–463. 1954.

Raj, H., and J. Liston. "Survival of Bacteria of Public Health Significance in Frozen Seafoods." *Food Tech.*, *15*(10): 429–434. 1961.

Rogers, R. E., and C. S. McClesky. "The Bacteriological Quality of Ground Beef in Retail Markets." *Food Tech.*, *11:* 318–320. 1957.

Romanoff, A. L., and A. J. Romanoff. *The Avian Egg.* John Wiley & Sons, New York. 1949.

Schlafman, I. H. "Community Milk Sanitation Problems and The Role of the Public Health Service." *Jour. Envir. Hlth.*, *26*(1): 26–29. 1963.

"Second Report Joint FAO/WHO Expert Committee on Meat Hygiene." *Jour. Sci. Food & Agric.*, *14:* ii–109. 1963.

Stokes, J. L., W. W. Osborne, and H. G. Bayne. "Penetration and Growth of Salmonella in Shell Eggs." *Food Res.*, *21*(5): 510–518. 1956.

Straka, R. P., and F. M. Combes. "The Predominance of Micrococci in the Flora of Experimental Frozen Turkey Meat Steaks." *Food Res., 16:* 492–493. 1951.

Todorov, D. "Viability of Salmonellae in Milk and Dairy Products." *Dairy Sci. Abst., 25:* 2655. 1963.

Tressler, Donald K., and Clifford Evers. *The Freezing Preservation of Foods.* 3rd ed. Avi Publishing Co., Westport, Conn. 1957.

U.S. Department of Health, Education and Welfare. National Shellfish Sanitation Workshop. 4th ed. Proceedings, 1962. Washington, D.C.

U.S. Public Health Service. "Manual of Recommended Practices for Sanitary Control of the Shellfish Industry." 1957–1959.

U.S. Quartermaster Food and Container Institute for the Armed Forces. "Dry Whole Milk; a Symposium." Chicago, Ill. 1955.

Walters, A. H. "The Isolation of Coagulase-positive Staphylococci from Routine Composite Milk Samples." *Jour. Appl. Bact., 22*(2): 248–252. 1959.

Weiser, Harry R. *Practical Food Microbiology and Technology.* Avi Publishing Co., Westport, Conn. 1962.

Wells, Frank Edwards. "Parameters of the Spoilage of Poultry Meats by Psychrophiles." Ann Arbor, Michigan Univ. Microfilm copy of typescript. *Abst. Dissertation Abstrs., 22*(7): 2134–2135. 1962.

White, James C. "Contaminants in Milk." *Amer. Milk Review, 23:* 112–115. 1961.

Yamamoto, R., W. W. Sadler, H. E. Adler, and G. F. Stewart. "Characterization of *Clostridium perfringens* (*welchii*) isolated from Market Poultry." *Appl. Micr.,* 9(4): 337–342. 1961.

# CHAPTER VII

# RESERVOIRS OF MICROORGANISMS CAUSING FOODBORNE GASTROENTERIC OUTBREAKS: FOOD SUPPLY

## PART II. FOOD SUPPLY OF PLANT ORIGIN

## PART III. PRECOOKED FROZEN FOODS

### Part II. Foods of Plant Origin

Fruits and Vegetables

*Contaminants*

Fruits and vegetables carry a natural flora which ordinarily does not include types pathogenic to man. The organisms causing spoilage in fresh and stored foods are not pathogenic to man either; for information on microbial spoilage of fresh and refrigerated plant foods, the reader is referred to Vaughn (1963).

The natural bacterial flora varies with the type of plant. The genera frequently encountered are *Achromobacter, Alcaligenes, Flavobacterium, Micrococcus,* the coliforms, and the lactics.

Plants may acquire human pathogens from contact with contaminated soil, water, human hands, animals, air, harvesting equipment, and so forth. The nature of the contamination depends on many factors. An important source of contamination is soil which contains raw sewage. Fortunately, in the United States, raw sewage is rarely used for fertilizing soil; and if it is used, it is by persons raising vegetable garden crops for their own use. However, in some other parts of the world fertilization with raw sewage is still practiced;

155

vegetable foods grown on such soil must be expected to be contaminated with human pathogens. Soil may also become contaminated from surface waters into which sewage has been directed.

## Fresh Fruits and Vegetables

The term "fresh" here implies that the plant materials were not processed, but they may have been cold-stored.

Fresh fruit may become contaminated from soil dust in the orchard. Fruit collected from the ground, and low-growing fruit, often becomes heavily contaminated with soil organisms. Dust from the road may be an important source when fruit is displayed on roadstands. One of the important sources from a public health point of view is human hands. During harvesting, subsequent sorting, and storing, fruit may acquire the flora adhering to the handlers' hands.

In the case of vegetables, contact with the ground makes contamination with organisms from the soil likely. Spore formers such as *Clostridium botulinum* and *C. perfringens* are inhabitants of soil. When the ground has been fertilized with night soil or similar products, the soil flora may include salmonellae originating from the human intestinal tract. For example, the outer leaves of lettuce and cabbage have been found to contain, on occasion, typhoid organisms and other species of *Salmonella*.

WASHING

In the case of fruit, mechanical washing is quite an efficient method for removal of soil, chemical residues, and microorganisms adhering to the outside, but washing does not render plant tissue sterile. Sometimes an accepted disinfectant such as chlorinated lime is added to the washing water. New methods of washing are constantly explored, including the use of detergents. Since washed fresh fruit may be recontaminated before it reaches the consumer, thorough washing is necessary to assure a clean product earmarked for consumption as a raw item.

In the case of vegetables, washing may remove much of the gross soil, but additional thorough washing remains to be done by the consumer. It is difficult to clean certain vegetables from all traces of gross soil; green vegetables are particularly stubborn in releasing dirt.

Along with the gross soil, microorganisms and animal parasites are only partially removed, complete removal being almost impossible. Therefore, vegetables to be consumed raw must never originate from sewage-polluted soil. Utmost care must be given to the cleaning of all vegetables to be served raw. And finally, it should be remembered that raw vegetables added to cooked items which already have received a terminal heat treatment may recontaminate these items.

STORING

Many fruits and vegetables may be kept fresh for long periods of time if stored under appropriate conditions, which include atmosphere controlled with respect to composition, temperature, and relative humidity. The reader is referred to the literature dealing with the science of pomology and vegetable crops.

## Processed Fruits and Vegetables

CANNED FRUIT

Canned fruit is safe from a public health point of view. Spore formers which may survive include some gas-producing butyric anaerobes, such as *C. pasteurianum,* and the aciduric flat sours, e.g., *Bacillus thermacidurans;* none are pathogens.

CANNED VEGETABLES

In properly canned vegetables the spores of *C. botulinum* have been destroyed. Commercially canned vegetables have had an excellent record for decades. However, heat-stable survivors may prove a nuisance and spoil canned vegetables under "tropical" conditions of storage. The thermophilic anaerobes are most frequently encountered in the medium-acid group of vegetables; the thermophilic flat sours and putrefactive anaerobes represent the more common survivors in the low-acid group of vegetables such as corn and peas.

DRIED FRUIT

Excellent dried fruit is available on the market and much of it is pasteurized. Fruit which has been sulfured has some of its microbial content reduced by that process. Molds constitute the greater percentage of the flora of dried fruit.

DRIED VEGETABLES

Vegetables may be dehydrated from the raw stage or they may be blanched before processing.

Raw dehydrated vegetables may be used to make fresh-like salads. Examples of vegetables processed in this way are peppers, carrots, and cabbage. These are first washed to reduce soil contaminants. Obviously, the kinds and numbers of microorganisms remaining on the product will depend on many factors including kind of soil, kind of vegetable, number of microorganisms, thoroughness of cleaning, and general sanitation during the operation. Germicidal rinses are sometimes used as an aid in reducing the number of bacteria remaining on the vegetable after washing. If the flora includes *Escherichia coli*, human or animal contamination must be suspected, and use of these vegetables as a raw item must be questioned.

Blanched dehydrated vegetables are more common. Blanching inactivates the enzymes and reduces the microbial content considerably. Sulfuring of vegetables reduces also total counts. The flora of the finished product is therefore largely acquired during processing following blanching. Contaminants often originate with the raw vegetables brought into the processing plant. These contaminants include *Aerobacter, Achromobacter, Bacillus, Clostridium, Escherichia, Micrococcus, Streptococcus, Pseudomonas, Lactobacillus, Leuconostoc,* and many others. Spores, micrococci, and microbacteria are quite resistant to drying and will linger, while other forms of bacteria gradually decrease in number. No multiplication of bacteria takes place in the dehydrated product if it is stored properly. The microbiology of various dehydrated foods has been discussed by Goresline (1963).

## FROZEN FRUIT AND JUICE

These items have not proven to be a problem from a public health point of view. Vaughn et al. (1957) reviewed the significance of microorganisms in frozen citrus products and found no known health hazard of bacterial origin.

Microorganisms of public health significance have been seen to survive for a while in fruit products. Larkin et al. (1955) found fecal streptococci after 147 days storage at $-10°F$ in orange concentrate. On the other hand, Hahn and Appleman (1952) found these organisms to disappear rather fast. The initial bacterial load may have something to do with this discrepancy of results; possibly, with a larger initial bacterial load the chance that survivors will be detected is greater.

Fecal streptococci were also isolated from commercially frozen grape juice, peaches, melon balls, and various citrus juices. As reported by Tressler and Evers (1957), survival after several months of freezer-storage was noted by Wallace and Tanner for several pathogenic strains of *Salmonella, Escherichia coli,* and *Proteus vulgaris* when these were introduced into cherries and frozen at 0 and $-40°F$. Survival in the juice was less than four weeks. The survival periods for several salmonellae in strawberries have been known to be as long as 6 months. The subject of survival of pathogenic contaminants has been reviewed by Tressler and Evers (1957).

FROZEN VEGETABLES

Vegetables are washed and blanched before freezing. Germicides may be used in the washing process. Washing and blanching remove much of the natural flora as well as the contaminants from soil and water.

Larkin et al. (1955) found that blanching with 190°F water destroyed *Streptococcus faecalis* in 1 minute. Recontamination of the blanched product may occur during cooling and further handling. Fecal streptococci in sufficient numbers to possibly be of public health significance were isolated from commercially frozen vegetables including green beans, corn, lima beans, and spinach.

Splittstoesser et al. (1965) determined the incidences of coagulase-positive staphylococci in 112 samples of peas, green beans, and corn collected at various stages of processing for freezing. The greater percentage of contaminated samples (65%) was obtained with corn; the highest counts (7.3 per gram) were found in peas. Major sources of the staphylococci were the hands of employees. The gravity separator used in the processing procedure was found to be a potential area for staphylococcal buildup.

DEFROSTING

Fruits and vegetables to be used without further heating are defrosted. The possibility that pathogenic contaminants may survive freezing and freezer-storage, points to danger when thawing is allowed to proceed at room temperature for a prolonged period. The fact that fruits and vegetables lose their textural quality quickly when allowed to remain warm for hours after thawing is fortunately a safeguard. With fruit, acidity is a safeguard also.

Vegetables to be cooked are, as a rule, cooked from the frozen state; this is a good practice.

## Cereal Foods

Several types of undesirable microorganisms may be associated with starch and flour, but none are of public health significance except possibly *Bacillus cereus*. This organism has been indicted in food-poisoning outbreaks in Norway. Hauge, as reported by Dack (1956), has studied this organism in its capacity to cause illness in man and he warns that potato and cornstarch may be frequently so contaminated, and that foods prepared with starches must not be allowed to remain at temperatures favorable to bacterial growth for any length of time. The spores of this organism are resistant to heating given to foods in routine cooking operations.

## Spices

Spices have a reputation for possessing germicidal qualities. It is a fact, however, that few spices seem to have this property. Some have some bacteriostatic action, but others may accelerate bacterial multiplication.

Oils from ground mustard, cinnamon, and cloves possess some bactericidal power toward certain bacteria. Garlic and onion have been shown to exert bactericidal power also. The bactericidal action of horseradish was investigated by Foter and Gorlick (1938), who reported that the active principle is allyl isothiocyanate. The activity of the vapors was dependent on temperature, the most favorable temperature being 99.5°F. These vapors were found to have a greater bactericidal power than garlic and onion.

The resistance of different bacteria to a particular spice varies; differences also exist in the reaction of a specific organism to different spices (Fabian et al., 1939).

It is an important fact that commercial spices harbor great numbers of microorganisms which may contaminate the menu items in which they are incorporated unless the spices have been heat-treated sufficiently to reduce their bacterial load. The microbial content of untreated spices was studied by Yesair and Williams (1942), who found staggering numbers in some. The microbial contents of common spices were combined by Weiser (1962) and are reproduced in Table 21. Strong et al. (1963) examined 20 spices for the presence of *Clostridium perfringens;* they isolated the organism from paprika, savory, and poultry seasoning.

## Nuts

Nut meats removed from the shell may harbor a variety of bacteria in large numbers. The presence of enterococci and staphylococci on broken nut meats has been demonstrated by Smith and Iba (1947) and Hyndman (1963). The bacterial load may be reduced by pasteurizing the nuts in 180–190°F water. Salmonellae have been demonstrated in shredded coconut. Since nuts are not natural hosts of salmonellae, the contaminants must have been added in the processing or in transport, storage, or other handling.

Since nuts are frequently added to highly perishable items, such

**Table 21. Microbial Content of Untreated Spices [Adapted from Weiser (1962)]**

|  | Untreated spice suspensions incubated at: 37°C (98.6°F)   Room temp. Total microorganisms per gram | |
| --- | --- | --- |
| Kind of spice or herb | Bacteria | Molds |
| Whole allspice | 1,000,000 | 70,000 |
| Ground allspice | 64,000 | 50,000 |
| Sweet basil | 525,000 | 50 |
| Whole cloves | 4,400 | 100 |
| Whole Zanzibar cloves | 190 | 0 |
| Ground China cinnamon | 36,000 | 60,000 |
| Crushed cinnamon | 8,000 | 600 |
| Ground ginger | 60,000 | 2,000 |
| Bay leaves | 15,000 | 350 |
| Ground Banda mace | 2,800 | 400 |
| Ground mustard | 1,800 | 0 |
| Ground East Indian nutmeg | 1,200 | 700 |
| Ground paprika | 680,000 | 5,000 |
| Ground red pepper | 2,190,000 | 1,220,000 |
| Ground white pepper | 42,000 | 9,000 |
| Decorticated pepper | 1,780,000 | 70,000 |
| Ground black pepper | 10,400,000 | 1,300,000 |
| Savory | 4,400 | 450 |
| Ground sage | 270,000 | 20,000 |
| Whole thyme | 2,700,000 | 12,000 |
| Ground thyme | 35,000 | 30,000 |
| Miscellaneous: | | |
| Celery seed | 1,150,000 | 10,000 |
| Onion powder | 6,000 | 0 |
| Garlic cloves | 200 | 20,000 |
| Onion juice | 30,000,000 | 100 |
| Ground garlic powder | 90,000 | 200 |
| Liquid garlic | 10,000 | 10,000 |
| Emulsified spice oil | 10 | 10 |

as puddings and other desserts, at the end of the cooking process, they may well be expected to recontaminate the items after these have received their terminal heat treatment.

Precautions are indicated which involve the removal of contaminants from the nuts through immersion in hot water; and prompt cooling to 45°F or below of perishable menu items to which nuts were added.

Principles of Control

These principles include the procurement of high quality foods and their protection during storage on the premises. Fruits and vegetables consumed raw should be washed thoroughly.

When raw vegetables and nuts are incorporated into potentially hazardous menu items and these are not sufficiently heated to kill the contaminants which may adhere, precautions aimed at precluding bacterial multiplication must be applied promptly.

### Part III.    Precooked Frozen Foods

This is a very diversified group of foods. The industry engaged in the processing of cooked frozen foods is relatively young; its history has been reviewed by Goresline (1962). An interest in these convenience food items arose in the early 1930's. Since World War II cooked and frozen menu items have become of increasing importance in the frozen food field. These items include an astounding array of menu items, from soups to desserts. Foter (1964) stated that it is estimated that more than 8000 food items are for sale in supermarkets, of which approximately 6000 were not available 15 years ago.

Processing

As the industry expanded, specific microbiological problems emerged, including public health considerations. Precooked frozen items have, in general, an excellent record in regard to food-poisoning outbreaks. In spite of this record, potential danger exists from grossly mishandled products. Surveys have shown that some products that were obviously mishandled contained large numbers of bacteria, including forms of public health significance.

The cooking, blanching, and pasteurizing of the raw material kills many microorganisms adhering to the food materials, but the chances for recontamination during subsequent handling cannot be ruled out. Many operations, such as deboning, sorting, and weighing, usually require the use of hands. Furthermore, during many operational steps the ingredients are at warm temperatures for some time.

Huber et al. (1958) made a survey of plants processing precooked frozen foods and were able to show that plant sanitation was closely related to the microbial quality of the product leaving the plants.

The Food and Drug Administration conducted a bacteriological survey of the frozen food industry from March 1958 to June 1959, as reported by Shelton et al. (1959). The FDA undertook the survey to evaluate the public health and sanitary significance of the micro-organisms found in products in interstate commerce. Sixty-three frozen food plants were inspected, and approximately 3000 samples representing 81 food items were examined.

The samples were analyzed for total counts, most probable number of coliforms, most probable number of *Escherichia coli*, and staphylococci. Coagulase tests were run on the staphylococci to assess the presence of potential food-poisoning strains. The foods were arranged into four groups on the basis of the amount of cooking which the product received at the plant plus the amount it is expected to receive when finally prepared in the consumer's kitchen (Table 22).

Group I contained products which do not require warming prior to serving, such as cream pies and cakes; counts varied from item to item. Total counts were very high in the products made with chocolate, although there was considerable variation in the bacterial content of chocolate cream pies from plant to plant. High counts could be explained by the use of unclean equipment and long holding of the chocolate base. Coagulase-positive staphylococci occurred in 6% of the samples. This fact was of relative comfort to the public health officials since Group I included highly perishable items.

Group II contained samples of 453 finished products, representing 20 different menu items. During the processing of these items, some ingredients were cooked early in the production schedule, then

**Table 22. Product Groups [Adapted from Shelton et al. (1959)]**

| Group | Product | Cooking required |
|-------|---------|------------------|
| I | Bakery products, cream pies, cakes. | Product does not require warming prior to serving. |
| II | Variety of products—spaghetti, macaroni and cheese, potato products, blintzes, knishes, and some other meat and sea-foods. | Product requires warming prior to serving. Cooked early in production process, then combined with other items before packaging or freezing. |
| III | Crab cakes, fish cakes, Chinese foods, and specialty products. | Product requires warming prior to serving. Cooked late in production just prior to packaging or freezing. |
| IV | Poultry, tuna, beef, and lobster pies, pizza, and raw breaded shrimp. | Product requires cooking prior to serving. |

mixed with other ingredients and handled more or less considerably before freezing. The members of this group need to be heated before they can be served, but not necessarily to temperatures high enough to destroy the bacterial contaminants. The *Staphylococcus* toxins would not be inactivated in such heat treatments.

High total counts and *Escherichia coli* counts could be explained partly on the basis of poor sanitation and partly on the basis of unduly long holding periods, or both.

Coagulase-positive staphylococci were detected in products that were manipulated, especially in those shaped by hand, such as shrimpburgers, crabburgers, and chicken croquettes. The elaborate handling in the deboning and slicing operations employed in connection with the cooked chicken resulted in large numbers of these organisms; the slight final browning of the croquettes did not eliminate these.

In Group III were combined 796 samples of 40 different menu items. These items differed from those in Group II, in that they were cooked late in the manufacturing process, but they too needed some additional heating prior to being served. In general, counts were lower in this group. There were some exceptions when equipment such as wooden surfaces had evidently recontaminated the cooked items. Coagulase-positive staphylococci again appeared in finished products containing cooked, deboned, and diced chicken: chicken chop suey, chicken chow mein, creamed chicken, and chicken a la king. Contamination with staphylococci also resulted from handling at the packaging line of the finished product.

Group IV contained food items which require cooking by the consumer. Analyzed were 226 product samples representing 11 foods. Of concern to the public health officials were the poultry, meat, and seafood pies, all being products which contained large numbers of staphylococci. The levels were not sufficiently high to be a health hazard per se; however, if the foods should be abused and allowed to thaw for extended periods, multiplication might take place, and the heating that the consumer applies would not inactivate the toxin once it is formed. The authors emphasize that such contamination, which obviously stems from the food handler, is not inevitable and that the control lies in strict sanitary measures. The plants varied a great deal in their standards of sanitation, some having very high standards.

In summary, the inspections of the plants manufacturing precooked frozen food items brought out the fact that these plants were, to varying degrees, below the level of sanitation which is desirable for a nonsterile food product not receiving a final heat treatment and which may be ingested by the consumer without being given a heat treatment sufficient to destroy microorganisms. The inspections also revealed that the sanitary problems pertained to two areas: (1) those which have an effect on the type and number of contaminating bacteria and (2) those pertaining to control of temperature and time in relation to opportunities for bacterial multiplication. Furthermore, the inspections revealed that some important sanitary principles, such as adequate handwashing, were not practiced as they should have been. Although in most plants the equipment was cleaned well at the close of the operations, it was often left unprotected overnight, and food contact surfaces were not sanitized. And finally, in some instances, the cooling rates of large batches of food were slow, and the foods remained at temperatures favorable to bacterial multiplication longer than is desirable and safe. Sometimes the flow of processing was slow and the processing of perishable ingredients delayed, which allowed for a greater chance for contamination as well as bacterial multiplication.

The use of properly sanitized equipment, sanitary working habits of employees, proper heat treatment during processing, avoidance of recontamination after cooking, and avoidance of delays during the entire process, up to freezing, are important means to keep counts low and staphylococci out.

## Fate of Bacteria in Frozen Foods

### Total Counts

Some microorganisms may temporarily multiply in foods during the freezing process. Most foods are not solidly frozen at 32°F, and lower temperatures are required, the exact temperatures depending on the type of food. While food is not solidly frozen, the solutes are available for bacterial multiplication.

Elliott and Michener (1960) found 150 records of growth at subfreezing temperatures scattered over approximately 100 reports. Most of the records for vegetables are for temperatures above 20°F for bacteria, although molds may grow at lower temperatures. These authors state that microbial growth was reported to occur at temperatures as low as 10°F, but that this is unusual. The psychrophilic bacteria may multiply at about 14°F.

Bacteria of public health importance such as *Staphylococcus aureus*, the salmonellae, and the fecal streptococci, are not known to multiply in solidly frozen foods. In fact, with the exception of *Clostridium botulinum* Type E, no food poisoning organisms are able to multiply below 40°F.

Although there is a paucity of information regarding the mechanism determining death and survival of bacteria during the freezing process and freezer-storage, it is known that during the freezing process the bacterial population may be expected to decline; further reduction takes place at freezer storage.

Elliott and Michener (1960, 1961) have reviewed important data available regarding the behavior of bacterial contaminants under conditions of freezing and freezer storage.

The killing effect of the freezing process varies with the type of microorganism, the rate of freezing, and other environmental conditions such as the substrate in which the organisms are frozen. Survival is apt to be higher in non-acid substrates, in menstrua containing protective substances such as meats, poultry, fish, and peas; and when freezing proceeds at a fast rate. Alternating freezing and thawing seems to have a detrimental effect on survival. In general, approximately 50% of the initial population dies off during the freezing process.

Unfortunately, conditions generally conducive to maintaining quality of frozen foods, such as fast freezing and storage at low non-fluctuating temperatures, are also conducive to the survival of contaminants. It is known that microbial contaminants have survived months of freezer storage.

It is difficult to generalize on the bacterial flora in precooked frozen foods when it reaches the consumer, because it is subjected to so many variables. Hucker and David (1957) stated that there seems to be a "base" of cold-resistant bacteria, and that there is a species–temperature relationship which determines the change in bacterial flora of the frozen product.

*Pathogenic Bacteria*

Pathogenic contaminants, and survivors, in frozen foods are known to include typhoid bacteria and other salmonellae, staphylococci, enterococci, and spore formers such as *Clostridium perfringens* and *botulinum*.

Proctor and Phillips (1948) showed that when *Staphylococcus aureus* and *Salmonella enteritidis* were added to cooked foods and these were frozen, the organisms survived for months (Fig. 11). Survival of *S. aureus* and enterococci in frozen chicken a la king was demonstrated by Buchbinder et al. (1949). In Figure 12 is shown a comparison of species of *Salmonella*. Survival varied with the species.

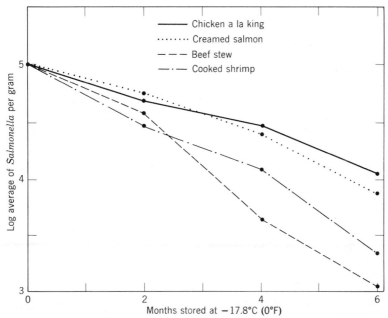

Fig. 11. *Experimental inoculation studies. Survival of Salmonella enteritidis in foods stored at −17.8°C (0°F) (three samples per point).* Adapted from Proctor and Phillips (1948).

Research data involving frozen items inoculated with *Clostridium botulinum* (Saleh and Ordal, 1955) indicated that there was danger when the products were grossly mishandled, i.e., when they were allowed to thaw and stand at warm temperatures for hours or days. However, no toxin was found in the frozen items or in items defrosted and immediately refrigerated.

Canale-Perola and Ordal (1957) examined frozen chicken and turkey pies produced by five manufacturers. Enterococci were present in all samples and coagulase-positive staphylococci in 37 of 40 pies. Five *Salmonella* cultures were isolated.

The bacterial content of frozen precooked dinners and pies was also studied by Ross and Thatcher (1958). The classical indicators of fecal contamination, *Escherichia coli* and enterococci, were commonly present. Salmonellae were not found, but coagulase-positive staphylococci were determined in numerous specimens (Table 23).

Woodburn and Strong (1960) studied survival of *Salmonella typhimurium*, *Staphylococcus aureus*, and *Streptococcus faecalis* in simplified food media and submitted these to freezer storage. The

**Table 23. The Bacteriological Content of Frozen Precooked Dinners and Pies [Adapted from Ross and Thatcher (1958)]**

| Index No. | Manuf. | Specimen | No. of specimens | Country of origin | Bacteriological findings[a] | | | | No. of specimens containing | |
|---|---|---|---|---|---|---|---|---|---|---|
| | | | | | Average No. of organisms per gram | | | | Coagulase pos. staph. | Paracolon organisms |
| | | | | | S.P.C.[b] × 10³ | E. coli | Entero-cocci | Staphylo-cocci | | |
| 1–7 | A | Chicken dinner | 7 | U.S. | 24 | 50 | 3.4 | 1,825 | 1 | 1 |
| 8–14 | A | Turkey dinner | 7 | U.S. | 90 | 444 | 295 | 861 | 1 | 2 |
| 15–21 | B | Beef dinner | 7 | Can. | 4 | 21 | 8.5 | 226 | 2 | 4 |
| 22–24 | A | Chicken pie | 3 | U.S. | 14 | 1.7 | 11.7 | 65 | 0 | 2 |
| 25–31 | C | Salisbury steak | 7 | U.S. | 740 | 33 | .7 | 490 | 0 | 3 |
| 32–38 | C | Swiss steak | 7 | U.S. | 30 | 0 | 38 | 18 | 2 | 0 |
| 39–44 | D | Steak and onions | 5 | Can. | 113 | 2 | 48 | 690 | 1 | 0 |
| 45–49 | D | Fillet of sole | 5 | Can. | 68 | 1 | 2,510 | 519 | 0 | 1 |
| 50–54 | E | Turkey pot pie | 5 | U.S. | 213 | 6 | 8,300 | 15,620 | 2 | 2 |
| 55–59 | E | Chicken pot pie | 5 | U.S. | 430 | 3 | 3,250 | 12,200 | 2 | 3 |
| 60–64 | E | Beef pot pie | 5 | U.S. | 5 | 3 | 0 | 14 | 0 | 3 |
| 65–69 | F | Chicken pie | 5 | U.S. | 7 | 4 | 59 | 526 | 1 | 4 |
| 70–74 | F | Beef pie | 5 | U.S. | 11 | 8 | 1,356 | 1,384 | 0 | 1 |
| 75–77 | F | Turkey pie | 3 | U.S. | 4 | 1.7 | 177 | 579 | 0 | 2 |
| 78–80 | G | Pork pie | 3 | Can. | 8 | 10 | 0 | 1,350 | 0 | 2 |
| 81–83 | G | Lamb pie | 3 | Can. | 15 | 0 | 1.7 | 65 | 0 | 2 |
| 84–86 | G | Veal pie | 3 | Can. | 16 | 0 | 1.7 | 433 | 0 | 1 |
| 87–89 | G | Chicken pie | 3 | Can. | 12 | 108 | 43 | 633 | 1 | 0 |
| 90–92 | G | Turkey pie | 3 | Can. | 10 | 568 | 18 | 120 | 0 | 1 |
| 93–95 | G | Beef pie | 3 | Can. | 3 | 0 | 0 | 237 | 0 | 3 |
| 96–98 | H | Beef pie | 3 | Can. | 7,525 | 43,500 | 48,550 | 334,000 | 1 | 0 |
| 99–101 | I | Chicken pie | 3 | Can. | 13 | 7 | 123 | 420 | 2 | 1 |
| 102–104 | I | Beef pie | 3 | Can. | 12 | 7 | 0 | 1,500 | 2 | 2 |
| 105–107 | I | Steak and kidney pie | 3 | Can. | 721 | 100 | 1,450 | 263 | 3 | 3 |
| 108–112 | E | Pumpkin pie | 5 | U.S. | 12 | 738 | 1,102 | 38 | 0 | 0 |
| 113–117 | E | Coconut pie | 5 | U.S. | 1 | 0 | 4 | 26 | 0 | 0 |

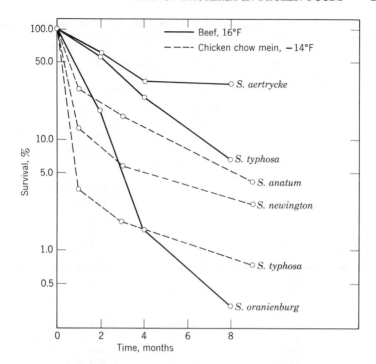

*Fig. 12. Storage survival: Comparison of species of Salmonella.* Adapted from Elliott and Michener (1960).

effect of freezer storage varied with the organism and temperature, survival being greater at $-22°F$ than at $12°F$.

According to Kereluk and Gunderson (1959), the rate of survival of enterococci frozen in chicken gravy at $6°F$ was better than that of coliforms (Table 24).

Georgala and Hurst (1963) reported that food-poisoning bacteria in frozen foods do not differ greatly from nonpathogens in their survival, that salmonellae are less resistant than are *S. aureus* or vegetative cells of *Clostridium,* and that bacterial spores and food-poisoning toxins are apparently unaffected. The protective effect of beef on the death of *S. aureus* is shown in Fig. 13. Georgala and Hurst stated that food-poisoning bacteria die more rapidly when stored between 32 and $14°F$ than at $1–4°F$.

Strong et al. (1963) examined 111 samples of commercially prepared frozen foods for *Clostridium perfringens.* The items included TV dinners, meat and poultry pies, and similar items; of these, three were positive for *C. perfringens.* In a laboratory experiment, Strong

**Table 24. The Effect of Storage at −6°F on the Longevity of the Coliform Bacteria and Enterococci [Adapted from Kereluk and Gunderson (1959)]**

| Days in storage at −6°F | Most probable number[a] | |
|---|---|---|
| | Coliform | Enterococci |
| 0 | 5,600,000 | 15,000,000 |
| 7 | 6,000,000 | 20,000,000 |
| 14 | 1,400,000 | 13,000,000 |
| 20 | 760,000 | 11,300,000 |
| 35 | 440,000 | 11,200,000 |
| 49 | 600,000 | 20,000,000 |
| 63 | 88,000 | 11,000,000 |
| 77 | 395,000 | 15,000,000 |
| 91 | 125,000 | 41,000,000 |
| 119 | 50,000 | 5,400,000 |
| 133 | 136,000 | 7,400,000 |
| 179 | 130,000 | 5,600,000 |
| 207 | 55,000 | 3,500,000 |
| 242 | 14,000 | 4,000,000 |
| 273 | 21,000 | 4,000,000 |
| 289 | 42,000 | 3,200,000 |
| 347 | 20,000 | 2,300,000 |
| 410 | 8,000 | 1,600,000 |
| 446 | 260 | 2,300,000 |
| 481 | 66 | 5,000,000 |

[a] Average of four determinations.

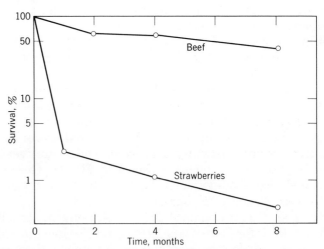

*Fig. 13. Survival of Staphylococcus aureus at 0°F.* Adapted from Elliott and Michener (1960).

and Canada (1964) demonstrated the survival of this organism in frozen chicken gravy. The survival rate was high when the inoculum was mixed with sterilized soil before it was added to the gravy.

In summary, contaminants capable of causing foodborne illnesses have been demonstrated to survive for months in precooked freezer-stored items.

Recognition of the inherent danger in the use of many types of precooked frozen foods has resulted in pressures for establishing standards for bacterial counts in these foods almost from the begining. The pros and cons of setting up bacteriological standards for precooked frozen foods are still under scrutiny.

The National Association of Frozen Food Packers has suggested, on a tentative basis, that a standard of 100,000 bacteria per gram be tried for precooked frozen foods. The Massachusetts Department of Public Health in "Rules and Regulations" (1961), allows a maximum of 50,000 bacteria per gram, a limit of 10 *E. Coli* per gram, no coagulase-positive staphylococci, and no representatives of the *Salmonella–Shigella* group.

The microbiological criteria used, their merits, limitations, and attainability are discussed in Chapter VIII.

The Food and Drug Administration is taking an active interest in the bacteriological quality of precooked frozen products, as indicated by their surveys and their close cooperation with industry (Surkiewicz, 1964). Industry is on the alert, and is working toward higher goals regarding the sanitary quality of these popular convenience foods.

Foter (1964) suggested the following guidelines to reduce contamination with microorganisms and their subsequent growth in foods during processing:

1. Use only raw materials which have been produced, stored and transported with minimal contamination.
2. Keep human contacts with foods to a minimum through mechanization, and indoctrinate personnel with clean habits by provision of adequate hand-washing and sanitizing facilities and rigid supervision of all hand operations.
3. Provide food-processing equipment designed, constructed, installed, and maintained to facilitate cleaning. After cleaning, subject all food contact surfaces to germicidal treatment.
4. Maintain time–temperature conditions which will prevent the growth of any pathogenic or spoilage organisms that may gain accidental entry.

In food service management the following principles are applicable:

1) Precooked frozen menu items should be purchased from reliable vendors, since even products processed under good conditions

may lose their quality due to failure to observe proper temperature control during storage and transportation.

2) Upon arrival at the food service premises frozen items should be immediately placed in appropriate cold storage (freezer) and held until needed. Holding time in freezer storage varies somewhat with the product, but is quite limited for precooked items.

3) At every step of preparation and service these items should be handled with the precautions due all potentially hazardous foods.

## References

**Part II**

Dack, G. M. (1956). *Food Poisoning.* 3rd ed. Univ. Chicago Press, Chicago, Ill.

Fabian, F. W., C. F. Krehl, and N. W. Little (1939). "The Role of Spices in Pickled Food Spoilage," *Food Research, 4:* 269–286.

Foter, M. J., and A. M. Gorlick. (1938). "Inhibitory Properties of Horseradish Vapors." *Food Res., 3:* 609–613.

Goresline, H. E. (1963). "A Discussion of the Microbiology of Various Dehydrated Foods." *In:* Slanetz, L. W., et al. "Microbiological Quality of Foods." Proceedings of a Conference held at Franconia, New Hampshire, August 27–29, 1962. Academic Press, New York. pp. 179–192.

Hahn, S. S., and M. D. Appleman. (1952). "Microbiology of Frozen Orange Concentrate." *Food Tech.,* 6: 156–158.

Hyndman, James B. (1963). "Comparison of Enterococci and Coliform Microorganisms in Commercially Produced Pecan Nut Meats." *Appl. Micr.,* 11(3): 268–272.

Larkin, E. P., W. Litsky, and J. E. Fuller. (1955). "Fecal Streptococci in Frozen Foods. I. A Bacteriological Survey of Some Commercially Frozen Foods. II. Effects of Freezing Storage on *Escherichia coli,* and Some Fecal Streptococci Inoculated Onto Green Beans. III. Effects of Freezing Storage of *Escherichia coli, Streptococcus faecalis* and *Streptococcus liquifaciens* Inoculated Into Orange Concentrate. IV. Effect of Sanitizing Agent and Blanching Temperatures on *Streptococcus faecalis.*" *Appl. Micr.,* 3(2): 98–101; 102–104; 104–106; 107–110.

Smith, W. W., and S. Iba. (1947). "Survival of Food Poisoning Staphylococci on Nut Meats." *Food Res., 12:* 400–404.

Splittstoesser, D. F., G. E. R. Hervey II, and W. P. Wettergreen (1965). "Contamination of Frozen Vegetables by Coagulase-Positive Staphylococci." *Jour. Milk & Food Tech., 28:* 149–151.

Strong, D. H., J. C. Canada, and B. B. Griffith. (1963). "Incidence of *Clostridium perfringens* in American Foods." *Appl. Micr.,* 11(1): 42–44.

Tressler, D. K., and C. F. Evers. (1957). *The Freezing Preservation of Foods.* 3rd ed. Avi Publishing Co., Westport, Conn.

Vaughn, R. H. (1963). "Microbial Spoilage Problems of Fresh and Refrigerated Foods." *In:* Slanetz, L. W., et al. "Microbiological Quality of Foods." Proceedings of a Conference held at Franconia, New Hampshire, August 27–29, 1962. Academic Press, New York. pp. 193–197.

Vaughn, R. H., D. I. Murdock, and C. H. Brokaw. (1957). "Microorganisms of Significance in Frozen Citrus Products." *Food Tech., 11:* 92–95.

Weiser, Harry H. (1962). *Practical Food Microbiology and Technology.* Avi Publishing Co., Westport, Conn.

Yesair, J., and M. H. Williams. (1942). "Spice Contamination and Its Control." *Food Res., 7:* 118–126.

### Part III

Buchbinder, L., V. Loughlin, M. Walter, and G. Dangler. (1949). "A Survey of Frozen Precooked Foods With Special Reference to Chicken a la King." *Jour. Milk & Food Tech.,* 12: 209–213.

Canale-Perola, E., and Z. John Ordal. (1957). "A Survey of The Bacteriological Quality of Frozen Poultry Pies." *Food Tech., 11*(11): 578–582.

Elliott, R. P., and H. D. Michener. (1960). "Review of the Microbiology of Frozen Foods." Conference on Frozen Food Quality, U.S. Department of Agriculture, Albany, Calif. pp. 40–61.

Elliott, R. P., and H. D. Michener. (1961). "The Microbiology of Frozen Foods." I. *Frosted Food Field, 32*(5): 26–27, 49. II. *Ibid.,* 33(1): 16. III. *Ibid., 33*(2): 38–40, 53.

Foter, M. J. (1964). "Bacteriology of Frozen Foods During Processing." *Jour. Envir. Hlth., 25*(4): 273–280. January–February.

Georgala, D. L., and A. Hurst. (1963). "The Survival of Food Poisoning Bacteria in Frozen Foods." *Jour. Appl. Bact., 26*(3): 346–358.

Goresline, H. E. (1962). "Historical Development of The Modern Frozen Food Industry." *In:* Proceedings, Low Temperature Microbiology Symposium. 1961. Campbell Soup Company, Camden, N.J., pp. 5–25.

Huber, D. A., H. Zaborowski, and M. M. Rayman. (1958). "Studies on the Microbiological Quality of Precooked Frozen Meals." *Food Tech., 12*(4): 190–194.

Hucker, G. J., and E. R. David. (1957). "The Effect of Alternate Freezing and Thawing on the Total Flora of Frozen Chicken Pies." *Food Tech., 11*(7): 354–356.

Kereluk, K., and M. F. Gunderson. (1959). "Studies on The Bacteriological Quality of Frozen Meat Pies. IV. Longevity Studies On the Coliform Bacteria and Enterococci At Low Temperature." *Appl. Micr., 7*(5): 327–328.

Massachusetts Department of Public Health. (1961). "Rules and Regulations Relative to the Storage and Distribution of Frozen Foods." Mass. Dept. Publ. Hlth., Bureau of Consumer Protection, Division of Foods and Drugs, Boston, Mass.

Proctor, B. E., and A. W. Phillips. (1948). "Frozen Precooked Foods." *Amer. Jour. Publ. Hlth., 38*(1): 44–49.

Ross, A. D., and F. S. Thatcher. (1958). "Bacteriological Content of Marketed Precooked Frozen Foods in Relation to Public Health." *Food Tech., 12*(7): 369–371.

Saleh, M. A., and Z. J. Ordal. (1955). "Studies on Growth and Toxin Production of *Clostridium botulinum* in a Precooked Frozen Food. I. Some Factors Affecting Growth and Toxin Production." *Food Res,,* 20(4): 332–339.

Shelton, L. R., Jr., H. V. Leininger, B. F. Surkiewicz, E. F. Baer, R. P. Elliott, J. B. Hyndman, and N. Kramer. (1959). "A Bacteriological Survey of the Frozen Precooked Food Industry." U.S. Department of Health, Education and Welfare, Food and Drug Administration.

Strong, D. H., J. C. Canada, and B. B. Griffith. (1963). "Incidence of *Clostridium perfringens* in American Foods." *Appl. Micr.,* 11: 42–44.

Strong, D. H., and J. C. Canada. (1964). "Survival of *Clostridium perfringens* in Frozen Chicken Gravy." *Jour. Food Sci.,* 29: 479–482.

Surkiewicz, B. F. (1964). "The Role of the U.S. Food & Drug Microbiologist in Frozen Food Plant Inspections." *Jour. Envir. Hlth.,* 26(4): 261–264.

Woodburn, M. J., and D. H. Strong. (1960). "Survival of *Salmonella typhimurium, Staphylococcus aureus* and *Streptococcus faecalis* in Simplified Food Substrates." *Jour. Appl. Micr.,* 8: 109–113.

## Additional Readings

Abrahamson, A. E., L. Buchbinder, J. Guenkel, and M. Heller. "A Study of Frozen Precooked Foods: Their Sanitary and Microbiological Standards for Control." Association of the Food & Drug Officials of the U.S., *Quart. Bull.,* 23(2): 63–72. 1959.

Anonymous. "All-Industry Coordinating Committee Takes Steps to Improve Frozen Food Handling." *Food Processing,* 21(8): 36–37. 1960.

Borgstrom, Georg. "Unsolved Problems in Frozen Food Microbiology." *In:* Proceedings, Low Temperature Microbiology Symposium, 1961. Campbell Soup Company. pp. 197–251. 1962.

Campbell Soup Company, Camden, N.J. 1962. "Low Temperature Microbiology Symposium." Proceedings, 1961.

Conference Report. "Microbiological Standards For Foods." *U.S. Publ. Hlth. Repts.,* 75: 815–822. 1960.

Desrosier, N. W. *The Technology of Food Preservation.* Avi Publishing Co., Westport, Conn. 1959.

Fanelli, M. J., and M. F. Gunderson. "Defrost of Prepared Frozen Foods. I. Defrost Temperatures of Frozen Fruit Pies, Frozen Meat Pies and Frozen Soups." *Food Tech.,* 15(10): 419–422. 1961.

Fitzgerald, G. A. "Are Frozen Foods a Public Health Problem?" *Amer. Jour. Publ. Hlth.,* 37: 695–701. 1947.

Frazier, William C. *Food Microbiology.* McGraw-Hill Book Co., New York. 1958.

Geldreich, E. E., B. A. Kenner, and P. W. Kabler. "Occurrence of Coliforms, Fecal Coliforms and Streptococci on Vegetation and Insects." *Appl. Micr.,* 12(1): 63–69. 1964.

Gunderson, M. F., and A. C. Peterson. "A Consideration of the Microbiology of Frozen Foods." Association of the Food & Drug Officials of the U.S., *Quart Bull.,* 28(1): 47–61. 1964.

Gunderson, M. F. "Health and Mishandling of Frozen Foods." *Quick Frozen Foods,* 24: 131–136. 1962.

Gunderson, M. F. "Microbiological Standards For Frozen Foods." *In:* Conference on Frozen Food Quality. U.S. Department of Agriculture, Western Utilization Research and Development Division, Albany, Calif. ARS–74–21. pp. 74–78. 1960.

Kereluk, K., A. C. Peterson, and M. F. Gunderson. "Effect of Different Temperatures on Various Bacteria Isolated From Frozen Meat Pies." *Jour. Food Sci.*, *26*(1): 21–25. 1961.

Litzky, W., I. S. Fagerson, and C. R. Fellers. "A Bacteriological Survey of Commercially Frozen Beef, Poultry and Tuna Pies." *Jour. Milk & Food Tech.*, *20:* 216–219. 1957.

Peterson, A. C. "An Ecological Study of Frozen Foods." *In:* Proceedings, Low Temperature Microbiology Symposium, 1961. Campbell Soup Company. pp. 157–195. 1962.

Peterson, A. C., J. J. Black, and M. F. Gunderson. "Staphylococci in Competition. I. Growth of Naturally Occurring Mixed Populations in Precooked Frozen Foods During Defrost." *Appl. Micr.*, *10*(1): 16–22. 1962.

Peterson, A. C., M. J. Fanelli, and M. F. Gunderson. "The Limits of Edibility of Defrosted Chicken Pot Pies." *In:* Slanetz, L. W., et al. "Microbiological Quality of Foods." Proceedings of a Conference held at Franconia, New Hampshire, August 27–29, 1962. Academic Press, New York. pp. 205–222. 1963.

Peterson, A. C., and M. F. Gunderson. "Role of Psychrophilic Bacteria in Frozen Food Spoilage." *Food Tech.*, *14*(9): 413–417.

Raj, H., and J. Liston. "Survival of Bacteria of Public Health Significance in Frozen Seafoods." *Food Tech.*, *15*(10): 429–434. 1961.

Slocum, G. G. "Microbiological Limits for Frozen Precooked Foods." *In:* Conference on Frozen Food Quality. U.S. Department of Agriculture, Western Utilization Research and Development Division, Albany, Calif. ARS-74-21. pp. 70–73. 1960.

CHAPTER **VIII**

# CONTROL: PROCUREMENT OF SOUND FOOD SUPPLY AND APPROPRIATE STORAGE OF PURCHASED ITEMS

The institutional buyer is concerned with the sanitary quality of the food purchased. He should know what the ever-changing food industry has to offer and should get the best buy, best in every respect, including sanitary quality. To keep abreast with the rapidly developing field of food technology is no small task. Fortunately, certain powerful agencies concern themselves with food protection and are an invaluable aid to the consumer in the assessment of the sanitary quality of the food he buys. In the United States and in Canada, certain governmental agencies, both federal and state, have some degree of influence in the control of sanitation in connection with processing of foods; the control is very stringent.

### AGENCIES AND ORGANIZATIONS CONCERNED WITH PROTECTION OF FOOD SUPPLY IN THE USA

The government agencies concerned with the protection of the food supply available to the consumer officiate as representatives at three levels—federal, state, and local—many times in close co-operation with industry. Other agencies which concern themselves with the sanitary aspects of foods are trade associations and institutes, professional societies, private associations, and foundations. The fundamental concern of all these agencies is the wholesomeness of the food supply as it reaches the consumer. The food-processing industries, and their associations, are increasingly active and effective in the promotion of the high sanitary quality of their products.

176

## Federal Agencies

Although a number of U.S. Government departments are involved in regulating the food supply, two stand out as being much concerned with the sanitary aspects of food protection: the U. S. Department of Health, Education and Welfare, and the U. S. Department of Agriculture.

## U. S. Department of Health, Education and Welfare

Within this department, two divisions are engaged in activities regarding food protection: the Food and Drug Administration and the Public Health Service.

### The Food and Drug Administration (FDA)

The powers and activities of this office apply to foods shipped in interstate commerce with the exception of meats and poultry. These latter products in interstate commerce are exempt in all points which are covered by the Meat Inspection Act and the Poultry Products Inspection Act and are regulated through the Agricultural Marketing Service, a branch agency of the United States Department of Agriculture.

The FDA enforces the Federal Food, Drug and Cosmetic Act of 1906, as revised in 1938 and 1958. The activities are briefly described in an FDA leaflet (U.S. Department of Health, Education, and Welfare, 1962). Among the many other specifications, the act specifies that food shipped in interstate commerce must be safe, pure, wholesome, and processed under sanitary conditions. Also, it authorizes the establishment of legal food standards of identity, prohibits adulteration and misbranding, and prescribes certain regulations for the labeling of canned and otherwise packaged foods. Consumers and law-abiding manufacturers and dealers need and welcome this protection.

The FDA, in enforcing the act, enters into many activities. As a part of its charge of policing the purity, quality, and labeling of foods, the agency makes periodic inspections of food establishments and examines samples; issues and enforces regulations which specify the kinds and quantities of new food additives allowable in or on foods; establishes the amounts of pesticide residues allowable on food crops and keeps check on shipment to verify that residues are within safe limits; checks imports of foods into the United States; cooperates with state and local agencies in the inspection and, if indicated, removal from the market of foods contaminated in the course of disasters; and assists industry in voluntary compliance with the Pure Food and Drug Law.

In connection with the microbiological aspects of food quality, the requirement that the food not be "adulterated" is of interest, since the presence of certain microorganisms, and/or their toxins, falls into the category of "adulterated foods." Frazier (1958) has called attention to this fact and states,

> the following descriptions of adulteration may have bacteriological implications: (1) if it [the food] bears or contains any poisonous or deleterious substance which may render it injurious to health . . . [unless naturally there at less than a harmful level]; (2) if it bears or contains any added poisonous or added deleterious substance which is unsafe . . . [i.e., above tolerances set]; or (3) if it consists in whole or in part of any filthy, putrid, or decomposed substance, or if it is otherwise unfit for food; or (4) if it has been prepared, packed, or held under insanitary conditions whereby it may have become contaminated with filth, or whereby it may have been rendered injurious to health; or (5) it if is, in whole or in part, the product of a diseased animal or of an animal which has died otherwise than by slaughter; or (6) if its container is composed, in whole or in part, of any poisonous or deleterious substance which may render the contents injurious to health.

Certainly, microorganisms capable of causing foodborne illnesses, and their toxins, are "injurious to health." Thus, it takes little imagination to see that the FDA can exert considerable power in forcing many foods so contaminated out of the market, at least those shipped in interstate commerce. The microorganisms, the toxins they produce, and other evidences of unsanitary processing need not be proved; the mere fact that their presence can be shown to be possible may lead to condemnation.

The activities of FDA in the control of foodborne salmonellae have been discussed by Slocum (1963).

### The Public Health Service (PHS)

The Public Health Service is the principal health agency of the Federal Government. This agency conducts a number of effective programs in the interest of public health (Burney, 1959). It develops health resources and improves health services. The PHS concerns itself with affairs of public health significance between the USA and other countries. It is legally responsible for the enforcement of the safety of foods and drinking water aboard interstate carriers such as trains, planes, buses, and ships operating under the flag of the United States. Otherwise, unlike the FDA, the PHS is not an enforcement agency. However, it provides powerful aids to other agencies entrusted with the enforcement of regulations pertaining to food sanitation and to the food-processing industry. Protection of the public from hazards arising from harmful microorganisms present in food and water is one of the main concerns of the PHS. This agency has made outstanding contributions in developing model sanitary standards for water, milk, and some other foods. In the area of food sanitation, the PHS conducts research, prepares manuals on sanitary procedures, and trains sanitarians and other persons active in fields related to the purity and wholesomeness of food. It is very instrumental in aiding the food industry in achieving and maintaining high standards of sanitation in processing. Regarding food service programs, the PHS feels that food sanitation programs should be flexible and adjusted to meet the needs of the situation, but that "certain basic principles must be understood and accepted if the program's objectives are to be achieved" (U.S. PHS Pub. No. 934, 1962). More will be said later about the various facets of a sanitation program as it applies to quantity food service. The principal considerations in connection with conducting an effective food sanitation program have been stated in the Food Service Sanitation Manual (1962).

CODES

Examples of model codes developed by the PHS are those for drinking water, milk, shellfish, poultry, and frozen desserts. Other codes pertain to eating and drinking establishments, and vending of foods and beverages (see "Additional Readings").

The model codes are widely adopted with or without revisions by health agencies of the individual states, counties, municipalities, or districts. The PHS will give aid to these agencies in making appropriate revisions to suit their specific needs and in the enforcement of these codes.

COOPERATIVE PROGRAMS

Certain cooperative programs have been developed with various states. One example is the cooperative State Public Health Service program for the certification of interstate milk shippers. Through the cooperative efforts of health agencies and producers and shippers of milk of high sanitary quality, milk can be moved from areas of overproduction to areas where milk shortage prevails. The program presented at the National Conference on Interstate Milk Shipments is described in a PHS publication (U.S. PHS Pub. No. 1040, 1963).

Another example of cooperative programs is the national shellfish sanitation program (U.S. PHS Pub. No. 33, 1962; No. 906, 1964).

Since 1925, the PHS has cooperated with the various states and industry to insure high sanitary quality of shellfish shipped in interstate commerce, each of the three participants having accepted specific responsibilities. The main responsibility of the PHS is the continuing appraisal of state sanitation programs pertaining to shellfish. The PHS is also responsible for certification of interstate dealers of shellfish. The list of certified dealers is made available to the various state and local health authorities. The food service manager or dietitian may obtain this important information from the local health authorities.

### RESEARCH

The food research of the PHS is conducted along various avenues, all projects having to do with the purity and wholesomeness of foods. Research is devoted to both fundamental and applied phases. The PHS supports various centers in which extensive research is carried forth, such as the National Institutes of Health at Bethesda, Maryland; the Robert A. Taft Sanitary Engineering Center at Cincinnati, Ohio; and the Communicable Disease Center at Atlanta, Georgia. The PHS awards research grants and fellowships to support research projects elsewhere.

### TRAINING

Training persons active in fields related to the wholesomeness of foods is an important function of the PHS. Persons taking advantage of this helpful service are those engaged in the processing, distribution, and service of food, and include dietitians, food service managers, sanitarians, scientists, and food engineers. These training courses provide factual information on newest developments in the various subject areas. They also give opportunity for practice in the application of techniques.

The courses applicable to food protection are usually held at the Sanitary Engineering Center at Cincinnati, but special training institutes and field courses are also held elsewhere. The PHS awards training grants to colleges and universities.

## U. S. Department of Agriculture (USDA)

The USDA engages in food protection in that it establishes, administers, and enforces a number of food standards through the branch agency known as the Agricultural Marketing Service (AMS) established in 1953. This office aids in making the tremendous national food marketing operation more orderly, efficient, and economical.

A considerable part of the research effort and regulatory activity of this agency is devoted to the goal of reducing the incidence of pathogenic and otherwise harmful bacteria in livestock, poultry, and food products. For example, through the efforts of the cooperative poultry improvement programs, pullorum was practically eradicated from poultry flocks, USDA specialists were successful in developing a workable method for pasteurizing egg white, and the USDA scientists have developed a recommended procedure for isolating salmonellae from meat products and animal feed.

## The Meat Inspection Act

The Meat Inspection Branch of the AMS enforces the Meat Inspection Act and regulations in connection with inspection of meat: that all meat and meat products shipped in interstate commerce, produced in the District of Columbia or in the U.S. territories, or imported from foreign countries must be inspected as regulated by the act and must be packed under a license. Among important activities are ante- and postmortem inspections of the animal for disease, and inspection for sanitation pertaining to processing procedures, plant maintenance, and personnel. The USDA inspects approximately 85% of all the meat sold commercially.

## The Poultry Products Inspection Act

Regulations similar to those applied to meat are used for poultry: ante- and postmortem inspection of the animals and inspection for sanitation regarding processing, personnel, and plant maintenance. The Poultry Division of the AMS gives this service. A high percentage of the poultry sold commercially is inspected.

## Acceptance-Type Inspection Service

This service provides, upon request, inspection service which allows an institutional food buyer to write his own specification to suit his needs. This service is discussed later.

## Commodities Other Than Meat and Poultry

Continuous inspection services are available for fruit and vegetable products, dairy products, egg products, and rabbit meat. Processing plants must at all times measure up to strict requirements for quality and sanitation, or service will be withdrawn.

## Grading

A large percentage of all the trading in foods is done on the basis of U.S. grades set up by the Agricultural Marketing Service. AMS grading service will provide certification of quality based on these grades.

## U. S. Department of Interior

The Fish and Wildlife Service, Bureau of Commercial Fisheries, administers the Agricultural Marketing Act as it extends to fish. The fish products which meet the official standards can carry the U. S. shield indicating the grade of the product and that it was packed under continuous supervision of a government agent. An increasing number of processors accept this service.

### State and Local Agencies

The food laws laid down by states and municipalities are, in general, fashioned after the regulations or recommendations set up by federal agencies. In the state of New York, the New York State Department of Agriculture and Markets concerns itself with problems of food production, protection, and marketing. For example, the Meat Division, effective since 1963, assumes responsibility for state-wide meat inspection and renders services such as sanitary surveillance of slaughter houses and meat-processing plants, counseling on construction plans for proper sanitation and efficient operation, ante- and postmortem inspection of animals, inspection during processing, and label evaluation and approval. Refrigerated warehouses and frozen food locker plants are licensed by the State of New York for the protection of producers as well as consumers; inspection is made periodically to check compliance with sanitary and temperature requirements of the warehouses and lockers and with other requirements, such as the length of time for which food items may be stored.

State food laws are usually enforced through the Department of Public Health. On the municipal level, the Department of Health and/or Board of Health may be involved.

### Other Agencies

Some trade associations and institutes are very active in upgrading and maintaining the sanitary quality of their products. The National Canners Association, the American Meat Institute, and the American Dry Milk Institute are examples of such organizations. Many processing plants set up their own sanitary standards, which are frequently fashioned after federal recommendations.

One of the very influential semiprivate agencies concerned with sanitation is the National Sanitation Foundation, which was organized by a group of industrial leaders and Public Health officials. It is a nonprofit, noncommercial organization which seeks solutions to problems involving cleanliness, and it sponsors and conducts research to find answers concerning sanitation. On the basis of results from research, minimum sanitation standards are developed for equipment, products, and devices that are generally acceptable to the health authorities. A manufacturer or producer may apply for the use of the National Sanitation Foundation Testing Laboratory Seal of Approval.

### Professional Societies

The American Public Health Association, the International Association of Milk and Food Sanitarians, and the Association of Food and Drug Officials are examples of professional societies which have published recommendations pertaining to methodology for investigation of food-poisoning outbreaks and the microbiological examination of foods.

## MICROBIOLOGICAL STANDARDS

Very rapid developments in the processing and distribution of foods which need little or no additional preparation in the kitchen are constantly creating new opportunities for potential hazards to public health. In connection with the concern over potential hazards (Slanetz et al., 1963), microbiological standards have been, and still are, ardently discussed.

### Definition

In the report by the Food Protection Committee (1964) of the Food and Nutrition Board entitled "An Evaluation of Public Health Hazards From Microbiological Contamination of Foods," the following definitions are given:

1. A *microbiological specification* is the maximum acceptable number of microorganisms or of specific types of microorganisms, as determined by prescribed methods, in a food being purchased by a firm or agency for its own use.

2. A *recommended microbiological limit* is the suggested maximum acceptable number of microorganisms or of specific types of microorganisms, as determined by prescribed methods, in a food.

3. A *microbiological standard* is that part of a law or administrative regulation designating the maximum acceptable number of microorganisms or of specific types of microorganisms, as determined by prescribed methods, in a food produced, packed, or stored, or imported into the area of jurisdiction of an enforcement agency.

Microbiological standards for processed foods, as Frazier (1958) has pointed out, may be of three types: (1) standards for the raw product and ingredients, (2) standards in connection with plant sanitation, packaging, storage and handling, and (3) standards concerned with the finished product.

Ideally, the standard in connection with freedom from pathogens of public health significance should include the pathogens most likely to be present in the particular foods. However, "indicator" organisms and total counts are most frequently used at present.

Frazier (1958) lists the chief purposes of microbiological standards as assurance that (1) the food will not be responsible for spreading pathogens causing disease and outbreaks of food poisoning; (2) the food is of high quality, that is, of good material that has not become deteriorated or unduly contaminated during processing, packaging, handling, and storing; (3) the food is acceptable from an esthetic point of view; and (4) the food has keeping quality expected of the product.

Application

Some microbiological standards are now in operation. The Public Health Service has set up recommendations for bacterial limits in drinking water, milk, and shellfish. Some powerful consumers, such as the U.S. Quartermaster Corps, have set tolerances for certain food items. The U.S. Food and Drug Administration has set microbiological standards for its own use. The Commonwealth of Massachusetts has promulgated bacteriological standards for precooked frozen foods, and so has the City of New York.

Canada has set up microbiological standards for certain food products and, according to Thatcher's (1958) report, with subsequent improvement in the sanitary quality of the food items involved.

Several industries—for example, the American Dried Milk Institute—have set up standards for their products. Cake-mix manufacturers have set up specifications for *Salmonella*-free processed eggs.

By the time this book has been printed, more standards may have been put into action.

In the United States, milk is presently the only food that is subject to strict microbiological control in every state of the Union. However, with more food preparation being shifted from the institutional kitchen to the processing plant, and with nationwide distribution of these items, strict and nationwide microbiological controls may be initiated for other potentially hazardous foods, although the difficulties in connection with the setting up of reasonably safe and acceptable standards will be formidable.

## Difficulties Encountered

The above-mentioned Food Protection Committee has stated these basic principles for setting up microbiological criteria. They should: (1) accomplish what they purport to do, that is, reduce public health hazards; (2) be technically feasible, that is, attainable under conditions of good commercial practice; and (3) be administratively feasible.

The difficulties encountered in developing and enforcing microbiological standards in foods are manifold. In contrast to water and milk which are nonviscous, homogeneous liquids, many other potentially hazardous foods are viscous and nonhomogeneous semisolids or solids which cannot be filtered, cannot be easily pasteurized or otherwise heat treated, and cannot be treated with germicides.

At present, the great variety of foods produced and variation in formulas make standardization of procedures that would ensure complete elimination of pathogens difficult. A special difficulty in establishing standards presents itself in connection with foods processed by special techniques such as freezing and vacuum packing.

It has been argued that standards not only tend to be too inflexible, but that they may even offer false security. It has also been said that their widespread application on a non-uniform basis may cause untold difficulties for the food industry, and even for the consumer, in the areas where controls are less strict.

It is for these and other reasons that microbiological standards for processed foods are difficult to establish and make legal. This does not preclude, however, that carefully worked-out specifications should not be set up for an increasing number of food products and used by the food buyer when purchasing. The effect should be one of general improvement of the sanitary quality of our food supply.

It has been suggested that control at the processing plant offers a sounder solution to the problem, namely, the inspectional program of the U.S. Food and Drug Administration, state agencies, and local agencies, especially if accompanied by educational programs in sanitation for food handlers.

The trend is now for the regulatory agencies to intensify close supervision of the food-processing industry through more frequent inspections and microbiological surveys; and perhaps even more important, industry seems to be increasingly aware of the microbiological implications in connection with its products they prepare.

The trend is for industry to either set up high standards of its own or to comply with existing government standards on a voluntary basis.

It seems an appropriate time for the managers of food service establishments and their professional organizations to make known their interest in food products of high sanitary quality. A demand for high-quality products would stimulate the food industry to adhere to high bacterial standards for its products through careful quality control.

Purchasing processed food of known microbiological quality would make it easier for the administrator of a food service operation to purchase by specification.

## Methods; Bacteria Used As Indicators

### Direct Counts

Bacteriological standards may be concerned with numbers regardless of kind, or with numbers of specific bacteria. They may be based on "direct bacterial counts," which include both living and dead cells. Direct counts have an advantage in that they give a fairly good indication of the past history of the product as far as contamination at some point of the production line is concerned. They also have certain disadvantages, the discussion of which is beyond the scope of this book.

### Total Counts

A frequently used basis for microbiological standards are "total counts" or "standard plate counts," which represent, hopefully, all living cells present in a food. Total counts include pathogens and harmless saprophytes.

As a quality control tool in the processing plant, total counts may reflect on a number of conditions, for example, the raw materials, processing procedures, personal hygiene, and temperature control. They are useful to the food processor in the evaluation of the sanitary aspects of his processing methods.

When foods spoil due to prolonged storage or mishandling, a microflora characteristic of the particular food and storage temperature develops. Thus, total counts will give excellent information as to the general microbial quality of the product. They are excellent indicators of the degree of decomposition of a food.

Total counts are particularly useful in evaluating the sanitary quality of preserved products in which the organism cannot multiply, namely, dried, salted, pickled, and frozen foods. They are, however, no aid in evaluating canned foods, since the heating process kills all contaminants except certain thermophiles.

High total counts in precooked foods would denote contamination following cooking, or possibly delay in processing procedure following cooking, or poor temperature control, or any combination of these.

Although standard plate or total counts are a rough measure of conditions in the food-processing plants, they have been said to be of limited value in denoting sanitary quality from a public health point of view. While high counts indicate that the product has been mishandled somewhere, somehow, along the way, low total counts do not necessarily indicate that mishandling has not occurred since a terminal heat treatment of freezer storage might have eliminated or reduced the original number of living cells. Moreover, food items of low total counts have been reported to be contaminated with pathogens.

In spite of these limitations, and the fact that bacteria may grow in milk, total counts are successfully used to evaluate the sanitary quality of milk. The reason is that milk is processed and handled under very standarized conditions. Probably no other perishable food item is as well controlled as milk.

In summary, high total counts, although they may represent harmless saprophytes, are likely to arouse suspicion of gross mishandling and thus, of possible contamination with pathogens. Low total counts, on the other hand, are not a guarantee for absence of pathogens.

*Indicators*

Specific bacteria of intestinal origin are being used as indicators of sanitary microbial quality. These are, before all, the coliforms, especially *Escherichia coli* and the fecal streptococci (enterococci). *Clostridium perfringens* has been mentioned as a possible useful indicator of pollution; it is being used in Europe.

The coliforms have been used as indicators of fecal pollution for many decades. Pollution of water is judged by the presence of members of the coliforms, and milk quality has also been assessed on the basis of the presence of these organisms.

The question of which one of these organisms should be used as an indicator of microbial quality of foods other than milk is a controversial one. The coliforms (except *E. coli*), the fecal streptococci, and *C. perfringens* are ubiquitous organisms and their presence does not necessarily indicate contamination with fecal matter. *Aerobacter* is a natural inhabitant of plant material. Even *E. coli* has limitations in that it is a common contaminant of vegetables raised on manured soil, and of meats and egg magma. The streptococci are part of the natural flora of cheeses. There is, however, no doubt that in pre-cooked foods the presence of coliforms or other enteric organisms would usually indicate recontamination after cooking or poor temperature control. It is therefore very important that the source of these contaminants be investigated when this organism is detected in a food.

### Pathogens

The question arises whether it would not be most desirable to base the microbial standards on the number of the various pathogens apt to be associated with certain food items, rather than general "indicators." Perhaps this will be possible some day. At present, the analysis of foods for pathogens such as *Salmonella* and *Staphylococcus aureus* has been judged to be inadequate to assess the degree of contamination with these pathogens. However, the methodology for detecting microorganisms of public health significance in foods is constantly being improved.

No methods are at present available for the identification of viruses in, and isolation from, foods.

The Food Protection Committee of the Food and Nutrition Board, National Academy of Sciences, National Research Council (1964) summarizes its discussion of microbiological standards as follows:

> Although the standard plate count of aerobic mesophiles and the coliform count cannot distinguish between hazards to health and organoleptic qualities, in most instances a food with high counts may be considered unwholesome from either standpoint. Since the presence of *Escherichia coli* indicates the likelihood of fecal contamination, it also indicates the potential presence of intestinal pathogens. Hazards from the presence of *Salmonella* in foods has been amply demonstrated. Thus, in the development of microbiological criteria aimed at lessening health hazards, consideration should be given to include limits for these organisms. The following are therefore recommended as useful microbiological criteria: counts of aerobic mesophilic bacteria and of coliform organisms, and demonstration of the presence or absence of *E. coli* and of *Salmonella*.
>
> Failure to recover a pathogen by sampling and analysis does not assure its absence, but such testing is of most value as a check on the adequacy of a procedure for destroying or removing the pathogen. Control measures based on positive laboratory demonstration of a pathogen such as *Salmonella* could do much to improve the relative safety of several foods.

### Dairy Products

The U.S. Public Health Service has set up recommendations in its Milk Ordinance and Code (revised 1965) and many states and municipalities base their standards on these. For dry milk, standards have been developed by the American Dry Milk Institute, Inc., and by the USDA (Agricultural Marketing Service). The bacterial standards set up for dairy products vary; it goes beyond the scope of this book to list all of them. Some states and cities permit the marketing of raw milk and have set standards for it. The reader is referred to recent editions of textbooks on food microbiology, processing of milk and other dairy products, and purchasing of foods for quantity food service.

## Chilled and Frozen Foods

The literature dealing with the subject of microbiological standards for this group of foods is not only extremely extensive, it is also quite controversial. Although the incidence of food poisoning from frozen foods is rare, results of laboratory studies are available which show that grossly mishandled precooked frozen foods may be dangerous. The need for bacteriological standards has been frequently stated, but the difficulties of devising meaningful standards are great.

The matter of fecal indicators for assessing the sanitary quality of chilled and frozen foods is a highly controversial one. The survival of the coliforms and fecal streptococci under conditions of freezer storage differs. It was found that *Escherichia coli* dies quickly, the other members of the coliform group die less quickly, and the enterococci are even more resistant. *E. coli* is quite sensitive to low pH and in acid citrus juices will be killed more readily than the enterococci.

On the other hand, it is argued that the reactions of *E. coli* are quite like those of the salmonellae and therefore this organism is more valuable as an indicator than the enterococci and that organisms which die off rapidly are useful in indicating recent contamination and danger from pathogens.

An excellent review of the subject has been presented by Elliott and Michener (1961) and the reader is referred to that publication for details. Summary tables prepared by these authors are given in Table 25.

Elliott and Michener (1961) list the principal precautionary arguments as follows:

1) A single set of microbiological standards should not be applied to foods as a miscellaneous group such as "frozen foods" or "precooked foods."
2) Microbiological standards should be applied first to the more hazardous types of foods on an individual basis, after sufficient data are accumulated on expected bacterial levels, with consideration of variations in composition, processing procedures, and time of frozen storage.

**Table 25. Suggested Microbial Limits in Chilled and Frozen Foods** (per gram, except as indicated) [Adapted from Elliott and Michener (1961)]

| Reference[a] | Total viable aerobes | Coliforms | Other organisms, comments |
|---|---|---|---|
| | *Frozen Precooked Foods* | | |
| Fitzgerald, 1947b | 100,000 | 1 | |
| Heller, 1952 | 2,000 | | Pathogens absent; designate methods |
| Goresline, 1959; Huber *et al.*, 1958; Johnson, 1960; Kereluk and Gunderson, 1959; U.S. Quartermaster Food and Container Institute, 1955 | 100,000 | 10 | Quartermaster purchases (USA) |
| Gunderson, 1960; Litsky, Fagerson, and Fellers, 1957; Rayman, Huber, and Zaborowski, 1955 | 100,000 | | |
| International Association of Milk and Food Sanitarians, 1957 | | 0 | |
| Abrahamson, 1958 | 100,000 | 100 | *Staphylococcus* 1,000; enterococci 1,000 |
| Abrahamson *et al.*, 1959 | 100,000 | | *Staphylococcus* absent; New York City tolerance |
| Hobbs, 1959 | 100,000 | 0.1 g[b] | *Staphylococcus* 1 g[b]; *Salmonella* 50 g[b]; 37°C count |
| Hobbs, 1959 | 500,000 | | 22°C count |
| Nickerson, Proctor, and Robertson, 1959 | 100,000 | | 5,000,000 direct count |
| Massachusetts Department of Public Health, 1959 (1960) | 50,000 | 10 | *Staphylococcus, Salmonella, Shigella* absent; Massachusetts law |
| Abrahamson and Clinton, 1960 | 100,000 | 100 | *Staphylococcus* 100; enterococci 1000; attainable in good practice |
| Robertson, 1960 | 50,000 to 100,000 | 100 | *Staphylococcus* 100; under AFDOUS consideration |
| | *Precooked Meats* | | |
| Heller, 1952 | 10,000 | | Sausage. Pathogens absent; designate methods |
| Heller, 1952 | | 0.1 g[b] | Pressed meats. Designate methods |

*(continued)*

Table 25 (*continued*)

| Reference[a] | Total viable aerobes | Coliforms | Other organisms, comments |
|---|---|---|---|
| *Precooked Meats (continued)* | | | |
| Goldenberg, Sheppey, and Robson, 1955 | 10 | | Canned hams. Enterococci, *Clostridium perfringens*, *Escherichia coli*: 1 g,[b] pathogens absent. Spores 10 |
| Anonymous, 1960e | 10,000 | | Canned hams. Gram-negative rods, fungi, and *Clostridium* absent |
| *Raw Meats* | | | |
| LeFevre, 1917; Marxer, 1903 | 1,000,000 | | Hamburger |
| Bates and Highlands, 1934; Brekenfeld, 1934; Elford, 1936; Geer, Murray, and Smith, 1933; Weinzirl and Newton, 1914, 1915 | 10,000,000 | | Hamburger. Recommended; Portland, Oregon, law 1936 |
| Fitzgerald, 1947a | 250,000 | | Hamburger, sausage |
| Nickerson et al., 1959 | 5,000,000 | | Hamburger |
| Fitzgerald, 1947a | 100,000 | | Meats, poultry |
| Ayres, 1955 | 10,000 to 100,000/cm² | | Anaerobes 5,000 to 50,000/g |
| Nickerson et al., 1959 | 5,000/cm² | | Poultry |
| Nickerson et al., 1959 | 10,000/cm² | | Cut meats |
| Hobbs, 1959 | 2,000,000 | 0.01 g[b] | Unfrozen meats. *Salmonella* 50 g[b]; *Staphylococcus* 0.01 g[b]; 37°C count |
| Hobbs, 1959 | 5,000,000 | | Unfrozen meats. 22°C count |
| Hobbs, 1959 | 500,000 | 0.1 g[b] | Frozen meats, *Salmonella* 50 g[b]; *Staphylococcus* 0.1 g[b]; 37°C count |
| Hobbs, 1959 | 2,000,000 | | Frozen meats. 22°C count |
| *Frozen Whole Eggs* | | | |
| Lepper et al., 1944, 1956 | 5,000,000 | | Direct microscopic count |
| Fletcher and Johns, 1951 | 10,000,000 | | Canadian regulations, 1947 |

(*continued*)

**Table 25** (*continued*)

| Reference[a] | Total viable aerobes | Coliforms | Other organisms, comments |
|---|---|---|---|
| | | *Frozen Whole Eggs* (*continued*) | |
| Fletcher and Johns, 1951 | 2,500,000 | | Canadian regulations, 1948 |
| Nickerson *et al.*, 1959 | 200,000 | | |
| | | *Fish, Shellfish, and Waters* | |
| Griffiths and Stansby, 1934 | 1,000,000 | | Fish stale and inedible |
| Fitzgerald, 1947*a*; Fitzgerald and Conway, 1937 | 100,000 | | Fish |
| Nickerson *et al.*, 1959 | 100,000 | | Fish. Direct count, 150,000 |
| | 500,000 | | Breaded shrimp. Direct count, 2,000,000 |
| U.S. Public Health Service, 1946 | | 2.3 | Oysters. U.S. Public Health Service code |
| Knott, 1951 | | | Oysters, *E. coli* 200/oyster |
| U.S. Public Health Service, 1954 | 50,000 | 160 | Oysters. Acceptable; USPHS code |
| U.S. Public Health Service, 1954 | 50,000 to 1,000,000 | 160 to 1,600 | Oysters acceptable on contion; USPHS code |
| U.S. Public Health Service, 1954 | over 1,000,000 | over 1,600 | Oysters. Rejectable; USPHS code |
| Kelly, 1958 | 500,000 | | Oysters. Acceptable on condition |
| Kachikian, Larken, and Litsky, 1960 | 100,000 | | Frozen breaded shrimp |
| U.S. Public Health Service, 1959 | | 0.7 | Shellfish waters. Approved for harvesting; USPHS code |
| U.S. Public Health Service, 1959 | | 0.7 to 7 | Shellfish waters. Restricted for harvesting; USPHS code |
| U.S. Public Health Service, 1959 | | over 7 | Shellfish waters. Prohibited for harvesting; USPHS code |
| Anonymous, 1960*e* | 100,000 | 100 | Crabmeat. Enterococci 1000; *Staphylococcus* 100; New York City tolerance |

(*continued*)

Table 25 (*continued*)

| Reference[a] | Total viable aerobes | Coliforms | Other organisms, comments |
|---|---|---|---|
| *Vegetables* | | | |
| Berry, 1941; Jones and Ferguson, 1957; Tressler, 1938 | 100,000 | | |
| Sanderson, 1941 | 100,000 | | *E. coli* absent |
| Nickerson, 1956 | 300,000 | | |
| Canada, Laws, Statutes, etc., 1954; Matthews and Young, 1957; Jones and Ferguson, 1956 | 100,000 | 0.1 g[b] | Canadian law suspended |
| Anonymous, 1958a; Schmitt, 1958 | 200,000 | | By soup manufacturers |
| Nickerson *et al.*, 1959 | 100,000 to 500,000 | | Direct microscopic count, 500,000 to 1,000,000 |
| Anonymous, 1945 | 400,000 | . | Peas |
| Hucker, 1950; Hucker, Brooks, and Emery, 1952 | 50,000 | | Peas. Before freezing |
| Hucker, 1950; Hucker *et al.*, 1952 | 100,000 | | Green beans. Before freezing |
| Hucker, 1950; Hucker *et al.*, 1952; Obold and Hutchings, 1947 | 150,000 to 200,000 | | Corn. Before freezing |
| *Ice Cream and Frozen Desserts* | | | |
| Buchan, 1910 | 1,000,000 | under 0.1 ml[b] | Enterococci under 0.001 ml[b], *Clostridium sporogenes* under 10 ml[b] |
| Beckler and Dusossoit, 1911 | 500,000 | | Boston law, August 4, 1906 |
| American Public Health Association, 1937; Fabian, 1926a, b, 1927, 1929, 1932, 1937, 1939; Fay and Olson, 1924; Fisher, 1935; Obold and Hutchings, 1947; Olson and Fay, 1925; Ostertag, 1950; Smith, Newman, and Nielsen, 1928 | 100,000 | | Recommended; also laws of California, Connecticut, other states |
| Fournelle and Macy, 1942 | | under 10 | |

(*continued*)

**Table 25** (*continued*)

| Reference[a] | Total viable aerobes | Coliforms | Other organisms, comments |
|---|---|---|---|
| *Ice Cream and Frozen Desserts (continued)* | | | |
| Kruse, 1950 | 100,000 | | *E. coli* absent |
| Dahlberg and Adams, 1950 | 50,000 to 100,000 | | Laws of 19 states and 20 cities |
| U.S. Federal Supply Service, 1953 | 50,000 | 20 | Federal purchases |
| Anonymous, 1935 | 5,000 to 500,000 | | Pathogens absent; laws of various countries |
| American Public Health Association, 1937; Fabian, 1937 | 10,000 to 25,000 | | Some firms could meet |
| Macy, 1937 | 100,000 to 500,000 | | Most states |
| Macy, 1937 | 25,000 | | Certain cities |
| International Association of Milk Sanitarians, 1939 | 75,000 to 500,000 | | 12 states |
| International Association of Milk and Food Sanitarians, 1956 | | 0 | 1 state |
| International Association of Milk and Food Sanitarians, 1956; Levowitz, 1939; Thomas, Jenkins, and Evans, 1938 | 100,000 | 0.1 ml[b] | New Jersey law |
| Buchbinder *et al.*, 1953; International Association of Milk and Food Sanitarians, 1956 | | 10 | 20 states |
| International Association of Milk and Food Sanitarians, 1956 | | 1 | 1 state |
| International Association of Milk and Food Sanitarians, 1956 | | 30 | 1 state |
| International Association of Milk and Food Sanitarians, 1956 | | 200 | 1 state |
| U.S. Public Health Service, 1940 | 50,000 | | Grade A, USPHS code |
| U.S. Public Health Service, 1940 | 100,000 | | Grade B, USPHS code |
| Adams, 1954 | 2,000,000 | | Milk or cream for |

(*continued*)

Table 25 (*continued*)

| Reference[a] | Total viable aerobes | Coliforms | Other organisms, comments |
|---|---|---|---|
| *Ice Cream and Frozen Desserts (continued)* | | | |
| Fabian, 1939 | 5,000 | | Ingredients for; after pasteurization |
| U.S. Public Health Service, 1940 | 200,000 | | Ingredients for; Grade A, before pasteurization; USPHS code |
| U.S. Public Health Service, 1940 | 800,000 | | Ingredients for; Grade A, direct count; USPHS code |
| U.S. Public Health Service, 1940 | 1,000,000 | | Ingredients for, Grade B, before pasteurization; USPHS code |
| U.S. Public Health Service, 1940 | 4,000,000 | | Ingredients for, Grade B, direct count; USPHS code |
| International Association of Milk Sanitarians, 1940 | 10,000 | 0 | Coloring solutions. Enterococci 0, yeasts and mold 10 |
| International Association of Milk Sanitarians, 1940 | 100 | 0 | Flavor extracts; Enterococci 0, yeasts and mold 10 |
| International Association of Milk Sanitarians, 1940 | 1,000 | 0 | Fruits. Enterococci 0, yeasts and mold 10 |
| International Association of Milk Sanitarians, 1940 | 100 | 0 | Nuts. Enterococci 0, yeasts and mold 10 |
| Rothwell, 1960 | 25,000 to 300,000 | 0 to 150 | Standards various countries |
| *Miscellaneous Foods* | | | |
| Sanderson, 1941 | 100,000 | | Frozen foods. *E. coli* 0.1 g[b] |
| Tressler and Pederson, 1951 | 100,000 to 200,000 | | Frozen foods |
| Buttiaux and Mossel, 1957; Mossel, 1956 | 100,000 | 1 g[b] | Fresh and frozen foods. Pathogens, fecal indicators 1 g[b] |
| Fitzgerald, 1947a | | 1 | Various foods; Direct count 1,000,000 |
| Fitzgerald, 1947a | 100,000 | | Fruits |

[a] For details regarding references, see Elliott and Michener (1961), or National Academy of Sciences, National Research Council, Wash., D. C., Pub. No. 1195 (1964).

[b] Absent from this portion.

3) When standards are chosen, there should be a definite relation between the standard and the hazard against which it is meant to protect the public.
4) Methods of sampling and analysis should be carefully studied for reliability and reproducibility among laboratories and chosen methods should be specified in detail as part of the standard.
5) Tolerance should be included in the standard to account for inaccuracies of sampling and analysis.
6) At first, the standard should be applied on a tentative basis to allow for voluntary compliance before becoming a strictly enforced regulation.
7) Microbiological standards will be expensive to enforce.
8) If standards are unwisely chosen they will not stand in courts of law.

Food handling codes and recommended procedures are constantly revised and new ones developed. The following agencies have recommended, or are regulating, these codes: The Association of Food and Drug Officials of the United States; the American Public Health Association; the U.S. Public Health Service; the Food and Agriculture Organization of the United Nations; the U.S. Department of Agriculture; the various states, municipalities, and localities of the United States; and the food industry and its associations.

These codes or recommendations are concerned with temperature of storage, design, and construction of frozen food processing equipment, and length of storage of frozen foods.

The criteria and codes need to be reevaluated periodically regarding their adequacy and usefulness. The Food Protection Committee of the Food and Nutrition Board, National Academy of Sciences, National Research Council (1964), emphasizes in the summary of "An Evaluation of Public Health Hazards from Microbiological Contamination of Foods," that

... a decision to formulate microbiological specifications, recommended limits, or standards for foods that are meaningful from the standpoint of public health would be premature at present. A number of weaknesses in our knowledge of the hazards from microbiological contamination of foods, in our understanding of potential hazards from newer foods and technologies, in our knowledge of what is technically feasible commercially, and in methodology to assure compliance with such criteria, all point to this conclusion. Nevertheless, microbiological specifications and recommended limits are used for a number of purposes, and have generally been successful. Eventually, legal standards, particularly for foods for which a demonstrable microbial hazard exists, might reasonably be advocated.

## THE ROLE OF THE DIETITIAN, FOOD SERVICE MANAGER, OR OTHER BUYER

The person entrusted with the purchasing of food carries the responsibility for obtaining the best he can for the money he spends, one important quality factor being the wholesomeness or sanitary quality of the items purchased. The Food Service Sanitation Manual of the Public Health Service (1962) states that "all food in food service establishments shall be from sources approved or considered satisfactory by the health authorities." It is the responsibility of the institutional food buyer to find out which sources are safe.

Wholesome food from safe sources can be subjected to contamination and spoilage. It is the responsibility of the food buyer to write into his specifications sanitary packaging and protection during transit against physical damage and damage resulting from lack of time–temperature control. It is also the responsibility of the buyer to check and inspect the incoming purchases.

The steps to effective institutional food buying, as listed by Frooman (1953), are these: (1) find out what the food industry is offering the institutional market; (2) determine what best fits your needs; (3) compile written specifications covering your selections; (4) work out a buying procedure and decide on a course of action; and (5) check and inspect all deliveries.

In many institutions, the dietitian or food service manager is the person who carries out all of these activities in addition to other responsibilities which involve supervision of the storage of the purchased goods, the preparation and service of menu items, and the storage of leftovers. In some large organizations, a purchasing agent may do the actual ordering and checking. Yet, the dietitian or food service manager may even then exert an influence by requesting that the purchasing agent specify certain quality characteristics of the various items he orders or by requesting the purchase of "new" items placed on the market. Therefore, the first step, "find out what the food industry offers," is indeed an important one.

This is a relatively easy task for the more conventional line of foods, but not so for the "new" foods, the products of recent and current developments in the food processing field. Standards of wholesomeness have not been developed for many of these new items.

## Some Recent Developments in the Food-Processing Industry

One of the most remarkable developments in the food industry has been the transfer of menu item preparation from the institution kitchen to the factory. The factory-prepared items include partially prepared as well as ready-to-eat products (Irmiter, 1963; Stahl, 1963; Hahn, 1963; Treadway, 1965). Improvement in speed of transportation and extensive use of refrigeration and freezing are making this development possible.

Actually, little is known about the microbiology of some of the "new" foods, foods processed by new methods and packaged in new ways. Bacteriological guidelines are being developed for some of these items. It has been stated in the "Report Of The Food Protection Committee" (1964) that guidelines are of greatest urgency in the case of convenience and mildly processed foods.

By keeping abreast of new developments in the food field and research on the sanitary quality of new products, the dietitian or food service manager not only furthers his own knowledge; if he puts this knowledge to work by using it in his specifications when contracting for food, if he requests products produced under conditions of high sanitary standards, he contributes toward a high goal of sanitation in the food field as a whole.

The dietitian or food service manager has various resources which he may use to inform himself on what industry has to offer. Some very important sources of information are professional organizations such as the American Dietetic Association, the American Hospital Association, the American School Food Service Association, the National Restaurant Association, and the various professional state associations. These associations sponsor meetings at which eminent speakers present, among other material, pertinent information on newly developed foods, including the microbiological aspects of their processing and packaging. Also, these national associations have professional journals which publish articles with pertinent information regarding problems related to the sanitary aspects of the food supply.

Information on new developments in the food field is also made available by the Consumer and Marketing Service of the USDA in the form of a monthly publication titled *Agricultural Marketing,* and by the cooperative Extension Services of the various states which transmit food-marketing information. Hospital management magazines, food service magazines, and trade association publications all bring food news to the customer. (Examples of articles are given under "Additional Readings.") Very little information on the sanitary aspects of newly developed food products is actually conveyed to the potential buyer to use as basis for writing specifications insuring sanitary quality. When he receives the food he has no way of quickly checking on this quality other than inspecting for gross signs of mishandling.

The training courses conducted by the Milk and Food Training Program of the Public Health Service for key personnel responsible for food service operations furnish excellent up-to-date information on the sanitary aspects of food as it applies to institutional food services. Persons interested in participating should direct inquiries to Training Program, Robert A. Taft Sanitary Engineering Center, Public Health Service, U.S. Department of Health, Education and Welfare, Cincinnati, Ohio.

## Purchasing by Specification

Specifying exactly what is wanted is of greatest importance in purchasing food of high sanitary quality. Precise specifications can and should be made for the food itself as well as the packaging whenever possible. The federal or trade grade, or the brand, of the food should be stated. The size, nature, and sanitary conditions of the container may be specified. There may be specific factors required for specific commodities which are important from the viewpoint of sanitation; these may concern sanitary standards of the food itself, sanitary condition of containers, conditions of shipping, and other factors.

The writing of specifications is made easier by the establishing of grades and familiarity with the product. Governmental agencies and local health authorities may help set up specifications for food items which lack established standards.

Foods of animal origin are in the class of "potentially hazardous foods" as defined in the Food Service Sanitation Manual of the Public Health Service (1962). Specifications set up by the institutional food buyer should cover the wholesomeness of the product at the source, nature of packaging, handling, and time–temperature control during transit.

### Dairy Products

The Food Service Sanitation Manual (1962) states, first, that:

All milk and milk products, including fluid milk, other fluid dairy products and manufactured milk products shall meet the standards of quality established for such products by applicable state and local laws and regulations.

and second, that

only pasteurized fluid milk and fluid milk products shall be used or served. Dry milk and milk products may be reconstituted in the establishment if used for cooking purposes only.

and third, that

all milk and fluid milk products for drinking purposes shall be purchased and served in the original, individual container in which they were packaged at the milk plant, or shall be served from an approved bulk milk dispenser: *Provided*, that cream, whipped cream or half and half, which is to be consumed on the premises, may be served from the original container of not more than one-half gallon capacity, or from a dispenser approved by the health authority for such service, and for mixed drinks requiring less than one-half pint of milk, milk may be poured from one-quart or one-half gallon containers packaged at a milk plant.

Frozen desserts like ice creams, sherbets, ice milks, ices, and mixes from which frozen desserts are made should all conform to the sanitary standards set up by state and local regulations.

The dietitian or food service manager assuming his duties in a locality new to him should consult with the local health authorities before setting up specifications. This is important, since some regulations differ from state to state, as well as from one locality to another.

## Meat, Poultry, and Products Made from Them

In the Food Service Sanitation Manual (1962) is stated that:

All meat and meat products shall have been inspected for wholesomeness under an official regulatory program: *Provided*, that the health authority may accept other sources which are in his opinion satisfactory and which are in compliance with applicable state and local laws and regulations.

A comparable statement is made for poultry and poultry products. It is extremely important that the food buyer check with the local health authorities regarding regulations for locally produced meat, poultry, and products made from meat and poultry.

Specifications for wholesomeness for frozen meats and poultry are the same as for the unfrozen.

Canned meats and poultry should, like all canned foods purchased for institutional use, be processed commercially.

The U.S. Department of Agriculture will provide, upon request, an acceptance-type inspection service which allows a food buyer to write his own specifications to suit his specific need for meats and poultry. Under the acceptance service, an institutional buyer can protect himself regarding wholesomeness in that many meats are required to be inspected during cutting. This would be of special advantage in cases of ground meat, which has been shown to often harbor dangerously high numbers of bacteria, among them forms capable of causing foodborne illnesses. A buyer can specify hamburger to come from certain cuts. Under the acceptance inspection service, the food buyer can rest assured that his orders are carried out as specified and that the specified cuts are used rather than trimmings which are apt to be more heavily contaminated.

Specifications regarding packaging should include a request for sanitary and previously unused wrappings and containers.

Specifications regarding transit would pertain to care in handling and control of temperature and time: protective wrappings should not become torn; temperatures should be maintained adequately to prevent bacterial growth; and the time should be related to the perishability of the specific item.

The perishability of mildly processed meats is of special interest here since they are frequently mishandled regarding temperature control. These items because they are not sterile, are vulnerable to warmth and should therefore be held under continuous refrigeration. In pasteurized meats the microbial balance is upset in that an assortment of heat-resistant forms may survive and grow when conditions allow this, while the forms which would normally multiply most vigorously and suppress pathogenic forms are absent.

The number of marketed items which fall into the category of mildly processed foods is on the increase. Included here are hams, other meats, and poultry. Because of the uncertainties in connection with the microbiological aspects of these and other items receiving light heat treatments, it is important that these items not be allowed to remain in the danger zone of bacterial multiplication except for brief periods. Carelessness in temperature control, anywhere and any time, may spell trouble.

It has been warned that food items packaged under vacuum might require particular attention since the anaerobic conditions would inhibit many spoilage bacteria, but not the anaerobics and the micro-aerophilics. However, this is still a controversial issue and requires further study.

Specifications for shipment of frozen meats and poultry and products made from them should require that these items be kept at temperatures appropriate to maintain the quality of frozen foods.

It is evident, then, that the reliability of the vendor of highly perishable and potentially hazardous items is of utmost importance. This quality of reliability cannot be overestimated. Marginal dealers have been known to enhance their profits by selling items containing chemicals to retard food spoilage, which is an illegal practice. Institutions which are offered donated foods should refuse these donations, on principle.

## Eggs

Eggs may be purchased by federal grades. Consumer grades (federal) are AA, A, B, and C; equivalent federal procurement grades for the wholesale trade are I, II, III, and IV.

Eggs graded by trade (wholesale) standards are Specials, Extras,

Standards, and Trades; these standards run close to AA, A, B, and C, respectively.

Eggs cannot receive a grade when dirty, cracked, or broken. This is important since eggs with dirty and broken shells cannot be trusted to be free from salmonellae, although they might be. Grades for eggs are based on exterior and interior conditions, and a discussion of these is not appropriate at this time. The reader is referred to the earlier discussion on egg quality (Chapter VI) and other literature pertaining to egg production and marketing listed at the end of this chapter.

Eggs may also be graded according to the buyer's specifications under the supervision of federal graders, this being the acceptance-type inspection which was discussed above for meat and poultry.

When writing specifications for eggs, the institutional buyer should be aware of the fact that egg quality deteriorates rapidly. Therefore, the maximum number of days allowed to elapse between grading and delivery should be specified; this period is usually restricted to a few days. Also, the temperature conditions under which the eggs are stored before delivery should be specified and should require that the eggs be held under refrigeration at all times. Ideally, the eggs should come from one and the same source known to produce eggs from a disease-free flock of hens under strictly sanitary conditions. Under conditions of competitive buying, contracting for eggs from one producer may be impractical.

For processed eggs, specifications can be written to assure minimum total bacterial counts as well as freedom from salmonellae. Whether a recent regulation requiring pasteurization of all egg prior to processing (be it freezing or drying, see Chapter VI) will completely eliminate the necessity for such specifications, cannot be stated at this time. More will be known about this after the regulation has been in effect for a time.

*Fish and Shellfish*

Fish and shellfish are highly perishable and do not tolerate long holding. Quality standards developed for fish under the Agricultural Marketing Act are administered by the Bureau of Commercial Fisheries, U.S. Fish and Wildlife Service, Department of the Interior. Only fish from sanitary sources and processed under sanitary conditions qualify. However, fish shipped in interstate commerce do not require a federal seal of approval for wholesomeness.

Most fresh fish is sold without labels and seemingly some confusion exists about guidelines writing specifications for fresh fish. A reliable local dealer should prove quite helpful; his advice might well be sought regarding the availability of the various fresh fish in season.

In writing specifications, the sanitary source and processing should be stressed as well as sanitary treatment in transit. This includes sanitary packaging and strict temperature control. Frozen fish must be kept solidly frozen at all times; wrappings and glazes should not indicate damage.

Shellfish, fresh or frozen, must come from unpolluted waters. The U.S. Public Health Service is entrusted with the supervision of the shellfish industry, the catching, processing, and marketing. The requirements are stringent.

In the Food Service Sanitation Manual of the Public Health Service (1962) recommendations are made regarding the sanitary supply of shellfish which are: "All oysters, clams, and mussels shall be from sources approved by the State shellfish authority: *Provided*, that if the source is outside the State, it shall be one which is certified by the State of origin." And furthermore, "Shell stock shall be identified with an official tag giving the name and certificate number of the original shell-stock shipper and the kind and quantity of shell stock. Fresh and frozen shucked oysters, clams and mussels, shall be packed in nonreturnable containers identified with the name and address of the packer, repacker, or distributor, and the certificate number of the packer or repacker preceded by the abbreviated name of the State," and finally, "shucked shellfish shall be kept in the original container until used."

The certification by state shellfish agencies is made available through the Public Health Service, which issues a periodic listing of certified shippers. The Public Health Service honors only the certification of state shellfish agencies whose sanitary control measures are acceptable to them. This listing is an important and effective means of assuring the health authority that shellfish which originates outside its authority is wholesome.

The institutional buyer should consult the local authorities about this listing or should request it from the office of the Public Health Service, Washington, D.C.

As is true for other frozen items, frozen shellfish must be kept solidly frozen at all times.

*Frozen Precooked Items*

It is important to order from reliable vendors who handle items processed by reputable food processors. Since there have been almost no standards set up for these foods, buyers ordering items in very large quantities may wish to establish their own specifications, which may extend to formulation as well as to bacteriological quality (see Table 25). Strictest time–temperature control during transit is another important point to be stressed. Temperatures must be maintained at 0°F or lower to retain quality in a frozen product—in the processing plant, during transit, in warehouse storage, and on the premises of the food service establishment.

### Foods Prepared Outside the Place of Service

When food which has been prepared outside the hospital, school, or other place of service is purchased, it should be obtained from sources which comply with the regulations of the state, locality, or municipality. This is true whether the food is served in the conventional way or through vending machines. Such food should be wholesome and be processed, prepared, stored, and transported in a sanitary manner. This requirement includes that all good contact surfaces of containers should be protected from contamination and that strict time–temperature control be exercised during processing, preparation, and transport.

In vending, next to malfunctioning of the machines themselves, the most important hazard seems to be related to improper processing and mishandling of the items prior to introducing them into the machine (Food Protection Committee, 1964).

### Protecting Foods in Storage

### Receiving and Checking

Promptly upon delivery, the purchased items should be checked and inspected to make certain that the products agree with specifications. Items that do not meet the requirements should be returned.

If cases or wrappings are damaged, or discolored, they should be opened and inspected. All deficiencies should be recorded.

Great speed is required in the inspection and subsequent storage of perishables requiring refrigeration or freezer storage. It is therefore essential to know the time when perishables are to be delivered and to be ready for them with adequate personnel and space. Speed protects the food received and reduces the length of time the refrigerator and freezer doors remain open.

Frozen foods should be checked for temperature using an unbreakable thermometer. Hayes et al. (1964) suggest that this be performed by one of two methods:

1. One method is to open the case and remove the top corner package. Use an ice pick to make a hole through the case from the inside, level with the second layer of product. Insert the thermometer stem into the hole about three inches into the case. Replace the package, close the case, and weight down with several additional cases to insure good contact. Read the temperature after five minutes.

2. The other method is to cut a flap opening in the case near the middle corner-package. Bend the flap back and insert the thermometer stem between the package layers. Close the flap, weight down with additional cases. Read the temperature after five minutes.

The authors warn that firm contact between package and thermometer must be established for accuracy.

As is true for other packaged goods, inspection for signs of physical damage is indicated. Signs of thawing should be looked for also. The experienced dietitian and food manager is familiar with these signs: coarse ice crystals, cavity ice, shrinkage, discoloration, leakage, and so forth.

Canned items are checked for abnormalities which might indicate that the product is not sterile or may not keep: broken seals, leaks, swells, rust, and so forth.

*Storage*

Storage serves to temporarily house the purchased food items. Storage has been called the "link between receiving and preparations" (Lukowsky et al., 1962). Storage facilities should provide quarters appropriate for the satisfactory preservation of food quality, including sanitary quality. For dry items such as staples and canned goods, "dry storage" is provided. For highly perishable items, refrigerator or freezer storage is necessary. Refrigerated storage is to be provided for dairy products, meat, poultry, eggs, fish, fruits, and vegetables; freezer storage for all frozen foods.

DRY STORAGE

This type of storage serves for food items which do not require refrigeration but must be protected from freezing, excessive heat, and dampness and from rodents and insects.

Dry storage rooms should be cool (50–70°F), well ventilated, and dry; a relative humidity of 50–60% is satisfactory for many products kept in dry storage.

The construction should be such that cleaning is easy. The stored food should be protected against invasion of rodents, infestation with insects, and bacterial contamination. Therefore, the floors, walls, and windows should be rodent- and insect-proof. Places where pipes enter and leave the walls should be well sealed off.

Dry storage rooms are very frequently located in a basement and, therefore, are usually given the doubtful benefit of all sorts of pipes which run along the ceiling such as water, heating, and sewer pipes. Leakage from these pipes is a common source of trouble in basement storage rooms. Especially ominous is leakage from sewer pipes, which may have most serious consequences caused through contamination of foods with pathogenic bacteria and viruses present in sewage. Sewer pipes need frequent checking for leakage.

Hot water and steam pipes may create unfavorably high temperatures in the storeroom and should therefore be well insulated. The temperature can also be increased to an undesirable degree by sunlight entering through glass windows. As was pointed out in an earlier chapter, canned goods are not completely sterile and contain heat-loving, heat-resistant bacteria which survived the canning process; when temperatures rise to tropical heights, these survivors may begin to multiply, spoiling the contents of the cans.

Foods should never be placed directly on the floor; shelving should be provided. Both wood and metal shelves are used, each having its good and poor points. Wooden shelves may be cheaper but they absorb moisture and are difficult to sanitize, while noncorrosive metal shelves are easy to clean and vermin proof. Lightweight, sturdy, adjustable metal shelving is commercially available for storerooms and refrigerators. Just how far the lowest shelf should be placed above the floor is a matter of judgment. For easy cleaning, a minimum of 6–8 inches should be allowed in any case. Lukowsky et al. (1962) suggest that 30 inches should be allowed and that the space underneath be used to store flour, sugar, and other items which can be placed on skids or in cans. For the storage of many types of foods, galvanized cans with lids provide excellent containers. For bags and case lots, slatted platforms raised at least 6 inches from the floor are often used.

The sanitary quality of the food stored should be constantly protected by providing excellent care of the storeroom. The physical structure, floors, walls, ceilings, and shelves, should be kept in excellent repair and immaculately clean. Frequent inspection for presence of rodents, insects, and leakage from pipes is mandatory.

Insects sometimes gain entrance with crates and boxes into otherwise well-maintained storerooms. To eradicate insects, a professional exterminator should be engaged. Professional services for the extermination of rodents are also recommended.

After every issue of food, spilled food items must be gathered up and eliminated, either by disposal in covered metal trash cans inside the storage area or by complete removal from the area.

The cleaning routine should be frequent. Highest sanitary standards for, and close supervision of, all activities in connection with storeroom use and care are absolutely essential to maintain the sanitary quality of the stored items.

Orderly procedures in the stocking and the withdrawal of foods are also necessary to assure that stocked items will be used within a reasonable period of time.

### FREEZER STORAGE

To maintain the culinary quality of frozen foods, storage of 0°F or below is recommended, except for ice cream. At these temperatures, no bacterial hazards need be expected. Ice cream is usually stored at 6–10°F because first, it is more easily handled at these warmer temperatures, and second, its culinary quality is enhanced.

Whenever possible, frozen foods should be stored in the original containers. If wrapping is done, moisture-vapor proof materials should be used

Problems in connection with defrosting will be discussed in Chapter XIII.

### REFRIGERATOR STORAGE

The various items to be kept under refrigeration require somewhat different temperatures for storage. Dairy products and eggs are stored near 40°F, meat and poultry at 30–36°F, fish is kept iced or near 32°F, fruits and vegetables between 35 and 45°F.

The control of relative humidity is very desirable for cold storage of food items. A relative humidity of 75–85% is most frequently recommended for dairy products, meats, and poultry; for eggs, 80–85%; for fruits and vegetables, 85–95%.

Too high humidity causes sliminess in meats and poultry, the condition being due to excessive bacterial multiplication. The current trend is to include the feature of controlled humidity in refrigerators.

Temperature control is impossible without checking and rechecking the temperatures that actually prevail in a refrigerator. Too often a refrigerator is simply assumed to provide temperature conditions which, in reality, do not exist. The fact that a sign is affixed to the refrigerator door announcing a certain temperature does not necessarily mean that the refrigerator lives up to that expectation. Temperatures should be so adjusted that the warmest spot within the refrigerator is not higher than the maximum desirable for the particular food housed. Frequent regular checks are necessary, since the refrigerator temperature will fluctuate with such factors as size and temperature of the food loads placed in it and cooling capacity of the unit.

Dairy products and eggs absorb odors from other foods and should be stored separately. Milk and cream should be covered, butter and cheese kept wrapped when stored. Eggs are stored with the pointed ends down and should not be disturbed more than is absolutely necessary. Crates should be stacked in a way to allow for circulation of air. Crates containing fruits and vegetables also should be stacked in a way to allow for ventilation.

It goes without saying that, at best, cold storage will prolong but not improve the quality of perishable items. Even though properly refrigerated foods may remain bacteriologically safe for a remarkably long time, their culinary quality may not survive. Among the dairy products, fluid milk assumes off-flavors readily. Among the meats, lamb, pork, and poultry do not take kindly to prolonged storage, whereas aged beef may be held for 5–7 days, and fresh beef even longer.

Eggs, when stored at the proper temperature and relative humidity, will keep fresh remarkably long. At room temperatures, egg quality deteriorates quickly. It is, therefore, a deplorable procedure to hold eggs issued in the morning for a day's use in kitchens and bakeshops. Small refrigerator units should be installed in strategic areas of use, to receive and cold-store the eggs.

Refrigerated fresh fish should be used within 24 hours if kept uniced. When held longer (3 days is maximum), icing should be employed.

Since the keeping quality of fruits and vegetables is not as important from a public health point of view, it will not be discussed.

Metal shelves are recommended for refrigerators. Sanitary care of the refrigerated storage areas involves frequent inspections of the food supplies and removal of items suspected of quality deterioration; regular, if possible daily, cleaning of floors; regular, if possible weekly, cleaning of other surfaces such as walls and shelving. For cleaning shelves, which have direct contact with the food, hot water, soap, a brush, and "elbow grease" are recommended, followed by a thorough rinse with hot water containing baking soda.

# References

"Agricultural Marketing." A publication of the USDA Consumer Marketing Service, United States Government Printing Office, Division of Public Documents. Washington, D.C. (Monthly).

Burney, L. E. (1959). "The Public Health Service." *In:* "Food; The Yearbook of Agriculture." U.S. Department of Agriculture, Washington, D.C.

Elliott, P. Paul, and H. David Michener. (1961). "Microbiological Standards and Handling Codes for Chilled and Frozen Foods." A Review. *Appl. Micr.*, 9(5): 452–468.

Food Protection Committee of The Food and Nutrition Board. (1964). "An Evaluation of Public Health Hazards From Microbiological Contamination of Foods." National Academy of Sciences, National Research Council Publication 1195. Washington, D.C.

Food Service Sanitation Manual. *See* U.S. Department of Health, Education, and Welfare (1962). PHS Publication No. 934.

Frazier, William C. (1958). *Food Microbiology.* McGraw-Hill Book Co., New York.

Frooman, A. A. (1953). *Five Steps to Effective Institutional Buying.* Institutions Publications, Inc. Chicago, Ill.

Hahn, Fred. (1963). "Evolution of Convenience Foods." *The Cornell Hotel and Restaurant Administration Quarterly,* 4(1): 91–92.

Hayes, K. M., C. E. Eshbach, F. M. Sawyer, and N. G. Cournoyer. (1964). "Frozen Foods in Food Service Establishments." Food Management Program Leaflet 2, SL–10–GP. Cooperative Extension Service, College of Agriculture, University of Massachusetts.

Irmiter, T. F. (1963). "New Trends in Foods." *Jour. Amer. Dietet. Assoc.,* 43(1): 15–18.

Lukowsky, R. L., C. Eshbach, and A. L. Wrisley, Jr. (1962). "Using Storage in Food Service Establishments." Food Management Program Leaflet 4, SL–18. Cooperative Extension Service, College of Agriculture, University of Massachusetts.

Massachusetts Department of Public Health. (1960). "Rules and Regulations Relative to the Storage and Distribution of Frozen Foods." 1959. Boston, Mass.

Slanetz, L. W., *et al.* (1963). "Microbiological Quality of Foods." Proceedings of a Conference held at Franconia, New Hampshire, August 27–29, 1962. Academic Press, New York.

Ayres, J. C. "Low Temperature Organisms as Indexes of Quality of Fresh Meat." pp. 132–148.

Elliott, R. Paul. "Limitation of Microbial Levels in Chilled and Frozen Foods." pp. 171–178.

Goresline, H. E. "A Discussion of the Microbiology of Various Dehydrated Foods." pp. 179–187.

Mallman, W. L. "Current Status of Microbiological Tests and Standards for Food Quality in Microbiological Quality of Foods." pp. 1–5.

Niven, C. F., Jr. "Microbial Indexes of Food Quality: Fecal Streptococci." pp. 119–131.

Peabody, Frank R. "Microbial Indexes of Food Quality: The Coliform Group." pp. 113–118.

Silliker, J. H. "Total Counts as Indexes of Food Quality." pp. 102–112.

Slocum, G. G. (1963). "Control by the FDA of Foodborne Salmonellae." *U.S. Publ. Hlth. Repts.*, *78:* 1085–1087.

Stahl, W. H. (1963). "Newer Methods of Food Processing and Quality Evaluation." *The Cornell Hotel and Restaurant Administration Quarterly*, *4*(1): 37–41.

Thatcher, F. S. (1958). "Microbiological Standards for Foods. II. What May Microbiological Standards Mean?" *Food Tech.*, *12*(3): 117–122.

Treadway, R. H. (1965). "New Food Products and Processes." Part I and II, *Hospitals*, *39*(16): 94–99; *39*(17): 96–103.

U.S. Department of Health, Education and Welfare. (1962). "Food and Drug Administration—What It Is and Does." FDA Leaflet No. 1. Washington, D.C.

U.S. Department of Health, Education and Welfare, Public Health Service. (1962). "Food Service Sanitation Manual." PHS Publication No. 934. Washington, D.C.

U.S. Department of Health, Education and Welfare, Public Health Service. (1962). "Shellfish Sanitation Manual." Cooperative Program for the Certification of Interstate Shellfish Shippers. PHS Publication No. 33. Washington, D.C.

U.S. Department of Health, Education and Welfare. National Conference on Interstate Milk Shipments (9th), Memphis, Tennessee, 1963. "Procedures Governing The Cooperative State—PHS Program for Certification of Milk Shippers." PHS Publication No. 1040. Washington, D.C. 1963.

U.S. Department of Health, Education and Welfare. "Requirements of the United States Food, Drug and Cosmetic Act." FDA Bulletin No. 2. Revised, 1964. Washington, D.C.

U.S. Department of Health, Education and Welfare, Public Health Service. (1964). The "Shellfish Sanitation Program of the Public Health Service." PHS Publication No. 906. Washington, D.C.

U.S. Department of Health, Education and Welfare, Public Health Service. (1965). "Milk Ordinance and Code—Recommendations." Revisions of PHS Publication No. 229. Washington, D.C.

## Additional Readings

Abrahamson, A. E., L. Buchbinder, J. Guenkel, and M. Heller. "A Study of Frozen Precooked Foods: Their Sanitary Quality and Microbiological Standards for Control." Association of Food & Drug Officials of the U.S. *Quart. Bull.*, *23:* 63–72. 1959.

American Hospital Association. "Hospital Food Service Manual." American Hospital Association Publication M 27–54. Chicago, Illinois. 1954.

Anonymous. "Microbiological Standards for Foods." *U.S. Publ. Hlth. Repts.*, *75:* 815–820. 1960.

Association of Food and Drug Officials of the U.S. "Proposed Frozen Food Code." Association of Food & Drug Officials of the U.S. *Quart. Bull.*, *24:* 23–42. Proceedings issue. September 1960.

Buchbinder, L. "Current Status of Food Poisoning Control." *Publ. Hlth. Repts.*, *76:* 515–520. 1961.

International Association of Ice Cream Manufacturers. "Digest of State Laws Affecting Ice Cream and Related Products; Standards, Ingredients, Labeling, Packaging, Sales, Sanitation, Licensing, Marketing Regulations." Washington, D.C. 1962.

Kotschevar, L. H. *Quantity Food Purchasing*. John Wiley & Sons, New York. 1961.

Lee, R. J. "Labeling of Poultry Products Under Poultry Products Inspection Act." *Food Tech.*, *19*(11): 48–49. 1965.

Stauffer, Lee. "Sanitation in Hospital Food Service." *Hospitals, 38*(16): 162–170. 1964.

Stitt, Kathleen, and E. Neige Todhunter. "Menu Planning, Food Buying For Small Hospitals and Nursing Homes." School of Home Economics, University of Alabama, University, Alabama. 1960.

Thatcher, F. S. "Microbiological Standards for Foods: Their Function and Limitations." *Jour. Appl. Bact.*, *18:* 449–461. 1955.

Tigner, Nancy C. "Community Meal Management." Cornell University Miscellaneous Bulletin 42, New York State College of Home Economics, Ithaca, New York. 1962.

U.S. Department of Agriculture, Agricultural Marketing Service. "Food Storage Guide for Schools and Institutions." Publication PA-403. Washington, D.C. November 1959.

U.S. Department of Health, Education and Welfare, Public Health Service. "Ordinance and Code Regulating Eating and Drinking Establishments— Recommendations of the PHS" PHS Publication No. 37. 1943.

U.S. Department of Health, Education and Welfare, Public Health Service. "The Vending of Foods and Beverages. A Sanitation Ordinance and Code—Recommendations." PHS Publication No. 546. Washington, D.C. 1965.

U.S. Department of Health, Education and Welfare, Public Health Service. "Drinking Water Standards." PHS Publication No. 956. Washington, D.C. 1962.

U.S. Department of Health, Education and Welfare. "Federal Food, Drug and Cosmetic Act, As Amended and General Regulations for its Enforcement." Title 21, Pt. 1. Act revised October 1962; Regulations revised August 1963.

U.S. Department of Interior, Fish and Wildlife Service. "Fresh and Frozen Fish Buying Manual." Circular 20. Government Printing Office, Washington, D.C. 1954.

Weckel, W. K. "Increasing Populations and Future Foods. *Jour. Milk & Food Tech.*, *28*(1): 19–22. 1965.

West, B. B., Levelle Wood, and Virginia Harger. *Food Service In Institutions*. 4th ed. John Wiley & Sons, New York. 1965.

Wright, Carlton, E. *Food Buying: Marketing Information for Consumers*. Macmillan Co., New York. 1962.

CHAPTER **IX**

# CONTAMINATION OF INGREDIENTS AND MENU ITEMS IN THE FOOD SERVICE ESTABLISHMENT

The conditions and practices which may lead to microbial contamination of food items on the premises of a food service establishment are so manifold that only the main sources of contamination and the more frequently indicted practices will be discussed.

The sources of contamination which are of interest from a sanitary point of view may be classified, although somewhat arbitrarily, as primary and secondary. The primary sources as the term is used here, are more or less identical with the reservoirs of foodborne pathogens discussed in Chapters V, VI, and VII—namely, man, sewage, soil, water, air, rodents, insects, and the food supply. The secondary sources include the equipment and utensils which are used in the preparation, service, and storage of food and the physical plant itself—floors, walls, ceilings, and the like.

### Primary Sources of Contaminants

## Man

The fact that the food handler is an important source of contamination in a food service establishment should be reiterated in spite of the fact that the human reservoir of pathogens capable of causing foodborne illnesses was discussed before (Chapter V). Needless to say, the human reservoir is important whenever and wherever man handles food, be it in the processing plant, in shipment, in the kitchen, or in the dining room. It seems important to now take a closer look at the circumstances under which the transfer of microorganisms

212

from man to ingredients and menu items may take place in the food service establishment, with regard to applying this information to effective control measures available to the food service manager, supervisor, and food handler.

Healthy man is known to be a potential source of *Staphylococcus aureus, Salmonella, Clostridium perfringens*, and fecal streptococci (enterococci). The staphylococci are common inhabitants of his skin, nose, mouth, and throat, and may be easily transferred to food. This potential source is available throughout the working hours of the food handler. Every time his hands make contact with his body parts harboring the staphylococci, he contaminates the hands, and subsequently the food he touches. Direct transfer of these cocci from the respiratory tract to food is made when the food worker coughs and sneezes without covering his nose and mouth. If he uses his hands or a hankerchief to cover his mouth, the hands become contaminated and unless they are immediately washed, they serve as a vehicle of transmission for many foods.

The intestinal organisms may get attached to the hands of the food handler when he visits the toilet and does not thoroughly wash his hands before returning to work. Pathogens of intestinal origin which are capable of causing foodborne illnesses include the salmonellae, the fecal streptococci, *Clostridium perfringens*, and some strains of *Escherichia coli*. After washing his hands the worker may easily recontaminate them if he touches soiled clothing, faucets, linen towels, doorknobs, and the like.

Respiratory as well as intestinal disorders are frequent causes of illness. Food handlers returning to work shortly after recovery from these disorders are likely to be especially rich reservoirs of the pathogens for a while.

The personal habits, also called "hand habits," of the food handler have a great deal to do with the chances of transfer of contaminants from person to food. These hand habits refer to involuntary movements of the hands, such as scratching the skin, rubbing the nose, smoothing or arranging the hair, touching the clothing, and the like.

Funk (1955) made a revealing study of certain habits of the food service employee which may lead to contamination of food. Habits believed to present sanitary hazards were under scrutiny. They were: restroom procedures, including washing hands after visiting the toilet; washing hands before reporting to work and before returning to work after meals and coffee breaks; and washing hands after touching body parts. Also studied were certain working habits in the preparation of sandwiches and salads, in portioning desserts, in handling prepared foods, and in dishwashing. Observations were made in three units of a university food service and of a local luncheon counter. It was found that employees who executed a variety of duties had more undesirable habits than employees doing specific jobs. The employees of the lunch counter operation performed more undesirable acts than the employees of the college food service. On warm days, body parts were touched more frequently; in particular, the hair was brushed away from the face. Length of service of the employee was not a factor affecting the performance of undesirable habitual acts. Busy persons had less time for these undesirable habits. Hands were washed more frequently when handwashing facilities were near the place of work.

The opportunities for contamination of hands are endless and cannot possibly be enumerated. Examples are: picking up a dangling shoe lace which needs to be tied, recovering a potholder from the floor, reaching into a drain which needs to be unplugged, and countless similar occasions where contact is first made with unsanitary articles and surfaces and then with food. That foods themselves can be reservoirs of undesirable pathogens was discussed in previous chapters; handling of certain foods likely to bear pathogens may also lead to contamination.

The bacterial flora of the hands of food service employees has been analyzed by Horwood and Minch (1951). Thirty-four food handlers were selected at random from 22 public eating places in Boston and Cambridge, Massachusetts. These establishments included cafeterias, lunchrooms, restaurants, and drugstores. No attempt was made to trace the origin of the bacteria. It is therefore likely that some bacteria were derived from the food that was handled. Extremely large numbers of bacteria were isolated. Among these, hemolytic staphylococci, streptococci, and *Escherichia coli* were types recovered frequently. The results of this study showed up a dire need for education and supervision in matters of personal hygiene.

The smoking habit, from a sanitation point of view, may represent a potential danger because of possible transfer of saliva to the hands of the smoker. Also, when a cigarette is laid down on surfaces which are used in food preparation, the saliva will contaminate the surfaces with organisms originating in the human respiratory system.

The habit of tasting food from cooking utensils is an unsanitary one, because the taster will inoculate his mouth flora, which is apt to contain staphylococci, into food. This tasting habit is not only esthetically undesirable but potentially dangerous, especially when it concerns food which will not be heated or sufficiently reheated to destroy the organisms transferred.

### Rodents and Insects

Rodents and insects are a menace to areas where food is stored and prepared. The danger of contamination with pathogens has been fully discussed in an earlier chapter.

Rodents and insect pests have been known to contaminate food in storage as well as in the preparation area. They have been known to contaminate menu items left in inappropriate places to cool; counters, equipment, utensils and working surfaces; in brief, almost anything left unprotected. Opportunity for entrance and subsequent activities of these pests is afforded wherever and whenever access from the outside exists. The importance of the exclusion of vermin from all areas where food is stored, prepared, and served cannot be overemphasized.

### Soil

Soil is carried into the food establishment on man's clothing, especially his shoes. Soil may be blown in through doors and windows as dust. It may reach the kitchen by adhering to certain foods like celery, root vegetables, and potatoes. Depending on its source, soil may contain almost any microorganisms and parasites, including pathogens causing foodborne illnesses, especially spores, since these remain viable in soil for long periods of time. Reports of outbreaks involving food items, such as pudding, which were allowed to cool in dusty and drafty hallways, have indicted soil as the source of the contaminants. Any food that drops to the floor may be considered contaminated by soil. Hands which pick up things from the floor become contaminated with soil.

McKillop (1959), who made a study of the bacterial contamination of food in a hospital over a period of $2\frac{1}{2}$ years, found that cooked cold chicken was frequently contaminated with fairly large numbers of *Clostridium perfringens* (*welchii*) and gave as the probable source kitchen dust. Hobbs (1960) has stated that *Clostridium welchii* (*perfringens*) spores can be routinely cultured from kitchen floors.

### Water

As was pointed out in an earlier chapter, the municipal water supply of our cities is, in general, excellent. However, the dangers involved in the use of water from unknown sources are great.

Contaminated water will contaminate food either directly or by way of hands, equipment, utensils, and the like.

If, in an emergency, water must be transported from an approved source to a food service establishment, it is important that contamination be avoided from unsanitary containers and through unsanitary methods of handling. The local health authority will give appropriate advice.

In some establishments a supply of nonpotable water may be available by permission of the health authorities for special purposes such as fire protecton and air conditioning. Such water is not intended as a food, and if it is used in connection with food or drink it may serve as a source of contamination.

### Air

Adequate ventilation is essential in a food service establishment, be it in the areas of food preparation, service, or storage. If adequately installed and well maintained, the ventilation system reduces condensation, which would otherwise be apt to promote microbial growth on walls and other surfaces. Contaminated water in the form of condensed droplets may fall into food and onto surfaces used in food preparation.

Ill-designed and ill-maintained ventilating systems, however, may cause a sanitary hazard in that they permit accumulation of condensates and grease which may contaminate food and working surfaces. Faulty intake air ducts or ducts poorly maintained may admit contaminating materials such as dust, dirt, and insects.

### Sewage

At first glance it must seem shocking that sewage is even mentioned in connection with the area of food preparation, service, and storage. Unfortunately, sewage is known to have caused serious illness and gastroenteric foodborne outbreaks which originated in food service establishments. Plumbing, either improperly installed or ill-maintained, has given rise to a variety of troubles, such as cross-connections, back siphonage, overhead leakage, and drainage system stoppage. Due to faulty plumbing, sewage has contaminated water, food, equipment, and utensils. In basement storage areas, leaky overhead plumbing is a frequent source of trouble.

In areas where a nonwater-carried sewage system is used, improper disposal of sewage may cause havoc in many ways, but mainly by contaminating the water supply and by attracting flies which in turn disseminate pathogens. Fortunately, nonwater-carried sewage systems are rarely used in connection with food service establishments, and if they are, they must have the approval of the health authorities.

## Food Supply

Cross-contamination may occur from raw to cooked foods in the storage area and kitchen. In the discussion of the various food groups it was brought out that foods may carry microorganisms most unwelcome to the kitchen, be they part of the food's natural flora or a flora acquired during processing, transport, storage, or other handling.

Of special concern to the food service manager are the foods which are known to be potential bearers of microorganisms capable of causing foodborne illness. Even if these foods are basically clean, wholesome, from sources which are approved or considered satisfactory by the health authorities, and safe for human consumption, a potential danger still exists. To recognize and accept the fact that certain foods are potential sources of food-poisoning organisms is the first step to successfully dealing with the problem, since the contamination of cooked food with microorganisms from raw food has been the frequent cause of gastroenteric episodes.

### Foods of Animal Origin

In the preceding chapters the flora of the food supply has been discussed in detail and the reader is referred back for information regarding the contaminants to be expected from specific food items.

Among the foods of animal origin, meats and poultry stand out as important sources of contaminants capable of causing foodborne illnesses. These foods have been shown to be frequently contaminated with representatives of various strains of *Salmonella, Clostridium perfringens*, fecal streptococci, and to a lesser degree, *Staphylococcus aureus*. Naturally, all foods touched by human hands may at sometime become contaminated with *S. aureus* and many comminuted meats, such as hamburger, are so contaminated.

COLD STORAGE

Uncooked animal foods are usually stored in separate refrigerators. This is a good practice since contaminants present on the meats are thus "kept to themselves."

When refrigerator space is limited and no provision exists for the separation of raw meats and cooked items, the chances for cross-contamination are greater. However, only the refrigerator which is poorly managed and ill-maintained will allow for such cross-contamination. The bacteria do not spread through the air to other substrates, rather, cross-contamination is usually performed by pieces of meat or other food which happen to drop into unprotected, uncovered items. Undersides and rims of containers, soiled racks, used covers transferred from one item to another, may contain particles of food harboring bacteria which may serve as an inoculum in other food substrates.

## FOOD PREPARATION AREA

When raw meats are handled, like in cutting, chopping, shaping and portioning, the hands of the food handler, his clothing, the working surfaces and equipment, all may become contaminated with the bacterial flora of the meat. In cases of trichina-infested pork, the trichinae may be spread to cooked food items.

The literature abounds with examples of foodborne illnesses traced to the contamination of cutting boards with bacteria—salmonellae, in particular—and also with enterococci and *Clostridium perfringens*. Grinders, cutters, and similar equipment are frequently indicated, and so are wooden pushers for grinders. Kitchen practices which allow raw foods to come in contact with cooked food, either directly or by way of contaminated equipment, may lead to trouble. Cooked foods are sterile; when seeded with an inoculum of food-poisoning bacteria, the stage is set for this inoculum to find a medium particularly attractive because it is devoid of competitors. In the case of trichinae, no multiplication will occur; however, a wholesome cooked product can be rendered contaminated through simple contact with trichinae-infested surfaces and equipment.

In many large food service establishments raw meats and poultry are handled in an area completely separate from the area where cooked foods are handled and the portioned meats are delivered to the kitchen ready to be cooked. The cutting, chopping, cubing, and slicing operations are carried out by employees who use implements solely reserved for this purpose. Meat-cutting areas which are air conditioned to low temperatures have the additional benefit of discouraging bacterial multiplication during the cutting operations. This is the ideal situation, but unfortunately not always possible, certainly not in small food service establishments. Therefore, it is very important for the operators, managers, and supervisors to fully understand and appreciate the potential dangers of cross-contamination from raw meats to cooked ingredients and menu items, and to pass the information on to their employees. They should either provide equipment and working surfaces which make possible complete separation of raw and cooked items, or enforce rigorous rules regarding sanitation of contaminated surfaces and equipment.

If raw meats and poultry must be handled in the kitchen along with cooked foods, the most meticulous housekeeping practices should be followed: washing hands following contact with raw meats; using separate cutting blocks or boards; and thoroughly cleaning and sanitizing chopping blocks or boards, grinders, choppers, knives, and other implements immediately after use.

Cooked ingredients or menu items that have been contaminated and are not promptly reheated or cooled are a real health hazard.

## Foods of Plant Origin

### COLD STORAGE

Uncooked plant materials such as fruits and vegetables should be stored in a separate refrigerator, if at all possible. If limited space prevents a complete separation, meticulous separation within the refrigerator is necessary so that cooked items will not be contaminated with the bacterial flora clinging to the plant material.

### FOOD PREPARATION AREA

Most food service establishments have a separate area for the cleaning of fruits and vegetables and for processes such as peeling and chopping. In establishments where such physical separation is not possible, meticulous housekeeping practices are indicated to avoid cross-contamination.

When raw vegetables are combined with an otherwise finished menu item which has received its terminal heat treatment, contaminants may be added along with the vegetables. Unless the contaminants are killed by reheating the item, they will remain viable and may even multiply, temperature and time permitting.

One example of a vegetable which is frequently added to a menu item "as the last thing," is parsley. Nuts are another ingredient frequently incorporated into finished menu items. Still another example is lettuce which could serve as a source of contaminants for a salad or sandwich filling. Leaf lettuce is an especially good source of soilborne bacteria because of its open structure which provides excellent chances for contamination with soil through splashing rains. Multiplication of the contaminant would, of course, depend on the suitability of the substrate for bacterial activity and on prevailing temperatures. Actually, in this country, the dangers from contaminants of vegetable origin are less acute than those associated with foods of animal origin.

## Equipment and Utensils

Material, design, construction, and state of repair are all of sanitary importance in equipment, large and small. In large floor-mounted equipment, installation plays a role also, since liquids or solid particles may settle in spaces not easily accessible to cleaning.

Equipment and utensils made of materials difficult to clean or so designed and constructed that thorough cleaning is inconvenient, are not apt to be cleaned regularly and thoroughly, and are therefore important sources of contamination in a food service establishment. But even equipment of sanitary construction and good cleanability may become a hazard if it is not maintained in a sanitary condition. Bacterial populations may build up to large numbers on first-rate equipment if this is not thoroughly and regularly cleaned.

Cleanability of equipment generally depends on first, the nature of the material used in construction and second, the general construction features and the ease with which the equipment is taken apart for cleaning purposes.

Examples of materials of poor wearability and sanitary quality are galvanized steel and iron, since the galvanized part wears off easily and soil gathers in its place. Wood, although light and popular as a chopping surface, does absorb and hold moisture, thus allowing penetration of bacteria; it is difficult to clean, especially when cracks are present, and it absorbs stains and odors. Wooden cutting surfaces and wooden pushers for grinders are still used a great deal in food preparation. The combination of wood and meat is very dangerous because meats and poultry are apt to be contaminated with microorganisms capable of causing foodborne illnesses and the contaminants may easily be spread to the next item by way of wooden surfaces. They may also multiply on the board to enormous numbers, and there is danger that since the cells continue to multiply on the meat juices and food remnants, they would be especially efficient contaminants because their lag phase would be brief and they would continue without interruption as soon as they landed in the new substrate.

General construction is considered poor if it does not permit easy cleaning of the equipment and its immediate surrounding. Examples are: large equipment poorly sealed to the floor; ill-fitting panels; poorly fitted steps and legs, drawers, and racks; fixed equipment too closely mounted to the wall; spouts that come out at an angle and do not empty effectively; ineffective draws; poorly fitted joints and seams; sharp corners and angles; screws, rivet heads, and other irregular protrusions that make direct contact with the food; food slicers, cutters, and grinders that are difficult to disassemble and reassemble; hollow handles on all kinds of utensils and equipment; ill-constructed rims of pots and pans; and seams which are rough or open and allow food particles to collect. In brief, all places where food particles may collect and where bacteria and vermin may feed.

The National Sanitation Foundation of Ann Arbor, Michigan, has been instrumental in stimulating interest in, and in giving directions regarding, the sanitary aspects of the design, construction, and installation of food service equipment. This organization is non-commercial and nonprofit. It conducts and sponsors research in order to form a basis for the establishment of minimum sanitation standards for equipment that are generally acceptable to health authorities.

Certain human traits aggravate the situation concerning the sanitary maintenance of equipment. Many cooks tend to be jealous of their small equipment such as knives, whips, and other small pieces; they tend to keep them near them, and if possible, hidden when not in use. Thus, these implements may escape the regular washing and sanitizing treatments. Stauffer (1964) has rightly pointed out that many cooks become so attached to certain implements like knives that they will use them to the last, even when the handles are held together with string or tape and are no longer cleanable.

Another common and undesirable kitchen habit is to forget about the periodic cleaning of certain equipment which is used by a number of persons during a workday, such as can openers and cutting boards. Can openers provided in connection with vended, canned foods represent a potential health hazard unless appropriate preventative provisions are made. More will be said about vending problems in Chapters X and XIII.

## Floors, Walls, Ceilings

Floors that are smooth and properly constructed are easily cleaned, whereas rough and absorbent floors are not. Especially in the food food preparation area and in walk-in refrigerators where spilling may occur, an absorbent floor is a potential hiding and feeding place for bacteria which have gained entrance. It is not easy to keep clean even if an effort is made toward that end. Floors originally smooth but in ill repair are a source of contamination for the same reason. Floors subjected to fluid wastes from cooking kettles and improperly drained may be a feeding ground for bacteria as well as insect pests.

Similarly, walls and ceilings which are rough or in a poor state of repair may harbor bacteria. *Staphylococcus aureus*, for example, may survive on such surfaces and contaminate food from these secondary sources. Floors, walls, and ceilings of poor basic construction are almost impossible to keep sanitary. However, even smooth structures are sources of undesirable contaminants unless they have regular and effective cleaning and repair.

Other places where contaminants may lodge are window sills, skylights, transoms, light fixtures, beams, rafters, joints, and the like. Kitchen and refrigerator shelves are of special importance as sources of contaminants for cooked foods. The significance of sanitary construction and effective maintenance will be discussed further in Chapter X.

Control measures include, first, understanding of the dangers of the sources of bacterial contamination, the chances for multiplication, and an appreciation of the role of every employee in reducing the dangers of undesirable bacterial activity in the food service establishment; and second, meticulous housekeeping at every step of food preparation, service, and storage. If management fails to provide adequate sanitizing facilities for equipment used in food preparation, if no directions are given for sanitary maintenance, and supervision is lacking, the employees lose interest in maintaining high standards. Inadequate facilities and lack of interest on the part of any management induce dissatisfaction and fatigue in employees, and the food service employee is no exception in this respect.

### References

Funk, Kaye. (1955). "A Study of Certain Habits of the Food Service Employee Which May Lead to Contamination." M.S. thesis, University of Washington, Seattle, Wash.

Hobbs, B. C. (1960). "Staphylococcal and *Clostridium welchii* Food Poisoning." *Roy. Soc. Promotion Hlth. Jour.*, *80:* 267–272.

Horwood, M. P., and V. A. Minch. (1951). "The Numbers and Types of Bacteria Found on the Hands of Food Handlers." *Food Res.*, *16:* 133–136.

McKillop, Elizabeth J. (1959). "Bacterial Contamination of Hospital Food With Special Reference to *Clostridium welchii* Food Poisoning." *Jour. Hyg.*, *57:* 31–46.

Stauffer, L. D. (1964). "Sanitation in Hospital Food Service—From Pots and Pans to Large Appliances: Equipment and Food Safety." *Hospitals, 38:* 80–87. Part I.

## Additional Readings

Browne, A. S., G. Lynch, A. R. Leonard, and G. Stafford. "A Clostridial or Enterococcal Food Poisoning Outbreak." *U.S. Publ. Hlth. Repts.*, 77(6): 533-536. 1962.

Dack, G. M. *Food Poisoning.* 3rd ed. Univ. Chicago Press, Chicago. 1956.

Kemp, G. E., R. Proctor, and A. S. Browne. "Foodborne Disease in California, With Special Reference to *Clostridium perfringens (welchii)*." *U.S. Publ. Hlth. Repts.*, 77(10): 910-914. 1962.

# CHAPTER X

# CONTROL: PRINCIPLES PERTAINING TO, AND MEASURES DIRECTED AT, PREVENTING CONTAMINATION OF COOKED INGREDIENTS AND MENU ITEMS IN THE AREAS OF PREPARATION, SERVICE, AND STORAGE

In previous chapters (V, VI, VII) the reservoirs of pathogens causing foodborne illnesses were discussed, and in a subsequent chapter (IX) possibilities for contamination to occur in the food establishment were scrutinized regarding both sources of contaminants and practices which aid in spreading bacteria in the areas of food preparation and storage.

The primary sources of contaminants of public health significance in connection with quantity food service are man, animals, sewage, soil, and certain foods; the secondary sources are equipment, utensils, and the food service premises themselves.

In the Food Service Sanitation Manual of the Public Health Service (U.S. PHS, 1962) it is stated that for appropriate food protection "all food being stored, prepared, displayed, served, or sold at food service establishments, or during transportation between such establishments, shall be protected from contamination."

### Control of Primary Sources of Contaminants

Man: The Food Handler

Attributes in a food handler which are important in connection with food sanitation are his health, cleanliness, and willingness to

224

learn. Good health reduces the chances for the food handler to be a dangerous reservoir of pathogens; cleanliness reduces the chances of spreading bacteria of which he may be a source; and his willingness to learn about sanitation in the food service department and his role in it is a prerequisite for a sanitation program to be effective.

## Health Control

A food service employee should not be on duty when he has an acute form of communicable disease, or while he is a carrier. The acute form is likely to be noticed by the supervisor, whereas the carrier escapes notice; the person who is a carrier appears healthy.

Either the ill person or the carrier is a menace in the food service department in that he may transmit the disease to other employees and to customers through direct contact or through food which he has contaminated. Food may serve in the capacity of a mere vehicle of transmission (Chapter III), in the same manner as doorknobs, money, and the like; or it may serve as a medium in which certain pathogens can multiply to enormous numbers, if conditions permit, causing outbreaks of food infections and food poisonings (Chapter IV).

In the Food Service Manual of the Public Service (U.S. PHS, 1962) the following recommendation is made:

> No person while affected with any disease in a communicable form, or while a carrier of such disease, or while afflicted with boils, infected wounds, sores, or an acute respiratory infection, shall work in any area of a food service establishment in any capacity in which there is a likelihood of such person contaminating food or food contact surfaces with pathogenic organisms, or transmitting disease to other individuals; and no person known or suspected of being affected with any such disease or condition shall be employed in such an area or capacity. If the manager or person in charge of the establishment has reason to suspect that any employee has contracted any disease in a communicable form or has become a carrier of such disease, he shall notify the health authority immediately.

### CONTINUOUS WATCHFULNESS

When a food handler is hired, he should come with a clean bill of health. This may or may not be supported by a statement from a physician. The medical checkup would show that the worker is not suffering from a communicable disease and is not a carrier at the time of the check. However, this clean bill of health would not prevent him from acquiring communicable diseases thereafter. Therefore, many food service operations try to get some protection by requiring periodic medical checkups of their food handlers. It seems desirable to require regular, frequent, fecal examinations of food handlers in geriatric institutions and hospitals, since salmonellosis is known to occur frequently in such institutions. The very young, the old, and the enfeebled are seemingly more susceptible to salmonellosis than the public at large. The efficacy of periodic checkups cannot be a complete safeguard, however. The U.S. Public Health Service in the 1962 Recommendations (Food Service Sanitation Manual, Section H) takes the stand that "pre-employment and periodic medical examinations of food service establishment employees are not required by this ordinance. . . . " This puts the burden of keeping track of their employees' health squarely on the shoulders of management.

There simply is no substitute for continuous watchfulness on the part of the supervisor for signs of illness in his or her employees, coupled with cooperativeness on the part of the employee.

It is the responsibility of the supervisor to see to it that employees are sent home when symptoms of illness are evident, to verify with the attending physician the nature of the illness, and to not allow the patient to return to work until the infectious stage has passed. In case of communicable diseases which may render a patient a carrier, his return may be delayed a long time.

It is the responsibility of the food handler to aid the supervisor in this endeavor. Some illnesses, such as intestinal illnesses, have symptoms not readily evident to other persons. Stauffer (1964), who called attention to the importance of health-conscious food handlers, stated that absenteeism is commendable whenever a food service employee has a condition as small as an inflamed hangnail. The reader is referred to this excellent series of five articles on sanitation in hospital food service.

Since the cooperation of the food handler is so very essential, he must be or become health conscious. His interest can be stimulated by education, and so can his motivation to contribute his part by not coming to work when afflicted with a contagious illness. As Stauffer (1964) rightly points out, in our present employment practices, continuous attendance is highly rewarded and absenteeism is frowned upon. There is also the fear of the employee of losing pay because of days missed and fear of being removed from the job. His motivation to cooperate toward the goal of high sanitary standards is indeed handicapped by these fears and probably additional ones. The dietitian, food manager, or supervisor has the responsibility to instill in employees a health consciousness which will overcome such fears.

## Cleanliness

Cleanliness and clean personal habits are extremely important in food handlers. They are not only desirable for esthetic reasons, but they are absolutely basic to sanitary food handling.

### PERSONAL HABITS

It has been said before, and must be reiterated here, that even the healthy person may carry microorganisms of public health significance on and in his body. These microbes, when allowed to contaminate food and multiply, may cause serious foodborne illnesses in persons who consume this food. These facts have been discussed in detail in Chapters III and IV.

Clean hair, skin, garments, and hand habits are essential to reducing contamination of food with the microbial flora for which the food handler is the primary source as well as a "middleman," since his hands and garments may, of course, spread microbes from other sources also.

Sneezes and coughs may spread pathogens in two ways, directly through the air and indirectly through the hands. It is therefore mandatory that the mouth and nose be protected when coughing and sneezing to avoid the direct transmission of germ-laden droplets to food, food preparation surfaces, and equipment; it is also mandatory to subsequently wash hands thoroughly. Every use of the handkerchief should be followed by washing of hands, whether the handkerchief was previously used or not. Every trip to the toilet should be terminated by thorough washing of hands.

In the Public Health Service Food Service Sanitation Manual (U.S. PHS, 1962) this recommendation is made:

All employees shall wear clean outer garments, maintain a high degree of personal cleanliness, and conform to hygienic practices while on duty. They shall wash their hands thoroughly in an approved hand-washing facility before starting work, and as often as may be necessary to remove soil and contamination. No employee shall resume work after visiting the toilet room without first washing his hands.

### HANDWASHING

Facilities for washing hands should be provided in dressing rooms, near the toilet room, and in the kitchen and the service area. A sink used in food preparation is not the place to wash hands. Many food service establishments lack a sufficient number of separate hand-washing sinks in the kitchen, or lack them altogether in the food preparation area. Sanitation education cannot succeed if provisions are not made for practicing what is preached.

The importance of washing hands and cleaning nails cannot be overrated. Management has an obligation to provide handwashing facilities in strategic points, thus making it convenient for the food handler to do the frequent hand cleaning required in his job.

Hands should be washed before starting work, after the coffee break, after smoking, after visiting the toilet, and each time when hands have been soiled in work or by touching soiled surfaces. These include body parts such as hair, nose, mouth, and ears, and soiled clothing. As was discussed earlier, many persons perform certain involuntary movements with their hands, touching various body parts; these are the so-called hand habits and their control is difficult but essential.

Sinks for handwashing should be provided with warm water. If one faucet provides cold water, the other very hot, the cold will be preferable to most persons because of fear of getting scalded. Therefore, mixing valves providing warm water of 110°–120°F have been suggested by Stauffer (1964). This same author recommends the use of soaps designed for handwashing in hospitals by physicians and nurses.

### USE OF TOBACCO

The use of tobacco should be prohibited in the food preparation area, in the food service area, in storerooms, and in the area where dishes, pots, pans, and utensils are washed. Usually, certain areas are provided by management where the employees may smoke. Hands should be washed after smoking because they are apt to become contaminated with the smoker's saliva.

### CLOTHING

Clothing must be clean, and if worn for more than one day, should be stored on the premises in clean lockers. Caps or nets should be used to prevent hair from contacting food surfaces and the food itself.

Management is responsible for an adequate, clean place in which the employee may change and store his clothing. In many institutions, uniforms are provided; in others, laundry service is available on the premises. It is, in general, undesirable to allow the worker to travel to his place of work in uniform, since the garments may become quite unsanitary enroute.

*Education in Principles of Personal Hygiene*

Education in the principles of personal hygiene is basic to the success of a training program in food sanitation. Personal hygiene is what it says: personal. Interference with personal freedom is likely to arouse in almost everyone a feeling of resistance or even resentment, unless one understands and fully appreciates the reasons for the restrictions. Therefore, education in the principles of sanitation should precede or accompany actual training in "how-to-do-it" matters of personal hygiene.

A discussion of educational programs in food sanitation will be presented in Chapter XIV.

## Man: The Customer

The customer may contaminate displayed food; therefore, displayed food must be protected from contact with him at all times. Wrapping food, when possible, will achieve that goal. Where unwrapped food is displayed, however, devices must be used which are effective in guarding food from customers' hands, sneezes, or coughs and which are easily cleaned. Tongs, forks, spoons, or other devices suitable to allow the particular food to be picked up by the customer should be provided.

Protection from hands and breath of customer should be exercised whenever a food item is subjected to possible contact and ensuing contamination.

## Animals

*Pets*

Pets, such as dogs and cats, may be rich sources of bacteria detrimental to public health, as was discussed previously (Chapter V).

The control of pathogens from pets is straightforward, in that pets absolutely must be kept out of all areas where food is stored, prepared, and served, except that guide dogs accompanying blind persons should have the right to be admitted to the dining room area (U.S. PHS, Food Service Sanitation Manual, 1962). Persons who have handled pets should wash their hands and arms thoroughly before touching food. These precautions should be remembered when food is prepared in the home for community meal service.

*Rodents and Insects*

RODENTS

The control of rats and mice is of great importance since rodents are hosts to many dangerous pathogens which they harbor in their intestinal tracts and carry on their feet and fur (Chapter V). Among these pathogens are salmonellae which are capable of causing outbreaks of foodborne infections in man.

In principle, rats and mice must be kept out of the food service department including storage rooms, kitchen, bakeshop, pantry, dining room, and garbage-storage rooms. The all-out important control measure is to effectively protect all openings to the outside against the entrance of rodents. Conditions of the building that may permit entrance include: windows near the ground; ventilation grills; holes in floors, walls, ceilings, especially near pipe lines; and doors with a base not flush with floor or threshold. The control measures consist of screening windows and ventilation grills, sealing openings with cement and/or metal plates or strips, and making doors flush with the floor threshold.

Further control measures require that harboring places where mice and rats might find temporary refuge should be eliminated. Such harboring places include unused crates, boxes, and rubbish piles. Good housekeeping practices should prevent these items from accumulating during the day, and inspection should be made each evening to assure that no such trash is being left around during the night.

Needless to say, food should never be left out during the night. Garbage should be protected from rodents at all times.

Eradication of rodents which have entered should be performed by an experienced professional exterminator. The local health authority should be consulted for advice.

Directions for the use of sanitation in the control of rodents have been given by Johnson (1960). Control methods against rodents are also discussed by Bjornson (1960). Information on rodent-proof methods of construction is made available through the Public Health Communicable Disease Center, Atlanta, Georgia.

### INSECTS

Insects, especially flies and cockroaches, are pests most undesirable in any food service establishment. They must not be allowed in areas where food is stored, prepared, and served. Unfortunately, cockroaches sometimes enter hidden in crates and in other food containers and wrappings.

Basic to effective control of insect pests is an understanding of their life cycles and feeding habits. The reader is referred to Chapter V for information, as well as to publications cited at the end of Chapters V and X.

The control measures directed against insect pests should include, first, preventing these animals from entering the areas where food is stored, prepared, and served and where garbage is stored and, second, eradicating the specimens which have gained entrance to these areas.

Some insects can be kept out by screening windows, skylights, transoms, doors, vents, and other openings to the outside, provided the screening is sufficiently dense for the exclusion of the smaller specimens. Screens of not less than 16 mesh per inch are recommended (U.S. PHS, Food Service Sanitation Manual, 1962). Screened and other doors should be self-closing.

Cockroaches may enter also through cracks in walls and floors. Therefore, control measures must include the elimination of such entering places. Frequent harboring and feeding grounds for cockroaches are places where large equipment such as steam-jacketed kettles is in poor contact with the floor or base. Food particles and moisture are apt to collect in cracks and crevices, providing food and drink, in addition to shelter, for the roaches. Through frequent inspection, such roach harbors must be located and appropriate action taken. These consist of sealing off cracks and crevices and eradicating the insect population. There is no doubt that constant vigilance in maintaining high standards of basic sanitation is an extremely important measure in the effective control of all vermin. Through effective basic sanitation, a buildup to large populations is prevented by depriving the insects of food, drink, and shelter, their three basic needs.

Whenever it is necessary to chemically eradicate insect pests present in a food service establishment, a professional exterminator should be retained. The suggestions of the local health authority will be helpful.

Besides flies and cockroaches, numerous other insects are apt to invade the food service department and cause a nuisance. Although these may not be as important as bearers of pathogenic bacteria as flies and cockroaches, they cannot be ruled out as disease carriers, and they can cause economic losses.

Moths, weevils, and beetles are insects often associated with dry foods such as flour, cereals, and dried fruit. They are typical pests of the "dry storage" area. Frequent inspection is necessary to prevent a buildup in population. Infestation can be recognized not only by the presence of the insects themselves but also by the fruits of their activities such as webbing, clumped-together food particles, holes in beans, holes in packaging, insect feces, and so forth.

Efforts should be made to (1) prevent infestation of the storage area by way of infested goods entering the area, although this is difficult when large shipments come in; (2) regularly and frequently inspect the storeroom; (3) avoid transfer of clean food to contaminated containers (in principle, food should be left in the original containers; if transfer is made, the previously infested container must be washed and sanitized); (4) avoid spills onto the floor, and immediately gather spilled food and place it in covered containers or completely remove it from the area; (5) regularly and frequently clean under bins, sacks, and other containers in which food materials are stored (Chapter VIII); and (6) if at all feasible, practice careful temperature control. Refrigerated storage provides excellent protection since none of the insect pests remain active at these low temperatures. In food service operations where refrigeration facilities are used for dry foods, items such as cereals, cocoa, chocolate, dried beans, powdered milk, dried fruit, nuts, and the like can be successfully stored for prolonged periods without risking losses caused by the activities of insects.

Control of insects in a food service establishment has been discussed by Johnson (1960), Scott and Littig (1962), and Scott (1963). A leaflet by the Entomology Research Division of the Agricultural Research Service (1962) deals with cockroaches and their control.

GENERAL ENVIRONMENTAL SANITATION IN THE CONTROL OF VERMIN

Because of the great importance of environmental sanitation in the control of vermin, the following points need to be reemphasized:

1) Rats, mice, flies, and cockroaches, to mention the most important pests, are attracted to food and odors from food regardless of whether the food is fresh or whether it is beginning to decay, as may be the case when garbage is stored.

2) These vermin are also attracted to human feces and unsanitary toilets.

3) Basic sanitation serves rodent control as well as insect control:
   a. Incoming produce must be kept covered, preferably in a screened area. The area must be kept clean from spills and wastes.
   b. Empty containers, crates, boxes, and the like must be disposed of frequently and regularly, and never left accessible to vermin overnight.
   c. Garbage and rubbish must be stored in containers constructed of durable metal or other materials which do not absorb odors, do not corrode, and are easily cleaned. The

containers should not leak. Garbage and rubbish cans should be covered with tight lids, unless they are stored in waste refrigerators or in vermin- and odor-proof rooms. Garbage should be removed frequently. Garbage containers should be thoroughly cleaned using special brushes and be decontaminated using hot (180°F) water or steam.

d. Food waste grinders must be installed in accordance with the regulations of the state and local health authorities, be suitably constructed, and be operated properly to prevent insanitary conditions in the food preparation area.

e. Toilet facilities must be kept immaculately clean and in excellent working order.

f. The floors and equipment in the areas where food is stored, prepared, and served should be maintained in a state of excellent repair and cleanliness. Regular inspection and cleaning schedules and efficient methods of cleaning are basic sanitary measures which will deprive vermin of shelter, food, and drink.

## Sewage, Water, Soil, Air

*Sanitary Sewage Disposal; Plumbing; Toilet Facilities*

### SEWAGE DISPOSAL

Sewage is one of the most dangerous sources of human pathogens (Chapter V) and should not make any contact whatever with food, drink, equipment, utensils, and any other surfaces which make contact with food. Therefore, sanitary sewage disposal is a prerequisite for good food sanitation. Sanitary sewage disposal should prevent the contamination of the ground and the water supply; it should also preclude access of rodents and flies to human feces. Proper sewage disposal is apt to be of special concern to those who operate temporary food service establishments. To prevent serious hazards from improper sewage disposal the U.S. Public Health Service recommends in the Food Service Sanitation Manual (1962) that "All sewage shall be disposed of in a public sewerage system, or, in the absence thereof, in a manner approved by the health authority."

In compliance with the above regulations set up by the Public Health Service, the following requirements should be met, as stated in the Food Service Sanitation Manual (U.S. PHS, 1962):

a. *Water-Carried Sewage:*
  (1) All water-carried sewage shall be disposed of by means of:
    (a) A public sewerage system; or

      (b)  An approved sewage disposal system which is constructed and operated in conformance with applicable State and local laws, ordinances, and regulations.

   *b.  Non-Water-Carried Sewage:\**
     (1)  Non-water-carried sewage-disposal facilities shall not be used, except where water-carried disposal methods have been determined by the health authority to be impractical. Under such conditions, only facilities which have been approved by the health authoritiy shall be used, and operation of these facilities shall be in conformance with applicable state and local laws, ordinances, and regulations.

## PLUMBING

Proper and sanitary plumbing is extremely important in food sanitation. If plumbing is not properly installed or is not properly maintained, serious troubles will ensue. Among these, back siphonage, stoppages, and cross-connections with the water system have frequently caused contamination in the food preparation and storage areas, with serious consequences. Leakage of sewer pipes is another common problem which must be kept under control. For the control of hazards from faulty sewerage plumbing, the U.S. Public Health Service states in the Food Service Sanitation Manual (1962):

> Plumbing shall be so sized, installed, and maintained as to carry adequate quantities of water to required locations throughout the establishment; as to prevent contamination of the water supply; as to properly convey sewage and liquid wastes from the establishment to the sewerage or sewage-disposal system; and so that it does not constitute a source of contamination of food, equipment, or utensils, or create an insanitary condition of nuisance.

The recommendation for compliance with these regulations is that all plumbing should conform to applicable State and local plumbing laws, regulations, and ordinances.

There are also specific recommendations concerning drains from dishwashers, steam kettles, refrigerating units, and vegetable peelers, in that these drains should be prevented from causing back flow of sewerage or flooding of floors. The latter trouble is a common one in some basements. Unfortunately, storage rooms are also frequently located in basements and may become subjected to flooding which contain raw sewage.

The local health authority should be consulted regarding the appropriate solutions to problems arising in connection with the sanitary aspects of plumbing.

---

\* Suggested standards and recommended practices are contained in Reprint No. 2461, from Public Health Reports–1950, "Individual Sewage Disposal Systems," and in Public Health Service Publication No. 526, *Manual of Septic Tank Practice*, and addendum dated August 1, 1959.

TOILET FACILITIES

Toilets must be of sanitary design, maintained in good working order, used properly, and kept in clean condition. Insanitary toilet facilities attract flies and other insects; they also are a hazard to clothing and hands of the food handler using the facility.

Management has a responsibility to see to it that toilets are adequate in number, construction, and maintenance. The following regulations are stated in the Food Service Sanitation Manual (U.S. PHS, 1962):

> Each food-service establishment shall be provided with adequate, conveniently located toilet facilities for its employees. Toilet fixtures shall be of sanitary design and readily cleanable. Toilet facilities, including rooms and fixtures, shall be kept in a clean condition and in good repair. The doors of all toilet rooms shall be self-closing. Toilet tissues shall be provided. Easily cleanable receptacles shall be provided for waste materials, and such receptacles in toilet rooms for women shall be covered. Where the use of non-water-carried sewage-disposal facilities have been approved by the health authority, such facilities shall be separate from the establishment. When toilet facilities are provided for patrons, such facilities shall meet the requirements of this subsection.

In compliance with these regulations, the Public Health Service has suggested that the following requirements be met: (1) that toilet facilities be conveniently located and accessible to the employees at all times; (2) that they conform to applicable state and local regulations, ordinances and laws, or be approved by the health authority; (3) that the design of stools and urinal be sanitary; (4) that the toilet rooms be completely enclosed and have tight-fitting, self-closing doors; (5) that the maintenance of toilets pertain to repair and regular cleaning of rooms and fixtures, control of odors, constant supply of toilet paper, and provision for waste receptacles; and (6) that provision be made for hand-washing facilities such as sinks, warm water, and adequate supply of soap, paper towels, and waste receptacles. The recommendation of the Public Health Services reads:

> Each food-service establishment shall be provided with adequate, conveniently located hand-washing facilities for its employees, including a lavatory or lavatories equipped with hot and cold or tempered running water, hand-cleansing soap or detergent, and approved sanitary towels or other approved hand-drying devices. Such facilities shall be kept clean and in good repair.

Knee-operated faucets are more sanitary than hand-operated faucets. In principle foot-operated faucets should be sanitary also. However, cleaning of the area between the foot pedal and the floor is inconvenient and apt to be slighted.

*Water*

The importance of potable water in a food facility has been discussed in Chapters V and IX. If contaminated water is used in a food service establishment, serious trouble will result.

In establishments where city water is used, the only control the food service manager needs to exert is to prevent the contamination of the potable water supply from faulty plumbing, as was discussed above.

The recommendations of the Public Health Service (1962) are:

> The water supply shall be adequate, of a safe, sanitary quality, and from an approved source. Hot and cold running water, under pressure, shall be provided in all areas where food is prepared, or equipment, utensils, or containers are washed.
>
> Water, if not piped into the establishment, shall be transported and stored in approved containers, and shall be handled and dispensed in a sanitary manner.
>
> Ice used for any purpose shall be made from water which comes from an approved source, and shall be used only if it has been manufactured, stored, transported, and handled in a sanitary manner.

When potable water is not piped into a food service establishment, the health authority must be consulted for applicable regulations. For information of what such regulations might be concerned with, the reader is referred to the recommendations of the U.S. Public Health Service (Food Service Sanitation Manual, Section E, 1962).

*Soil, Air*

Soil is carried into the food service establishment by way of doors, windows, airshafts, and ventilation systems, on employees' shoes and other clothing and on certain foods and their wrappings (Chapters V, IX). The control of soil in the kitchen is achieved by measures preventing its entry and by its prompt removal. If the outdoor air is dusty, doors and windows may have to be shut and ventilation may have to be accomplished through intake systems equipped with filters. Filters, where used, must be readily removable for cleaning or replacement.

It is very important to maintain intake air ducts well, or they may admit contaminated particles and insects.

All ventilation systems must comply with applicable local or state laws pertaining to fire prevention. Also, ventilating systems should not constitute a nuisance to the neighborhood.

Employees' street shoes can be eliminated as an important source of soil if they are exchanged for shoes worn only indoors.

Root vegetables and other foods and wrappings which can be a source of soil should be kept out of the area where cooked food is prepared.

In general, the food service manager should analyze his establishment for actual or potential sources of soil and apply appropriate control measures. Daily cleaning of floors and frequent cleaning of walls, hoods, ceilings, and other dust-catching surfaces is a basic requirement for the control of soil. Foods such as baked goods allowed to be held in the kitchen before serving should be covered to protect them from dust.

## The Food Supply

### Foods Serving as Potential Sources of Bacteria Capable of Causing Outbreaks of Foodborne Illnesses

Foods serving as important reservoirs of pathogens capable of causing foodborne illnesses have been discussed in Chapters VI and VII; the paths of contamination in the food preparation area have been presented in Chapter IX and purchasing procedures for the procurement of wholesome foods were outlined in Chapter VIII.

In this chapter, the fact should be reemphasized that certain food items, even when produced and processed under high sanitary standards, must be treated as potential sources of pathogenic bacteria. Therefore, control measures directed at preventing these foods from contacting cooked and vulnerable food items are a must. Vulnerable are all the so-called potentially hazardous items, namely, "any perishable food which consists in whole or in part of milk or milk products, eggs, meat, poultry, fish, shellfish, or other ingredients capable of supporting rapid and progressive growth of infectious or toxigenic microorganisms" (U.S. PHS, Food Service Sanitation Manual, 1962).

### Meat, Poultry

Among the foods of animal origin, two stand out as carrying a microbial flora which frequently includes bacteria capable of causing foodborne illnesses; these are meat and poultry which have not undergone processing to destroy pathogenic contaminants. Contaminating pathogens frequently associated with meats and poultry are strains of *Salmonella*, *Clostridium perfringens*, and the fecal streptococci and, to a lesser extent, strains of *Staphylococcus aureus*.

Canned products have all pathogenic contaminants removed. Products processed by mild heating are not sterile, however, and cannot be completely eliminated as a potential source of the above-named contaminants, however poor this source may be.

## Control in Storage

Meat and poultry and the products made from them, except the canned (sterilized) products, should be kept in a separate refrigerator. If the raw items are stored along with cooked foods, there is danger of cross-contamination (see Chapter IX).

It is most important that cooked and partially cooked foods should always be stored in a refrigerator designated for the sole purpose of storing this kind of food. Even then they must be protected from contamination from soil possibly adhering to containers and shelving. They should be covered; and containers should be stored off the floor, on dollies or racks.

## Control in Food Preparation Area

### PHYSICAL REMOVAL OF CONTAMINANTS

Washing is effective in removing bacteria, provided that running water is used and the bacteria are flushed away. Not all foods can, or should be, washed. However, whenever washing is indicated to remove soil, many bacteria also will go down the drain. All raw fruits and vegetables must be washed before being cooked or served. Moldy foods should be discarded.

### ELIMINATING CHANCES FOR CROSS-CONTAMINATION

Separate surfaces should be used for the cutting, cubing, and portioning of raw meats and poultry, and for cooked food items. There is no easier way for cooked foods to become contaminated with pathogens such as *Salmonella* and *Clostridium perfringens* than by contact with contaminated work surfaces.

Other equipment commonly used for raw meat and poultry as well as for cooked items are grinders, choppers, and the like. Separate equipment for raw and cooked items is not required for this kind of equipment, provided that it is thoroughly cleaned and sanitized after each use. Appropriate cleaning and sanitizing will be discussed later on in this chapter.

Because frequent cleaning is time consuming, some large institutions have a separate area where raw meats and poultry are handled and separate equipment is provided.

## Eggs

Dirty cracked shell eggs and egg products processed from unpasteurized raw material could serve as a source of pathogens, especially of salmonellae. Control measures mentioned earlier are the purchase of clean and high-grade shell eggs and the purchase of egg products specified to come from pasteurized raw material. Legislation pertaining to the pasteurization of egg magma used in the freezing and drying processess should, in the future, eliminate the danger of salmonellae from these egg products.

*Fish and Other Items*

Fresh fish which needs cleaning and portioning is used in institutional food services in some parts of this country. If raw fish must be handled, it should be kept separate from cooked items; precautions used for raw meat and poultry apply to raw fish also.

All uncooked materials are unsterile and present a threat to cooked and sterile foods, especially the items which are good media for bacterial growth, namely, the "potentially hazardous" items, and those which are apt to carry a flora of pathogenic contaminants.

## The Food Worker's Hands

In handling foods which are potential sources of pathogens, the food handler's hands play a very important role. Hands and their significance in food sanitation have been discussed previously on several occasions; however, the importance of hands in connection with the transfer of pathogens from uncooked to cooked food items is so great that they must be mentioned again. Each time a worker has had contact with uncooked items, which must be suspected of carrying pathogens, he must wash his hands before handling cooked items. Unfortunately, the lack of a conveniently located sink is frequently the reason that he does not wash them. If handwashing facilities are distant, he will, instead of washing his hands, use his apron, a towel, dishcloth, or whatever is at hand. This kind of cleaning does not do the job. In fact, the cloth used may spread contaminants to the next person picking it up and using it.

In some food service establishments it is customary to use food preparation sinks for handwashing. This is not a good idea since the sink, as well as the food it is used for, becomes contaminated.

In principle, the use of hands in the preparation of potentially hazardous food is to be discouraged. The Public Health Service recommends that "meat salads, poultry salads, potato salads, egg salads, cream filled pastries and other potentially hazardous prepared food shall be prepared (preferably from chilled products) with a minimum of manual contact, and on surfaces which are clean and which, prior to use, have been sanitized" (Food Service Sanitation Manual, 1962). Convenient and suitable utensils should be provided and should be used in the preparation as well as in the service of these items.

### Control of Secondary Sources of Contaminants

## Sanitary Equipment and Utensils

### Sources of Contaminants

Equipment and utensils have many chances of becoming contaminated. Knowing the source of contamination will aid in the understanding and the application of effective measures.

Equipment and utensils are known to have become contaminated with pathogens which come from the human reservoir, from rodents and insects, from sewage originating from faulty pipes and drains, from nonpotable water, from condensates created in connection with faulty ventilation, and from contaminated food.

### Sanitary Design, Construction, Installation

The reasons equipment and utensils of poor design, construction, and installation may become important sources of contaminants have been discussed in Chapter IX. It was shown that such equipment and utensils, poorly repaired and maintained may harbor food residues which serve as media in which bacteria may multiply. It was also pointed out that food residues may attract vermin.

It has also been shown (Chapter III) that equipment and utensils made with zinc, lead, and cadmium may lead to metal food poisoning if contact is allowed between the metal and acid foods or beverages.

The Food Sanitation Manual of the U.S. Public Health Service (1962) states that:

> All equipment and utensils shall be so designed and of such material and workmanship as to be smooth, easily cleanable, and durable, and shall be in good repair; and the food-contact surfaces of such equipment and utensils shall, in addition, be easily accessible for cleaning, nontoxic, corrosion resistant, and relatively nonabsorbent: *Provided*, that, when approved by the health authority, exceptions may be made to the above materials requirements for equipment such as cutting boards, blocks and bakers' tables.
>
> All equipment shall be so installed and maintained as to facilitate the cleaning thereof, and of all adjacent areas.
>
> Equipment in use at the time of adoption of this ordinance which does not meet fully the above requirements may be continued in use if it is in good repair, capable of being maintained in a sanitary condition, and the food contact surfaces are nontoxic.
>
> Single-service articles shall be made from nontoxic materials.

Control measures pertaining to the design, construction, and materials have been greatly aided by some fundamental efforts in the development of standards. The Public Health Service cooperates with several agencies in developing these standards: the National Sanitation Foundation, the Baking Industry Sanitation Standards Committee, the Automatic Merchandizing Health Industry Council, and the Committee for 3-A Sanitation Standards for Dairy Equipment are examples. For food service equipment and utensils, the main points emphasized pertain to:

1) Durability and capability of withstanding scrubbing and the corrosive action of foods as well as of cleaning and sanitizing agents
2) Smoothness; good state of repair; cleanability of movable and in-place equipment
3) Nontoxicity of base materials and solders
4) Freedom from hard-to-clean corners and crevices
5) Accessibility for cleaning
6) Sanitary design of spouts, corners, seams, and lubricated bearings and gears

Of interest is the fact that in these recommendations the use of wooden cutting blocks and boards is not eliminated; this would probably be too unrealistic. However, it is recommended that cutting blocks and boards and bakers' tables be of hard maple or equivalent material which is nontoxic, smooth, and free of open places such as faulty seams, crevices, and cracks.

Actually, wood has been eliminated as a meat-contact surface in some institutions. Cutting boards of hard rubber, as well as metal pushers for grinders and choppers, have been substituted for the implements made of wood. Undoubtedly, wood is one of the most difficult materials to sanitize. The detailed recommendations are presented in Section D of the Food Service Sanitation Manual (U.S. PHS, 1962).

Control measures pertaining to installation of equipment on tables and counters include mounting which will facilitate cleaning of the equipment itself as well as the surrounding area. Control measures pertaining to floor-mounted equipment include sealing to the floor; or mounting on raised platforms of concrete, with the purpose to control the seeping and settling of liquid and debris into inaccessible places; or elevating such equipment several, at least 6, inches from the floor. In any case, all mountings should be such that cleaning is easily achieved and no hidden places are left where food and moisture can collect.

Further specifications deal with aisle space and spaces between pieces of equipment; these should be large enough to allow the employees to move about freely without danger of contaminating food through contact with their body parts or clothing.

Attention is also called to a listing of NSF Standards and Criteria presented under "Additional Readings" at the end of this chapter. A Manual on Installation of Food Service Equipment is being prepared (Farish, 1965). The standards and criteria were developed through the cooperation of the NSF with industry groups and with a Joint Committee on Equipment Standards. In this Joint Committee leading official health and sanitation organizations are represented along with dietitians, food service consultants and engineers, the restaurant industry, and the Armed Forces.

The NSF authorizes the use of the NSF Seal of Approval for equipment which has been constructed in accordance with NSF criteria, tested in NSF laboratories, and approved.

Some other NSF Seal of Approval programs deal with tests and evaluation of plastics for containers for potable water and for various other purposes of interest from a sanitation point of view.

The buyer of institutional equipment and kitchenware should make use of the excellent services of the NSF and include NSF approval when setting up their specifications.

VENDING MACHINES

Vending machines are moving into food service establishments in ever-increasing numbers. Therefore, the sanitary aspects of the design and construction of these machines need to be discussed. Many items dispensed from the machines are of a highly perishable nature.

The National Sanitation Foundation (1963) classifies vending machines on the basis of dispensing one or more of the foods and beverages categorized as follows:

Class No.  1:    Hot bulk food or beverage
Class No.  2:    Cold bulk food or beverage
Class No.  3:    Hot packaged food or beverage
Class No.  4:    Cold packaged food or beverage
Class No.  5:    Hot readily perishable bulk food or beverage
Class No.  6:    Cold readily perishable bulk food or beverage
Class No.  7:    Hot readily perishable packaged food or beverage
Class No.  8:    Cold readily perishable packaged food or beverage
Class No.  9:    Bulk food or beverage
Class No. 10:    Packaged food or beverage

The NSF suggests that the manufacturer should affix to the interior of the vending machine a plate showing the class or classes of food and/or beverages which can be dispensed in accordance with the NSF Seal of Approval Listing.

Vending has introduced problems not normally encountered in conventional food service establishments. In the interest of uniformity, industry and health authorities (state and local) have requested the Public Health Service to develop an ordinance and code stating requirements for machine design and construction and for operation procedures. The ordinance and code have been adopted by numerous states and local jurisdictions.

Construction features of importance are these: that the machine be of sturdy construction and be so designed, fabricated, and finished as to facilitate its being kept clean externally and internally and to keep out rodents and insects. The interior should be so finished that all product contact surfaces are smooth, nontoxic, corrosion resistant, relatively non-absorbent, and should withstand repeated cleaning and sanitizing treatments of accepted procedure. All food-contact surfaces should be protected against contamination. For compliance regulations, the reader is referred to the "Ordinance and Code" (U.S. PHS, 1965).

Basic and special criteria for the evaluation of manually activated and/or coin-activated vending machines for foods and/or beverages have been adopted by the Joint Committee on Food Equipment Standards in cooperation with representatives of industry, including users of such equipment; they were approved by the Council of Public Health Consultants, published in 1958 by the National Sanitation Foundation and revised in 1963.

The local health authority should be consulted by food service operators who wish to install vending machines. Advice may be sought from the National Automatic Merchandising Association, Chicago, Illinois. This organization sponsors machine evaluation facilities at the Michigan State and Indiana University Schools of Public Health and maintains a listing of machines certified to meet code requirements. The first responsibility of the vending operator is to install only equipment which meets public health standards. For discussion of other problems in connection with vending see Chapter XIII.

## Cleaning of Equipment and Utensils

### CLEANING

An effective cleaning job should remove soil from equipment. However, both the "when" and the "how" of cleaning are essential.

If the principles of sanitation are to be effectively applied, the time factor is of tremendous importance: not only is cleaning immediately after use more easily effected, but the time span, which might allow bacterial populations to increase greatly, is reduced. A grinder, for example, in which meat was ground, or a slicer, or a chopping board used for slicing and portioning of meat, if left unattended for more than the "danger time" may be teeming with bacteria and thus represent a dangerously rich source of contaminants in the food preparation area. The dangers of contamination of cooked, sterile food by soiled equipment, although mentioned several times before, should be stressed again. In gastroenteric episodes caused by *Salmonella* and *Clostridium perfringens*, the contaminated equipment is frequently found to be an important link in the chain of events.

Therefore, cleaning must eliminate the contaminants. Effective cleaning involves the prompt removal of food particles after the close of the operation during which the equipment is used; or, if the equipment is used for extended periods, at predetermined intervals spaced to prevent microbial buildup. For example, if a piece of equipment is used all day, a cleaning schedule must insure well-spaced cleaning operations during the day. The higher the room or kitchen temperature, the shorter the intervals should be between cleanings. The cleaning schedule in such continuous operations should be acceptable to the health authority.

There are these basic steps to cleaning:

1) Scraping, possibly additional soaking to remove gross soil, followed by prerinsing.
2) Washing in hot (120°F) water containing a suitable detergent, using a stiff brush and "elbow grease."
3) Rinsing in hot (140°F) water.
4) Sanitizing, when required, using 170–180°F water; a booster may have to be installed to provide water sufficiently hot. In an emergency, appropriate chemical agents of appropriate strength may have to be substituted for hot water.
5) Air drying.

In the Food Service Sanitation Manual (U.S. PHS, 1962), the following statement is made:

All eating and drinking utensils shall be thoroughly cleaned and sanitized after each usage.

All kitchenware and food-contact surfaces of equipment, exclusive of cooking surfaces of equipment, used in the preparation of serving of food or drink, and all food-storage utensils, shall be thoroughly cleaned after each use. Cooking surfaces of equipment shall be cleaned at least once a day. All utensils and food-contact surfaces of equipment used in the preparation, service, display, or storage of potentially hazardous food shall be thoroughly cleaned and sanitized prior to such use. Non-food-contact surfaces of equipment shall be cleaned at such intervals as to keep them in a clean and sanitary condition.

After cleaning and until use, all food-contact surfaces of equipment and utensils shall be so stored and handled as to be protected from contamination.

All single-service articles shall be stored, handled, and dispensed in a sanitary manner, and shall be used only once.

Food-service establishments which do not have adequate and effective facilities for cleaning and sanitizing utensils shall use single-service articles.

For full details the reader is referred to Section D of the Food Service Sanitation Manual (U.S. PHS, 1962).

SANITIZING

Sanitizing involves "effective bactericidal treatment of clean surfaces of equipment and utensils by a process which has been approved by the health authority as being effective in destroying microorganisms, including pathogens" (Food Service Sanitation Manual, 1962). The effort spent in sanitizing is wasted unless a thorough job of cleaning by which all soil is removed has preceded the sanitizing procedure.

In the Manual is stated that:

1) All tableware should be sanitized, after each use.
2) All kitchenware and food-contact surfaces of equipment being used in the preparation, service, and storage of "potentially hazardous foods" should be sanitized prior to such use. Sanitizing should also be done following interruption during which contamination may have occurred and at regular intervals when equipment is used on a prolonged or all-day basis.

Actually, the requirement to sanitize applies to almost all equipment and all utensils used in food preparation; there are few exceptions. Detailed information is given on the methodology employed in washing and sanitizing equipment and utensils in Section D of the Food Service Sanitation Manual (1962).

The sanitizing procedure may take one of three paths:

1) Immersion for at least one-half minute in clean hot water, 170–180°F; this is the method applicable to most situations where food is prepared for and served to the public.
2) Use of a sanitizing solution approved by the health authority (suggestions for chemicals and strength are given in the Manual). Chemical sanitizing may have to take the place of hot water, if the latter is not available.
3) For large equipment use of live steam from a hose or rinsing

with boiling water; or spraying with a sanitizing solution twice the minimum strength required for small equipment sanitized by immersion.

Many factors must be taken into consideration when applying any physical or chemical agents to destroy bacterial populations. When using hot water, time–temperature effects must be considered. When using disinfectants, toxicity to microorganisms and nontoxicity to humans, solubility, noncorrosiveness, freedom from odor, and capacity to avoid combination with organic (food) materials are important factors to consider, along with homogeneity, capacity to penetrate, deodorizing capacity, detergent capacity, and such considerations as cost and availability.

A three-compartment sink is required whenever washing and sanitizing of equipment and utensils are done by hand. For equipment and utensils not used in the preparation of potentially hazardous foods, like bread pans, a two-compartment sink may be used for washing the kitchenware which need not be sanitized. However, most utensils and equipment are used at one time or another in connection with potentially hazardous foods. Also, even for bakeshops, a three-compartment sink might be more practical and usable for soaking, washing, and rinsing.

Mechanical dishwashing operations and the principles underlying them have been so well covered elsewhere that they will not be included in the present discussion (see "Additional Readings" at end of this chapter).

For years, much attention has been given to cleaning and sanitizing tableware, and good dishwashing procedures are now generally well accepted and applied in this country. Unfortunately, however, this cannot be said for the cleaning and sanitizing of food preparation equipment and utensils. This is indeed a serious situation, and must be remedied. For example, one contaminated pan in which a potentially hazardous item such as cream filling or turkey salad is stored, one contaminated slicer on which a roast is sliced, may make hundreds of persons ill. These possibilities are not yet fully appreciated by many food service operators.

STORAGE OF CLEAN EQUIPMENT AND UTENSILS

Whether simply washed, or washed and sanitized, all cleaned implements must be kept clean and prevented from being recontaminated. Knives, forks, spoons, whips, spatulas, and the like should be picked up by their handles and stored away from dust. All small equipment and utensils should be stored on airy racks off the floor and be protected from dust. Pots, pans, and other containers should be inverted. Fixed equipment, after cleaning, should also be protected by suitable means.

### SINGLE-SERVICE ARTICLES

These articles are used only once; until used they should be stored in closed cartons, inaccessible to contamination from dust, persons, rodents, insects, etc. At all times, these articles must be handled in a way which will prevent contamination of surfaces which make contact with the food or the user's lips.

## Vending

Regular and efficient cleaning is essential to vending sanitation. Cleaning should pertain to the machines themselves as well as the surroundings.

### GENERAL AREA

As was stated earlier, the location of the machines is of importance since there should be no constant sources of dangerous contaminants such as overhead sewer pipes and excessive dust.

There should be a sufficient number of receptacles for trash, and these should be prevented from overflowing by regular servicing. If a sanitation room is provided by management where parts of the machine may be washed and sanitized, this room should be kept in an immaculate state of cleanliness.

### VENDING OPERATIONS

Almost all vending facilities are operated by vending specialists, or operators, who own and install the equipment, provide the food, and service the machines; the services include cleaning operations.

The PHS Service Ordinance and Code (U.S. PHS, 1965) contains provisions for servicing and sanitation of vending machines used to dispense milk and other foods. Some regulations for milk are these:

All parts of any bulk milk vending machine which come into direct contact with the milk or milk product shall be effectively cleaned and sanitized at the milk plant: *Provided,* That single-service dispensing tubes which receive sanitizing treatment at the fabricating plant and which are individually packaged in such manner as to preclude contamination, may be exempted from this provision. The can or other bulk milk container shall be filled only at the milk plant and shall be sealed in such manner as to make it impractical to withdraw any part of its contents or to introduce any substance without breaking the seal or seals. The delivery tube and any milk-contact parts of the dispensing device shall be attached at the milk plant, and shall be protected by a moisture-proof covering, or housed in a compartment with a moisture-tight closure which shall not be removed until after the container is placed in the refrigerated compartment of the vending machine.

Regulations pertaining to foods other than milk say:

... all multiuse containers or parts of vending machines which come into direct contact with potentially hazardous food shall be removed from the machine daily and shall be thoroughly cleaned and effectively sanitized at the commissary or other approved facility: *Provided*, That the requirement for daily cleaning and sanitizing may be waived for those food-contact surfaces which are maintained at all times at a temperature of 45°F. or below, or 140°F. or above, whichever is applicable, and an approved cleaning frequency is followed. Such parts shall, after sanitizing, be protected from contamination.

Other regulations, dealing with the less perishable foods, specify that the methods used for cleaning and frequency of cleaning must conform with the regulations of the health authority and that a record of cleaning operations must be maintained by the vendor in each machine, and that it must show the record for the past 30 days at least.

SUPPLEMENTAL EQUIPMENT AND UTENSILS

Condiment dispensers sometimes create a sanitary nuisance because of spattering and use by many careless hands. Can openers not frequently cleaned may represent a real health hazard. All such equipment and utensils must be subjected to frequent and effective cleaning.

Recommendations are also made for the purchase, storage, and handling of single-service containers.

## Sanitation of the Physical Plant

### Construction, Repair, and Cleaning

Proper construction, good repair, and appropriate cleaning of floors, walls, and ceilings are part and parcel of good plant sanitation (see Chapter IX).

In the Food Service Sanitation Manual (U.S. PHS, 1962) the following statement is made:

The floor surfaces in kitchens, in all other rooms and areas in which food is stored or prepared and in which utensils are washed, and in walk-in refrigerators, dressing or locker rooms, and toilet rooms, shall be of smooth, non-absorbent materials, and so constructed as to be easily cleanable; *Provided*, that the floors of non-refrigerated, dry-food-storage areas need not be non-absorbent. All floors shall be kept clean and in good repair. Floor drains shall be provided in all rooms where floors are subjected to flooding-type cleaning or where normal operations release or discharge water or other liquid waste on the floor. All exterior areas where food is served shall be kept clean and properly drained, and surfaces in such areas shall be finished so as to facilitate maintenance and minimize dust.

The walls and ceilings of all rooms shall be kept clean and in good repair. All walls of rooms or areas in which food is prepared, or utensils or hands are washed, shall be easily cleanable, smooth, and light-colored, and shall have washable surfaces up to the highest level reached by splash or spray.

In compliance with these requirements the floors should be of smooth, durable, cleanable, non-absorbent materials. Suggested are terrazzo ceramic tile, concrete, good grade plastic or linoleum, or dense wood impregnated with plastic. Floor drains are an essential feature in situations where water flushing must be used for cleaning. A coved juncture between floor and wall is required for all concrete, terrazzo, and ceramic tile floors installed in the areas of food preparation, storage and utensil washing, walk-in refrigerators, dressing rooms, locker rooms, and toilet rooms.

Wall coverings should leave no open spaces or cracks which might accommodate vermin and permit accumulation of dust, grease, and other debris.

### REFRIGERATORS

The importance of sanitary care of refrigerators and freezers cannot be overemphasized. Care should include these basic points: maintaining the mechanical parts in good working conditions; preventing the accumulation of food items; and cleaning. Unfortunately, the care of refrigerator storage often leaves much to be desired.

Refrigeration units, whether they serve coolers or freezers, are complex and intricate mechanisms and require the know-how and skill of an expert for maintenance or repair of certain components. A schedule of systematic inspections by a specialist is recommended. The manufacturer or distributor should suggest the service agency to consult with regard to appropriate maintenance and repair. The manufacturer may also suggest points of refrigerator maintenance which can be followed through by the regular staff employed by the food service establishment.

It is important to remember that the warm summer months place heaviest demands on refrigeration equipment; therefore, a thorough checkup previous to those months is desirable. Doors should be inspected for faulty gaskets, hinges, and latches. Drains must be kept clean at all times. Poor maintenance of drains causes foul odor, corrosion, and general unsanitary conditions, and may lead to the destruction of the insulating materials in the refrigerator. Regular, careful cleaning, followed by flushing with baking soda in warm water, is recommended.

Defrosting should precede cleaning of coolers and freezers unless these automatically defrost. Above-freezing temperature type refrigerators should be defrosted at least once weekly. Freezers need defrosting when the frost builds up to approximately ¼ inch. Heavy coats of ice on evaporators act as insulators and overwork the compressors.

Before cleaning refrigerating units, food items, as well as shelves, hooks, dollies, and other accessories, should be removed. Walls, floors, and accessories should be thoroughly washed. Baked-enamel or stainless steel surfaces should be cleaned with a mild soap or detergent solution and then rinsed with clear water.

Coolers and freezers are not to be used as catch-alls. Coolers should be checked daily and freezers at regular frequent intervals to insure that food is being stored in appropriate containers or securely wrapped. Employees should be taught the proper procedure for storage.

VENTILATION

Hoods should be regularly inspected for, and maintained in, good working order and kept clean from accumulations of dust and grease; regular cleaning schedules should be set up.

The Manual (1962) of the U.S. Public Health Service has this to say:

> All rooms in which food is prepared or served or utensils are washed, dressing or locker rooms, toilet rooms, and garbage and rubbish storage areas shall be well ventilated. Ventilation hoods and devices shall be designed to prevent grease or condensate from dripping into food or onto food-preparation surfaces. Filters, where used, shall be readily removable for cleaning or replacement. Ventilation systems shall comply with applicable State and local fire prevention requirements and shall, when vented to the outside air, discharge in such manner as not to create a nuisance.

LIGHTING

Ample, properly distributed light must be available for preparing and serving food in a sanitary way. Certainly, effective cleaning and handwashing are not possible unless the employees see what they are doing. According to the Manual (1962) of the U.S. Public Health Service, compliance with the requirement of good lighting involves provision of at least 20 foot-candles of light on all working surfaces, less intense light being required for certain other strategic places where food is cooked, utensils washed, hands washed, and the like. The reader is referred to this important publication for full details.

GENERAL HOUSEKEEPING

Good housekeeping is most essential in the food service establishment and should pertain to every part of it through appropriately spaced schedules for cleaning and other activities related to the sanitary upkeep of the establishment. The following steps are essential: first, establish the requirements for the cleaning program; second, provide the tools; third, show the method; fourth, supervise the job and inspect the results.

A sample of a checklist suggested by the Public Health Service (1962) for inspection reports on the sanitation of food service establishments is presented in Chapter XIV.

## References

Bjornson, B. F. (1960). "Control of Domestic Rats and Mice." U. S. Department of Health, Education and Welfare, Public Health Service, PHS Publication No. 563.

Entomology Research Division, Agricultural Research Service. (1962). "Cockroaches—How to Control Them." U. S. Department of Agriculture Leaflet No. 430. Revised.

Farish, C. A. (1965). "Sanitary Design and Evaluation of Food Service Equipment." *Jour. Milk & Food Tech.*, *28*(8): 252–256.

Johnson, Wilfred H. (1960). "Sanitation in the Control of Insects and Rodents of Public Health Importance." U. S. Department of Health, Education and Welfare, Communicable Disease Center, PHS Publication No. 772. Training Guide: Insect Control Series Part 4.

National Sanitation Foundation. (1963). "Basic and Special Criteria for the Evaluation of Manually Activated and/or Coin Activated Vending Machines for Food and/or Beverages." No. C–1. Ann Arbor, Michigan.

Scott, H. G. (1963). "Household and Stored-Food Insects of Public Health Importance." U. S. Department of Health, Education and Welfare, Public Health Service, Communicable Disease Center, Atlanta Georgia. PHS Publication No. 772. Training Guide: Insect Control Series Part 12.

Scott, H. G., and K. S. Littig. (1962). "Flies of Public Health Importance and Their Control." U. S. Department of Health, Education and Welfare, Public Health Service, Communicable Disease Center, Atlanta, Georgia. PHS Publication No. 772. Training Guide: Insect Control Series, Part 4.

Stauffer, Lee. (1964). "Sanitation in Hospital Food Service." *Hospitals, 38:* 162–169, July 16; 80–87, Aug. 1; 84–88, Aug. 16; 116–121, Sept. 1; 88–97, Sept. 16.

U. S. Department of Health, Education and Welfare, Public Health Service. (1962). "Food Service Sanitation Manual." PHS Publication No. 934. Washington, D.C.

U.S. Department of Health Education and Welfare, Public Health Service. (1965). "The Vending of Food and Beverages." A Sanitation Ordinance and Code. PHS Publication No. 546. Washington, D.C.

## Additional Readings

Giles, H. C. "Effective Dishwashing Procedures." *School Lunch Jour.*, *13:* 66–67. 1959.

Gunderson, Harold. "Rodent and Insect Control." *School Lunch Jour.*, *13:* 37–39. 1959.

Hartley, David E. "Automatic Merchandizing—75 Years of Progress." *Jour. Milk & Food Tech.*, 25(3): 78–82. 1962.

Hartley, David E. "Sanitation Safeguards in Vending Machine Operation." *The Cornell Hotel and Restaurant Admin. Quart.*, *4*(1): 63–65, 86. 1963.

Hopkins, Edward. *Practice of Sanitation.* 2nd ed. Williams and Wilkins, Baltimore, Md. 1954.

Iverson, R. "Modern Pot and Pan Washing Methods." *School Lunch Jour.*, *13:* 68–71. 1959.

Jasper, H. C. "Cleaning with Acid Detergents." *School Lunch Jour.*, *13:* 44–45. 1959.

Ludewig, E. "Food Sanitation Course." Lecture Notes. Bureau Food and Drugs. New York City Department of Health, New York, N.Y. 1947.

Mallman, W. L. "Factors Involved in Cleaning and Sanitizing." *Jour. Amer. Diet. Assoc.*, *28:* 505–508. 1952.

Merrick, Maxine, and Neil M. Hathaway. "Cleaning Large Equipment—Food Flavor Protection." *School Lunch Jour.*, *13:* 33–35. 1959.

Miller, Samuel. "Sanitation and Dishes—Aspects Old and New." *Jour. Amer. Diet. Assoc.*, *43*(1): 23–28, Part I; 29–33, Part II. 1963.

National Sanitation Foundation. (1964). "Evaluation of Special Equipment and/or Devices." Number C–2. Ann Arbor, Michigan.

National Sanitation Foundation. "National Sanitation Foundation Standards." Ann Arbor, Mich.

NSF Standard No. 1. Soda Fountain and Luncheonette Equipment. 1952.

NSF Standard No. 2. Food Service Equipment and Appurtenances. Revised 1964.

NSF Standard No. 3. Spray-type Dishwashing Machines. 1956.

NSF Standard No. 4. Gas Commercial Cooking and Warming Equipment. Reprinted as amended 1963.

NSF Standard No. 5. Commercial Gas Fired and Electrically Heated Hot Water Generating Equipment. 1960.

NSF Standard No. 6. Dispensing Freezers, Including Recommendations for Installation. 1960.

NSF Standard No. 7. Commercial Refrigerators and Storage Freezers.

NSF Standard No. 8. Commercial Powered Food Preparation Equipment. 1961.

Nolan, A. J. "The Vending Industry Keeps Pace with Public Health." Association of Food and Drug Officials of the U.S., *Quart. Bull.*, *26*(2): 85–91. 1962.

Proud, Dorothy M. "Sanitary Food Handling in Church, Community Centers and Camps." Cornell Extension Bulletin 844. Reprinted 1961.
Ridenour, Gerald M., and E. H. Armbruster. "Bacterial Cleanability of Various Types of Eating Surfaces." *Amer. Jour. Publ. Hlth.*, *43*(2): 138–149. 1953.
"Vending Machine Food Service." Operation Law, Regulations and Interpretive Guide. Ohio Department of Health, Cincinnati, Ohio. Revised 1962.
West, B. B., L. Wood, and V. Harger. *Food Service in Institutions*. 4th ed. John Wiley & Sons, New York. 1965.

# CHAPTER XI

# MULTIPLICATION OF BACTERIAL CONTAMINANTS IN INGREDIENTS AND MENU ITEMS:

## PART I. EFFECT OF FOOD AS SUBSTRATE

This chapter deals with chances for multiplication of contaminants in the areas of food preparation, service, and storage, as affected by the food substrate.

Actually, the factors affecting multiplication under conditions of quantity food service are in principle the same as those applicable to the food processing plant where precooked frozen foods are handled (Chapter VII, Part III). Therefore, the present discussion will emphasize factors of importance to a food service operation. These factors include the nature of ingredients and menu items regarding composition, moisture, physical structure and presence of inhibitors. The effect of the time–temperature relationships during the preparation, service, and storage of ingredients and menu items will be discussed in Chapter XII.

### Effect of Composition, Moisture, Physical Structure, and pH of Foods

Composition

Food items can be grouped on the basis of their ability to support multiplication of organisms which are dangerous from a public health point of view. The Food Service Sanitation Manual of the U.S. Public Health Service (1962) states that

254

POTENTIALLY HAZARDOUS FOOD shall mean any perishable food which consists in whole or in part of milk or milk products, eggs, meat, poultry, fish, shellfish, or other ingredients capable of supporting rapid and progressive growth of infectious or toxigenic microorganisms.

Food items of vegetable origin support growth of pathogens causing gastroenteric outbreaks less readily than do items of animal origin. Exceptions are vegetables of relatively high pH, such as peas and corn. The ability to multiply at low pH varies with the pathogen. Under anaerobic conditions, *Clostridium botulinum* grows well in a variety of vegetable media, including acid ones; the pH values of some common vegetables were previously given (Table 2).

Complete menu items vary much in composition and thus in ability to support bacterial multiplication. Items which contain a preponderance of ingredients of animal origin must be expected to be excellent media for the multiplication of pathogenic bacteria and to be potentially dangerous. The pH of some common menu items will be discussed later.

Of increasing interest are the so-called "synthetic" foods—for example, cream fillings. It has been claimed by some manufacturers that pies made from these cannot support bacterial growth and that they can be marketed without refrigeration.

A synthetic cream filling contains, in general, these basic ingredients: starch, sugars, sodium chloride, artificial and natural flavoring, stabilizers, emulsifiers, preservatives, and other miscellaneous additives. Crisley et al. (1964) set out to check on the advisability of following the manufacturers' claims regarding safety. Using an enterotoxigenic strain of *Staphylococcus aureus*, they inoculated fillings and pies made from synthetic mixes. The results were enlightening. It was found that the fillings, in general, supported the inoculum of *S. aureus* poorly, unless a proteinaceous material was part of the powder. The natural contaminants of the powder showed abundant growth. However, since the powders when made up with water alone result in a product of poor culinary quality, they are usually improved by the baker through addition of some animal proteins such as milk and/or eggs. The authors found that synthetic fillings enriched this way supported growth of the staphylococci very well indeed.

Finally, these same workers studied the effect of the crust on staphylococcal growth. They found that profuse multiplication was achieved even when water alone was used in these fillings. Evidently, some nitrogenous material originating from the flour in the crust, probably wheat gluten, provided enough nourishment for the staphylococci. Since these small amounts were sufficient to support multiplication of *S. aureus* the authors wonder whether in a meringued pie traces of egg white might not provide similar stimulation. More research is needed to clarify the safety of these so-called synthetic products.

McKinley and Clarke (1964) also tested the ability of an imitation cream filling to support growth of food poisoning staphylococci, after two cases of food poisoning were attributed to doughnuts containing such filling, which were dispensed from an unrefrigerated vending machine. It was shown that the three cultures used for this test grew well on the imitation cream filling at 25 and 32°C (77 and 89.6°F). Therefore, it is advised that cooked synthetic fillings be kept refrigerated at all times.

### Moisture

The moisture content of many potentially hazardous foods is sufficient for bacterial multiplication, except when these foods have been dehydrated. For example, contaminants of dried eggs or dried milk will not multiply. However, growth is resumed when the powders are reconstituted. Keeping dry foods dry is a very important sanitary measure.

It has been pointed out by Adame et al. (1960) and McCroan et al. (1964) that lettuce added to dry sandwich fillings introduces moisture which improved the conditions for bacteria to multiply.

### Physical Structure

The effect of the physical structure of food must be considered. When food materials are cubed, chopped, minced, or ground, their surface area is much increased, and the contaminants are spread over these new surfaces. The spread of microorganisms is facilitated by the release of juices liberated by the processes of comminution, peeling, and skinning.

### pH and Inhibitors

*Soups*

Research data pertaining to the response of *Staphylococcus aureus* to change in pH of certain menu items, including soups, were reported by Longrée et al. (1957). The investigation was initiated because information was needed as to the potential hazard of menu items likely to be served in camps, community meal service, social gatherings, and other types of food service in which cooling facilities are frequently inadequate, and where the persons entrusted with the handling of large batches of food are often unaware of bacteriological dangers. A potential source of trouble is the slow cooling and heating rates of large food batches which allow these foods to remain in the danger zone of bacterial multiplication for long periods of time.

The study was divided into two parts. In the first part, information was obtained on the effect on staphylococcal growth of adding various ingredients like meat, fish, and vegetables to liquid bases such as chicken broth, milk, and thin white sauce; the proportions of these ingredients were 3.3, 10, 16.6, 25, 33.3, and 50 per cent. In the second part of the study, complete soups of varying formulation were used as media for the staphylococci. All inoculated mixtures were incubated at 30°C (86°F).

The results showed that in the mixtures containing solid ingredients at a 3.3% level, the counts were highest in chicken broth. However, as the amounts of ingredients were increased, the counts were greatly affected by the kind of ingredient added. In general, counts were higher in mixtures containing peas, corn, mushrooms, green beans, clams, and veal than in mixtures containing potatoes, spinach, asparagus, eggplant, and onion. An inhibitory effect on bacterial growth was exerted by acid ingredients such as tomatoes, canned okra, and green peppers. In general, as the pH of the mixtures approached 4.5, bacterial counts became quite low. However, an inhibitory effect of carrots on bacterial growth of the staphylococci was also observed, and this effect could not be explained on the basis of low pH. Some of the data are given in Table 26.

Table 26. Bacterial Growth and pH in Chicken Broth Mixtures as Affected by Kinds and Amounts of Added Ingredients [Adapted from Longrée and White (1957)]

| Ingredient | pH of Ingredient | No ingredient in broth | | 16.6% ingredient in mixture | | 25.0% ingredient in mixture | |
|---|---|---|---|---|---|---|---|
| | | pH | Log final count per ml. | pH | Log final count per ml. | pH | Log final count per ml. |
| Carrot, fresh | 5.6 | 7.2 | 7.6 | 5.3 | 5.1 | 5.2 | 4.4 |
| Sweet green pepper, fresh | 5.2 | 7.6 | 7.3 | 5.6 | 5.2 | 5.7 | 4.3 |
| Okra, canned | 4.1 | 7.0 | 7.2 | 4.9 | 4.5 | 4.8 | 3.1 |
| Tomato, fresh | 4.3 | 7.5 | 7.5 | 4.5 | 5.6 | 4.3 | 3.3 |
| Veal, fresh | 5.9 | 7.5 | 6.5 | 6.1 | 6.1 | — | 6.8 |
| Green bean, frozen | 5.8 | 7.0 | 8.0 | 5.4 | 7.2 | 5.2 | 7.7 |
| Mushroom, canned | 6.1 | 7.9 | 7.2 | 6.4 | 7.5 | 6.3 | 7.3 |
| Pea, frozen | 6.8 | 6.7 | 7.6 | 6.4 | 7.7 | 6.4 | 8.1 |

In the second part of the study, complete soups of varying formulation were used as substrates for *Staphylococcus aureus*. Formulations were adjusted to include ingredients known to have an inhibitory effect. Bacterial growth response to one or several of these variations were tested: omission of peas; increase in, or addition of, tomatoes; increase in, or addition of, carrots; and increase in, or addition of, green peppers. Culinary acceptability of the soups of different formulation was also determined. Eighteen soups found to be poor supporters of the test organism were listed. Examples of soups of low pH (4.0–4.9) are: soups high in tomato, such as consomme Madrilene; stockless vegetable soup; and tomato bouillon. Examples of soups of high pH (6.0 and above) are: corn chowder, the cream soups except cream of tomato, New England clam chowder, oyster stew, and potato chowder. The majority of soups fell into the intermediate pH range. Some of the data are presented in Table 27.

Table 27. pH and Bacterial Growth in Soups Prepared in Quantity [Adapted from Longrée and White (1957)]

| | Proportion of selected ingredients, % | | | | | |
| | Canned tomato | Fresh carrot | Fresh green pepper | Total | pH | Log final count per ml. |
| --- | --- | --- | --- | --- | --- | --- |
| Tomato bouillon | 51.0 | — | — | 51.0 | 4.2 | 2.1 |
| Consomme madrilene | 24.0 | — | — | 24.0 | 4.6 | 2.1 |
| Creole | 25.5 | — | 2.0 | 27.5 | 4.7 | 2.1 |
| Mock turtle | 18.6 | 4.7 | — | 23.3 | 4.8 | 3.2 |
| Stockless vegetable | 28.6 | 5.0 | — | 33.6 | 4.8 | 2.1 |
| Dixie vegetable[a] | 14.8 | 4.5 | 0.2 | 19.5 | 4.9 | 3.7 |
| English beef broth | 23.6 | 5.5 | 2.7 | 31.8 | 4.9 | 4.7 |
| Minestrone | 20.6 | 4.1 | 2.7 | 27.4 | 5.0 | 4.5 |
| Spanish bean | 24.5 | — | — | 24.5 | 5.0 | 4.2 |
| Chicken gumbo | 7.3 | 5.5 | 7.3 | 20.1 | 5.1 | 4.5 |
| Cream of tomato | 46.2 | — | — | 46.2 | 5.1 | 2.1 |
| Cream of tomato and mushroom | 47.3 | — | — | 47.3 | 5.1 | 2.1 |
| Mulligatawny | — | — | — | 0 | 5.5 | 4.3 |
| | — | — | — | 0 | 5.6 | 4.4 |
| Split pea | 18.6 | 10.0 | — | 28.6 | 5.6 | 5.1 |
| Tomato-clam bisque | 22.4 | — | — | 22.4 | 5.7 | 4.5 |
| Cream of carrot | — | 26.8 | — | 26.8 | 5.8 | 4.3 |

[a] Contained 1.7% peas.

## Entrees or Main Dishes

Most entrees are proteinaceous, and are therefore potentially hazardous menu items. Longrée (unpublished data) made a study of pH of some common entrees and inoculated them with *Staphylococcus aureus*. Menu items of relatively high pH, above 6, included beef stew, creamed dishes, scalloped eggs, meat loaves, meat balls, items made of fish and shellfish, meat and vegetable pies, fish and vegetable pies, chicken a la king, and turkey a la king. Bacterial growth was excellent in these items.

Low pH values (below 5) were found in mixtures such as chili con carne, creole spaghetti, and creole franks (the franks were cut into thin slices). Baked beans made with a high percentage of tomato juice and catsup were in the low pH class, and so were Spanish rice and vegetable chop suey. Bacterial growth was poor in these items.

In the intermediate pH range were items containing some small amounts of an acid ingredient, like tomato or mayonnaise. This group included items which are apt to vary a great deal in formulation; in some of them, the pH increased with holding as the neutral and acid portions became more thoroughly mixed.

The pH of "made" dishes was greatly affected by the proportions of acid and non-acid ingredients. Items containing a high percentage of acid ingredients such as tomato sauce were of relatively low pH. It was found that the acid ingredients such as tomato sauce were effective in significantly lowering the pH of the entree only when the proportion of the acid ingredient was high and when the meat was in small pieces or finely divided. This allowed the acid to thoroughly penetrate the meat. On the other hand, entrees involving relatively large pieces of meat and small amounts of acid-containing sauce were of medium acidity. Besides, the pH had a tendency to change toward the neutral, as the juice from the meat oozed into the surrounding sauce.

It was not surprising, then, that a high proportion of the entrees allowed excellent growth of *Staphylococcus aureus*. Exceptions were chili con carne and "creole" dishes such as creole spaghetti, Spanish rice, creole franks (meat was finely sliced), all of which contained a large proportion of tomato, no large pieces of meat, and were of a low pH (below 5). The formulas are available (Longrée et al., 1960). Only when the directions for the preparation of these menu items are carefully followed, especially regarding the proportion of acid and non-acid ingredients, will these formulas be an aid to the keeping quality and bacteriological safety of these items.

In conclusion, the author wishes to warn that all menu items made with a high proportion of proteinaceous ingredients are potentially hazardous, unless acid ingredients are incorporated in amounts sufficient to decrease the pH of the mixtures to near 4.5. This is difficult to achieve and requires that a relatively large proportion of acid ingredients be used, and that the proteinaceous ingredients be finely divided to allow penetration of the acid into the meat.

## Mayonnaise

Preliminary to a discussion of the effect of pH changes on bacterial multiplication in salads and sandwich fillings, a brief discussion on mayonnaise seems indicated. Mayonnaise is an important salad ingredient and is commonly used as a spread in sandwiches.

Mayonnaise has been defined by government identity standards as a semisolid emulsion of edible vegetable oil, egg yolk or whole egg, vinegar and/or lemon juice, with one or more of the following: salt, other seasoning used in preparation of the mayonnaise, and/or dextrose. It is required that the finished product contain not less than 50% edible oil.

Salad dressing looks similar to mayonnaise, but may differ in oil content which can be less than 50%. Rather than using egg alone to make the emulsions, water and fillers are also used.

Fabian and Wethington (1950) made bacterial and chemical analyses of mayonnaise, salad dressing, and related products. The samples were collected from all over the United States. It was found that in composition, mayonnaise varied least and French dressing most. The pH of the various samples are presented in Table 28.

Nunheimer and Fabian (1940) reported that, at a given pH, acetic acid was more inhibiting to food poisoning organisms than other organic acids. According to Levine and Fellers (1940) the following concentrations of acetic acid were germicidal: a 3% solution for *Sal-*

Table 28. Acidity (pH Values) of Commercial Salad Dressings [Adapted from Fabian and Wethington (1950)]

| Product | Number of samples | Range of pH values |
|---|---|---|
| Mayonnaise | 25 | 3.0–4.1 |
| Salad dressing | 40 | 3.0–3.9 |
| French dressing | 30 | 3.0–4.4 |
| Tartar sauce | 15 | 2.9–3.6 |

*monella typhosa,* a 4% solution for *Escherichia coli,* and a 9% solution for *Staphylococcus aureus.* These authors stated that acetic acid is more toxic to bacteria, at the same pH, than lactic acid or hydrochloric acid.

Mayonnaise is of special interest because salads made with mayonnaise have been indicted in food poisoning episodes many times, and it has become simply customary to blame the mayonnaise. Wethington and Fabian (1950), who made a study of food poisoning staphylococci and salmonellae in salad dressing and mayonnaise, found that the pathogens did not multiply in these media and finally died.

The salmonellae varied in their ability to withstand effects of low pH, *Salmonella typhimurium* and *S. schottmuelleri* being more resistant than *S. enteritidis, S. pullorum, S. parathyphi, S. cholerasuis,* and the staphylococci. The shortest survival time was 24 hours and the longest 144 hours. According to Lerche (1962), *S. typhimurium* and *S. thompson* were quite resistant to low pH, while *S. senftenberg* was the least resistant among the strains tested. Another interesting observation was made by the same author: when mayonnaise was inoculated with *Salmonella* and the contaminated mayonnaise was then used for the preparation of meat salad, the meat became invaded by the contaminant. This implies that mayonnaise, although it will not support growth, could serve as a vehicle of contamination, provided the time elapsing between contamination of the mayonnaise and its use in food preparation would be sufficiently short to allow for survival.

*Salads Made with Mayonnaise*

A special problem among the entrees are certain salads. Meat, egg, poultry, and potato salads are menu items which have been indicted in many foodborne gastroenteric episodes. Although these menu items are acid, the degree of acidity will vary with formulation. Besides, the chances are excellent for the various ingredients to become contaminated with pathogens clinging to chopping boards, knives, choppers, and human hands. Lewis et al. (1953) stated that there is a certain amount of contamination during deboning of poultry and cutting of the meat which seems unavoidable. The question is, then, under what conditions will multiplication usually occur.

With this in mind, Longrée et al. (1959a) made an investigation of potato and turkey salads. They studied the effect on pH and bacterial counts of varying formulation and of varying certain preparation procedures used for the salads. For the potato salads, the ingredients varied in amount of mayonnaise, pickle, and egg. For the turkey salads, the varied ingredients were mayonnaise, pickle, and celery. The highest amounts and lowest amounts of mayonnaise used were chosen on the basis of culinary acceptability of formulas. The variation in preparation procedures was that some inoculated samples were immediately marinated with part of the acid dressing, while others were held for several hours at room temperature following inoculation with the test organism, *Staphylococcus aureus*.

The results showed that in the high-mayonnaise salads the pH values and bacterial counts were lower than in the low-mayonnaise salads. The addition of a larger amount of pickle had a similar effect. On the other hand, the higher amounts of egg increased pH and bacterial counts. Marinating the ingredients with the acid dressing immediately after inoculation had a pronounced effect in that the final bacterial counts were relatively low. This treatment with acid was particularly effective in the salads made with a high amount of acid dressing. Some of these results are presented in Table 29.

## Sandwiches Made with Mayonnaise

Sandwiches are of interest because they are often made with mayonnaise and are frequently held at temperatures favorable for

Table 29. pH Values and Bacterial Counts of Potato Salads and Turkey Salads[a] [Adapted from Longrée et al. (1959a)]

|  | Not marinated | | Marinated | |
|---|---|---|---|---|
|  | pH | Log final count per gram | pH | Log final count per gram |
| Potato |  |  |  |  |
| High mayonnaise, plain | 5.21 | 8.34 | 4.79 | 5.90 |
| high egg | 5.46 | 8.13 | 5.01 | 6.88 |
| high pickle | 4.60 | 5.28 | 4.60 | 3.51 |
| Low mayonnaise, plain | 5.51 | 9.10 | 5.15 | 8.29 |
| high egg | 5.91 | 8.85 | 5.41 | 8.59 |
| high pickle | 4.69 | 6.61 | 4.75 | 5.33 |
| Turkey |  |  |  |  |
| High mayonnaise, plain | 5.70 | 8.30 | 5.52 | 8.01 |
| high pickle | 5.13 | 6.41 | 5.12 | 4.34 |
| Low mayonnaise, plain | 5.94 | 8.39 | 5.60 | 8.29 |
| high pickle | 5.65 | 8.61 | 5.79 | 7.16 |

[a] Inoculated potatoes or turkey were held at room temperature for 3 hours before remaining ingredients were added.

bacterial multiplication. Several studies were made of bacterial multiplication in sandwich fillings of varying acidity.

Longrée et al. (1959b) changed the formulation of three basic fillings made with protein bases of ham, egg, or turkey. The fillings were varied to include different amounts of lemon juice as well as other ingredients, some of then acid, some spicy. Among the acid ingredients were pickle, cranberry, pineapple, raisin, and apricot; among the spicy were mustard, garlic (dry), onion (dry), and Worcestershire sauce. The test organism was *Staphylococcus aureus*. Culinary acceptability was determined. Highest pH values and highest bacterial counts were found in the egg-base fillings, and lowest pH and lowest bacterial counts in the turkey fillings. The addition of lemon juice, pickle, cranberry, and apricot reduced bacterial counts, but some of the acid additives were not acceptable organoleptically. Acceptable mixtures of low counts were egg filling with lemon juice and sweet relish pickle; ham with lemon juice and sweet relish pickle; ham with lemon juice and sweet pickle or raisin; and turkey with lemon juice and pickle, pineapple, and cranberry. Some of the data are presented in Table 30.

Adame et al. (1960) undertook a bacteriological study of some selected commercially prepared, wrapped sandwiches. As the survey

Table 30. pH Values and Bacterial Counts of Protein-Base Sandwich Fillings [Adapted from Longrée, White, and Lynch (1959b)]

| Type of filling | Variable | No lemon juice in filling | | Lemon juice in filling | |
|---|---|---|---|---|---|
| | | pH | Log final count per gram | pH | Log final count per gram |
| Egg base | Plain (control) | 6.07 | 9.33 | 5.50 | 9.41 |
| | Sweet relish pickle[a] | 5.01 | 5.82 | 4.76 | <4.50 |
| Ham base | Plain (control) | 5.90 | 9.06 | 5.85 | 8.43 |
| | Sweet relish pickle[a] | 5.13 | <4.50 | 5.18 | <3.50 |
| | Raisins[a] | 4.83 | <4.50 | 4.70 | <3.50 |
| Turkey base | Plain (control) | 6.00 | 8.97 | 5.65 | 7.41 |
| | Cranberry[a] | 5.36 | 4.66 | 5.12 | 5.20 |
| | Dill pickle[a] | 5.66 | 5.07 | 5.37 | 4.50 |
| | Sweet relish pickle[a] | 5.09 | 3.22 | 4.98 | 2.94 |
| | Pineapple[a] | 5.48 | 5.00 | 5.19 | 4.11 |

[a] 15.0% substitution.

showed, sandwiches are frequently prepared 17–20 hours prior to sale and held during this period at ambient air temperatures, which for the Los Angeles area (the place of the survey) was given as 23–30°C (73–86°F). The sandwiches were prepared by hand. Analyses were made for total counts, coliforms, enterococci, spores, and staphylococci.

Among the salad-type or "wet" sandwiches, the egg sandwiches had higher counts than the tuna sandwiches. The pH of the egg sandwiches ranged from 4.90 to 6.20; the pH of the tuna sandwiches ranged from 4.60 to 5.35. The "dry" sandwiches were made of ham, cheese, salami, hot beef and cheese, and hot ham and cheese; the pH ranged from 5.40 to 6.30.

*Staphylococcus* counts were high, in general. No evidence of *Clostridium perfringens*, salmonellae, or shigellae were found. The authors were careful to point out that in spite of higher counts in the salad-type sandwiches, it should not be assumed that the "dry" type sandwiches were free from danger.

McCroan et al. (1964) called attention to the fact that although many sandwiches are bacteriologically abused by being transported in panel trucks, displayed for up to 96 hours on unrefrigerated shelves of filling stations, fruit stands, and the like, very few gastroenteric outbreaks caused by sandwiches have been discussed in the literature. However, these authors go on to say that if one chooses to review the food poisoning history of sandwiches in general, the story is not

Table 31. Average Findings for Commercially Prepared Wrapped Sandwiches Inoculated with Coagulase-Positive Staphylococci (combined results of 10 sandwiches in each sample) [Adapted from McCroan, McKinley, Brim, and Henning (1964)]

| Kind of sandwich and sample number | Average coagulase-positive staphylococci per gram | | Average pH | |
|---|---|---|---|---|
| | Fresh | 48 hours | Fresh | 48 hours |
| Spiced ham and cheese | | | | |
| 1 | 300,000[a] | 6,200,000 | 5.78 | 5.74 |
| 2 | 170,000[a] | 4,300,000 | 5.80 | 5.80 |
| 3 | 59,000[b] | 62,000,000 | 6.78 | 6.12 |
| 4 | 53,000[b] | 63,000,000 | 6.34 | 6.06 |

[a] Inoculum placed on the slice of spiced ham in contact with the bread and mayonnaise.

[b] Inoculum placed between the slice of spiced ham and the slice of cheese.

as favorable: according to data gained by these authors from Morbidity and Mortality Weekly Reports of the Public Health Service, it is evident that between 1951 and 1963, sandwiches were incriminated in 133 foodborne outbreaks of gastroenteritis and that 5947 victims were involved.

These same authors made a study in Georgia, with the purpose of getting a measure of the potential hazards of commercially prepared, wrapped sandwiches. They examined 820 fresh sandwiches from 15 different manufacturers for pH, average plate count, average coliform count, and coagulase-positive staphylococci, and again analyzed them after 48 hours of exposure to conditions of ambient temperatures routinely encountered. The average pH values of the blenderized sandwiches ranged as follows: chicken salad, 4.24–5.39; deviled egg, 4.83–6.18; spiced ham and cheese, 5.35–5.97; and ham and cheese, 5.51–6.21. The imitation chicken salad consisted of chopped pork, pork skins, pork stomachs, vinegar, and spices; pH values ranged from 5.02 to 5.11. It was found that coliform counts tended to decrease in salad-type sandwiches during holding and no salmonellae were isolated. Staphylococci were at times numerous, but few coagulase-positive types were detected, and no significant increase in these could be demonstrated upon holding.

In a laboratory study, a group of sandwiches, among them chicken salad, imitation chicken salad, spiced ham, and deviled egg, were inoculated with coagulase-positive staphylococci and held at room temperature for 48 hours. Multiplication did occur during this period in the chicken salad sandwiches, but none in the imitation chicken salad and deviled egg sandwiches. An impressive multiplication of these coagulase-positive staphylococci occurred in spiced ham and cheese sandwiches (Table 31). It is important to note that the pH values of these types were fairly high.

Of practical implication is the observation that the staphylococci grew far better when placed between the slices of ham and the slice of cheese, than when dropped onto the surface of a slice of ham, which, when the sandwich was completed, made contact with the mayonnaise and bread. This information points again toward the inhibitory effect of mayonnaise and suggests that it may well be a good practice to spread perishable fillings on both sides with mayonnaise to discourage multiplication of food poisoning bacteria.

*Poultry Stuffings*

A special problem is posed by poultry stuffings which have often been the critical foods in gastroenteric episodes. Many stuffings contain high-protein ingredients. In quantity food service it is considered good practice to bake the stuffing separately and to roast the turkey without stuffing. This is a sound rule, as will be discussed later, because heat penetration into the center of large stuffed turkeys is very slow. Within the long period of moderate temperatures prevailing in the stuffing during roasting, an opportunity for bacterial multiplication is afforded.

However, in view of the fact that to stuff poultry is still a popular practice, Longrée et al. (1958) initiated an investigation to determine the effect on the growth of *Staphylococcus aureus* of varying certain ingredients in poultry stuffings. In three basic stuffings containing a bread base, onion, shortening, seasoning, and chicken broth, the bread base was varied to include white bread, bulgar wheat, and cornbread. The liquid was varied to change the pH of the mixture by using orange juice in place of part of the broth. In addition, substitution was made for part of the liquid and bread in the basic stuffing using apple, apricot, cranberry, celery, green pepper, parsley, ripe

Table 32. pH and Bacterial Growth of White Bread Stuffings[a] [Adapted from Longrée and White (1958)]

| Stuffing | All broth | | Half orange juice and half broth | |
|---|---|---|---|---|
| | pH | Log final count per gram | pH | Log final count per gram |
| Basic[b] (controls) | 5.26 | 7.41 | 4.54 | 4.16 |
| Apricot[c] | 4.50 | 3.00 | 4.40 | 3.00 |
| | 4.70 | 4.00 | 4.20 | 4.00 |
| Cranberry[c] | 4.62 | 3.92 | 4.10 | 3.64 |
| | 4.62 | 4.00 | 4.32 | 4.00 |
| Egg[c] | 5.30 | 7.61 | 4.68 | 3.88 |
| | 5.26 | 6.00 | 5.03 | 3.00 |
| Giblet[c] | 5.40 | 7.41 | 4.34 | 4.00 |
| | 5.48 | 6.00 | 4.56 | 3.00 |
| Oyster[c] | 5.10 | 7.44 | 4.52 | 3.96 |
| | 5.11 | 7.97 | 5.05 | 3.00 |
| Raisin[c] | 4.68 | 3.00 | 4.35 | 3.00 |
| | 4.49 | 4.00 | 4.69 | 3.00 |

[a] All stuffings were of acceptable palatability.
[b] Values are averages of all controls.
[c] At 5% substitution.

olives, walnut, raisins, egg, giblet, and oyster. The inoculated samples were incubated at 30°C (86°F) for 24 hours. The culinary quality of the mixtures was assessed before inoculation. A total of 117 different combinations of ingredients were tested. Some of the results are presented in Tables 32 and 33. In general, the bacterial counts were highest in the cornbread stuffing. Acid ingredients which were effective in keeping bacterial multiplication at a low level were apricot, cranberry, orange juice, and raisin. Very high bacterial counts were encountered in the mixtures containing egg, giblet, and oyster. Many mixtures of low pH and low counts were acceptable organoleptically.

## Desserts

Of the varied items used as desserts, the cream-filled pastries, cream pies, and puddings fall under the category "potentially hazardous foods" because they consist in whole or in part of milk or milk products and eggs. These items are known to have caused gastroenteric outbreaks many times.

Table 33. pH and Bacterial Growth of Cornbread Stuffings[a] [Adapted from Longrée and White (1958)]

| | All broth | | Half orange juice and half broth | |
|---|---|---|---|---|
| Stuffings | pH | Log final count per gram | pH | Log final count per gram |
| Basic[b] (controls) | 5.96 | 8.58 | 5.25 | 6.50 |
| Apricot[c] | 5.40 | 4.00 | 4.90 | 4.00 |
| | 5.20 | 4.00 | 4.40 | 4.00 |
| Cranberry[c] | 5.70 | 7.60 | 4.70 | 4.00 |
| | 5.20 | 7.89 | 5.00 | 4.00 |
| Egg[c] | 6.18 | 8.60 | 5.47 | 7.23 |
| | 6.30 | 7.96 | 5.40 | 7.31 |
| Giblet[c] | 6.00 | 8.78 | 5.40 | 6.84 |
| | 6.19 | 9.27 | 5.60 | 7.93 |
| Oyster[c] | 5.95 | 8.49 | 5.35 | 6.60 |
| | 5.90 | 7.84 | 5.26 | 3.94 |
| Raisin[c] | 5.47 | 5.00 | 4.93 | 4.00 |
| | 5.62 | 3.00 | 4.83 | 3.94 |

[a] All stuffings were of acceptable palatability.
[b] Values are averages of all controls.
[c] At 5% substitution.

Plain unfilled cakes, unfilled pastry, and cookies will be omitted from the discussion, because of their good record with respect to bacteriological safety. These items are heated to high terminal temperatures in baking.

Ryberg and Cathcart (1942) studied the response of bacterial pathogens to pure fruit fillings and custard fillings. The fruits and their juices used in fillings were lemon, pineapple, orange, strawberry, and apricot. Standard custards with varying amounts of added lemon juice and rind were also used in the experiments. Also investigated was the effect on bacterial growth of incorporating milk into the fruit fillings. The test organisms were *Staphylococcus aureus* and *Salmonella enteritidis*. The data showed that the growth of both organisms was decreased as the pH of the fillings was decreased from approximately 6.8 in the plain custard to approximately 3 in the lemon fillings. In the other fillings the pH values ranged like this: in apricot, 4.17–4.38; in strawberry, 4.02–4.15; in orange, 3.80–3.86; and in pineapple, 3.48–3.68. The inhibitory effect of the acid ingredients on the inoculum was greater for the salmonellae than for the staphylococci. Although the degree of inhibition paralleled, in general, a decrease in pH, there were some other effects at play. For example, when strawberry filling was prepared in such a way that its pH was similar to that of the pineapple filling, the strawberry had a greater inhibitory effect than the pineapple.

The addition of lemon juice and rind to a standard custard did not have a marked retarding effect on the multiplication of *Staphylococcus aureus* until it was used in such high amounts that the acidified custard was no longer palatable, and even then the counts were not sufficiently decreased to make such an acidification of practical value. The addition of milk reduced the inhibitory action of the fruits on bacterial multiplication.

Cathcart and Merz (1942) studied the effect of chocolate and cocoa fillings on growth of *S. aureus*. Standard custards were prepared as control. The fillings were made with water, sugar, starch, butter, and chocolate or cocoa. Most formulas contained egg; some did not. The amounts and kinds of chocolate and cocoa were varied. The pH values were determined, and it was found that the amounts of the chocolate or cocoa had some effect on pH, the pH decreasing with increasing amounts of these ingredients. Their inhibitory action on bacterial multiplication was assumed by the authors as being due to a combination of decrease of the pH with some unidentified substance, or substances, in the nonfat part of the chocolate or cocoa.

Omission of egg had a profound inhibitory effect on the growth of the inoculum.

Cathcart et al. (1947) investigated the growth of *S. aureus* in commercial dry-mix puddings, made with and without milk; prepared vanilla fillings; pie fillings made from pumpkin, squash, and sweet potato; fruit fillings; cheese cake mixes; and whipped-cream type mixes. Some of these items were modified by the addition of varying amounts of lactic acid, citric acid, and sodium propionate. The inoculated fillings and mixes were incubated for 24 hours at 37°C (97°F). The commercial dry-mix puddings which included vanilla, chocolate, and butterscotch, when made with milk, supported the growth of the test organism very well. When water was substituted for milk, growth was poor but the products were unacceptable organoleptically. Good growth was found in the pie fillings made from pumpkin, squash, and sweet potatoes, the cheese cake fillings, and whipped-cream mixtures.

The fruit fillings made with peach contained sufficient acid to halt the multiplication of the test organism, and in those made with raspberry a substantial decrease of viable bacteria was noted. In another experiment, vanilla fillings and cheesecake fillings were altered in pH by use of various acids. In the vanilla fillings, the addition of citric acid in amounts sufficient to lower the pH to 3.43 and 3.65 successfully checked the proliferation of the staphylococci but the products tasted sour and were therefore unacceptable. The filling supported growth well when no acid was added.

In the cheesecake fillings, a decrease of pH to below 5.12 was effective in gradually checking the multiplication of the test organism. It was observed that the use of lactic acid produced a filling of better flavor than the use of citric acid, and it effectively controlled the growth of the staphylococci at pH values between 4.42 and 4.87.

Castellani et al. (1955) reported that staphylococcal growth could be checked in unmeringued fruit cream fillings of pH 4 when incubated at 37°C (97°F) for 48 hours, but that in meringued pies prolific growth took place at the interface between the fillings and the meringue and some bacterial penetration into the filling could be noted. At a pH of 3.5 and a temperature of 37°C (97°F) no staphylococcal multiplication was noted in the fillings, but extensive growth occurred at the meringue–filling interface. At a temperature of 30°C (86°F) no growth was observed at the interface of filling and meringue. With a filling at pH 3.8, a bactericidal effect was observed against *Salmonella meleagrides* and *Streptococcus faecalis* throughout the pie fillings.

The effect of baking time and temperature on heat penetration to the interface of filling and meringue, and temperatures attained at the interface, will be discussed in a later chapter.

## Adjustment of pH Applicable to Quantity Food Service

Among many other factors, the acidity (pH) of the food in which the contaminating bacteria find themselves controls the extent to which they multiply. This effect has been discussed previously (Chapters II and IV). A pH of 4.5 is the approximate level below which little multiplication need be expected of bacteria which are capable of causing foodborne gastroenteric outbreaks.

A pH of 4.5 indicates a fairly acid condition. Many fruits, but only a few vegetables, have pH values as low as this (see Table 2). Fruits and vegetables, pickles, relishes, and vinegar can be combined with non-acid ingredients into mixtures which are of low pH and are poor supporters of bacterial growth.

Appropriate amounts of ingredients inhibitory to bacterial multiplication can be successfully incorporated in certain menu items if formulation is carefully worked out, provided attention is paid to the resulting pH as well as the culinary quality of the items.

### Applicability to Community Meal Service

Formulation for high acidity (low pH) can have a purposeful and practical application in community meal service. When facilities for meal preparation at the site of service are limited, and they frequently are, some menu items are usually prepared in the home. These home-prepared items are apt to be exposed to long holding periods. It is only logical that in planning community meals, menu items high in acid (of low pH) should be the ones prepared in the home, whereas the potentially dangerous ones, those of near neutral pH, should be prepared at the place of meal service. In a Cornell Extension Bulletin by Longrée et al. (1960), information is presented along these lines and menu items are listed which are of low pH, if prepared with the formulas developed for this purpose.

### Applicability to the Average Food Service Operation

As a routine measure to control bacterial multiplication, adjustment of pH has several limitations under average conditions of food service. Although some acid menu items are well accepted by the public, most menu items cannot be readily acidified without becoming unpalatable. After all, menu items prepared for service to the public must appeal to the tastebuds of the average customer. Moreover, the number of ingredients sufficiently acid to effect a substantial change of pH is extremely limited; it would be very tiresome to see and taste, for example, tomato in almost everything.

It is difficult to measure acidity under conditions of actual food preparation. There is no gadget comparable to a thermometer which could be used by a cook to determine pH. And finally, even if determinations of pH were not required (measurements could be omitted if strictly standardized recipes were used) difficulties might arise in connection with general rules given to the employees for the sanitary handling of cooked foods, in that employees who have been educated to regard cooked foods as vulnerable and who have been trained to act accordingly would probably become confused by exceptions, and more harm than benefit would be the result.

Formulation with the intent to discourage bacterial growth is an excellent supporting measure in the control of bacterial multiplication but is no substitute for vigilance in temperature control.

### Timing the Incorporation of Acid Ingredients in Preparing Salads

In the preparation of salads made with mayonnaise, such as potato, egg, turkey, seafood, or chicken salads, the time at which the acid ingredients are combined with the basic ingredients is of great importance. For information on the growth-inhibiting effect of mayonnaise and other acid dressings, the reader is referred to the earlier part of this chapter. In the past, mayonnaise has been unjustly blamed as the culprit in food-poisoning episodes. Mayonnaise, however, is a very acid ingredient and is inhibitory to bacterial multiplication if used at the right time and in sufficient amounts.

The acid should be put to work immediately after contamination is likely to have occurred. Opportunities for contamination are afforded through handling and through contact with soiled cutting boards, grinders, slicers, and the like. If the operations during which contamination is likely to occur are brief, the acid may well be added at the end. However, if these operations are drawn out over several hours, the acid should be added at regular intervals which should be sufficiently brief to prevent bacterial multiplication. The acid ingredient should be thoroughly distributed over the surfaces of the individual pieces. It is advised for potato, egg, seafood, meat, and poultry salads, to incorporate at least one-third of the acid dressing, possibly in the form of a simple vinegar and oil marinade, during or immediately following the cutting or slicing operations.

May it be said, with emphasis, that acidification is to be looked upon as an additional aid in discouraging bacterial multiplication but is not a substitute for these other precautions: that hands and nails be thoroughly cleaned and food contact equipment sanitized and that the period during which the food is held at warm temperatures be kept at a minimum. After the acid ingredient has been added the food portions should be promptly cooled in shallow pans.

Salads made with meats, poultry, seafood, egg, and potato should be made using chilled ingredients.

## Contact of Acid Ingredients with Potentially Hazardous Ingredients in Sandwiches

If acid ingredients, like mayonnaise, are to inhibit bacterial multiplication, they must be placed where they are needed, namely, on the food item likely to be contaminated and/or preferred as food by bacteria. For example, in the case of meat or egg sandwiches, the mayonnaise should make contact with the meat or egg, not necessarily with the lettuce, bread, or other less hazardous portions. In fact, spreading mayonnaise onto both sides of the meat, cheese, poultry, or egg is good procedure in making sandwiches. Pickle or acid ingredients would also restrain bacterial contaminants from multiplying. The sandwiches should be kept cold until served.

## References

Adame, J. L., F. J. Post, and A. H. Bliss. (1960). "Preliminary Report on a Bacteriological Study of Selected Commercially Prepared, Wrapped Sandwiches." *Jour. Milk & Food Tech.*, *23*(12): 363–366.

Castellani, A. G., R. Makowski, and W. B. Bradley. (1955). "Inhibiting the Growth of Food Poisoning Bacteria in Meringue-topped Fruit Cream Pies." *Bact. Proc. Soc. Amer. Bact.*, *55*: 20.

Cathcart, W. H., W. J. Godkin, and G. Barnett. (1947). "Growth of *Staphylococcus aureus* in Various Pastry Fillings." *Food Res.*, *12*(2): 142–150.

Cathcart, W. H., and A. Merz. (1942). "Staphylococci and *Salmonella* Control in Foods. III. Effect of Chocolate and Cocoa Fillings on Inhibiting Growth of Staphylococci." *Food Res.*, *7*(2): 96–103.

Crisley, F. D., R. Angelotti, and M. J. Foter. (1964). "Multiplication of Staphylococcus aureus in Synthetic Cream Filling and Pies." *U.S. Publ. Hlth. Repts.*, *79*(5): 369–376.

Fabian, F. W., and M. C. Wethington. (1950). "Bacterial and Chemical Analysis of Mayonnaise, Salad Dressing and Related Products." *Food Res.*, *15*(2): 138–145.

Lerche, M. (1962). "The Viability of *Salmonella* Bacteria in Mayonnaise and Meat Salad." *Biolog. Absts.*, *37*(5), No. 19212.

Levine, A. S., and C. R. Fellers. (1940). "Action of Acetic Acid on Food Spoilage Microorganisms." *Jour. Bact.*, *39*: 499–515.

Lewis, M. N., H. H. Weiser, and A. R. Winter. (1953). "Bacterial Growth in Chicken Salad." *Jour. Amer. Dietet. Assoc.*, *29*(11): 1094–1099.

Longrée, Karla, Rose F. Padgham, James C. White, and Brenda Weisman. (1957). "Effect of Ingredients on Bacterial Growth in Soups." *Jour. Milk & Food Tech.*, *20*(6): 170–177.

Longrée, Karla, and James C. White. (1958). "Bacterial Growth in Food Mixtures." 32nd Annual Rept., N. Y., State Milk Sanit.

Longrée, Karla, James C. White, Kathleen Cutlar, Debrah Hogue, and Janet M. Hayter. (1958). "Bacterial Growth in Poultry Stuffings." *Jour. Amer. Dietet. Assoc.*, *34*(1): 50–57.

Longrée, Karla, James C. White, Kathleen Cutlar, and Anna R. Willman. (1959a). "Bacterial Growth in Potato and Turkey Salads: Effect of Formula Variation." *Jour. Amer. Dietet. Assoc.* *35*(1): 38–44.

Longrée, Karla, James C. White, and Corrine Lynch. (1959b). "Bacterial Growth In Protein-Base Sandwich Fillings." *Jour. Amer. Dietet. Assoc.*, *35*(2):131–138.

Longrée, K., A. R. Willman, and M. Knickrehm. (1960). "Soups and Main Dishes For Your Community Meals." New York State College of Home Economics, Cornell University Miscellaneous Bulletin No. 35.

McCroan, J. E., T. W. McKinley, A. Brim, and W. C. Henning. (1964). "Staphylococci and Salmonellae in Commercial Wrapped Sandwiches." *U.S. Publ. Hlth. Repts.*, *79*(11): 997–1004.

McKinley, T. W., and E. J. Clarke, Jr. (1964). "Imitation Cream Fillings as a Vehicle of Staphylococcal Food Poisoning." *Jour. Milk & Food Tech.*, *27*(10): 302–304.

Nunheimer, T. D., and F. W. Fabian. (1940). "Influence of Organic Acids, Sugars and Sodium Chloride Upon Strains of Food Poisoning Staphylococci." *Amer. Jour. Publ. Hlth.*, *30*(9): 1040–1049.

Ryberg, R. E., and W. H. Cathcart. (1942). "Staphylococci and *Salmonella* Control in Foods. II. Effect of Pure Fruit Fillings." *Food Res.*, *7*(1): 10–15.

U. S. Department of Health, Education and Welfare, Public Health Service. (1962). "Food Service Sanitation Manual." PHS Publication No. 934. Washington, D.C.

Wethington, M. C., and F. W. Fabian. (1950). "Viability of Food Poisoning Staphylococci and Salmonellae in Salad Dressing and Mayonnaise." *Food Res.*, *15*(2): 125–134.

# CHAPTER XII

# MULTIPLICATION OF BACTERIAL CONTAMINANTS IN INGREDIENTS AND MENU ITEMS:

## PART II. TIME–TEMPERATURE RELATIONSHIPS

In quantity food service the ingredients and the partially prepared and fully prepared menu items, are subjected to a wide range of temperatures—from those prevailing in freezer storage, which may be as low as −40°F, to those which the foods attain during cooking.

Perusing the literature dealing with reports on foodborne episodes, one is impressed with the fact that the implicated foods were usually allowed to remain at temperatures favorable to bacterial multiplication for long periods. Therefore, a knowledge of the handling conditions and practices which prevent bacterial multiplication, and of the conditions which cause bacterial death, is basic to effective temperature control measures. The Food Service Sanitation Manual of the Public Health Service (U.S. PHS, 1962) states that "safe temperatures, as applied to potentially hazardous food, shall mean temperatures of 45°F or below, and 140°F and above." It will be well to remember this important temperature span throughout the following discussion on time–temperature relationships.

In relating food-handling practices to time–temperature effects on microorganisms in foods, it is convenient to arrange the temperatures at which foods are handled into several zones. These are: 1) freezing, defrosting and chilling zone—in this zone the temperatures should prevent multiplication of organisms causing foodborne intoxications and foodborne infections over an extended storage period; 2) growth or hazardous temperature zone—in this zone the temperatures allow bacterial multiplication; 3) warming zone—the temperatures are aimed at preventing multiplication but usually do not kill the organisms; and 4) cooking zone—the temperatures should be sufficiently high to destroy the vegetative cells of bacteria within a brief span of time.

It will be learned from research data presented in this chapter that in reality the hazardous temperature zone may extend into the refrigeration as well as the cooking zones.

## Freezing Zone

### General Quality Aspects

Many ingredients and menu items can be successfully frozen. However, certain items deteriorate quickly; among these are hamburger, fatty kinds of fish, turkey, and pork.

Some food groups do not lend themselves to freezing, since they suffer severely in quality. Among these are creamed foods, custards, gravies, sauces, and puddings—in short, all cooked and uncooked foods in which freezing, storage, and reheating causes detrimental textural changes.

### Microbial Aspects

As was pointed out earlier, freezing temperatures do not have an all-out bactericidal effect. Although freezing reduces the numbers of viable microorganisms, it does not eliminate them. It is therefore essential that foods to be frozen be of excellent sanitary quality. Precooked foods should, if at all possible, receive some terminal heat treatment which is sufficiently rigorous to eliminate pathogenic contaminants. This is an important point to remember when freezing leftovers, and other much-handled items under conditions of quantity food service.

Although some multiplication of bacteria may take place in bulky batches during the freezing process, growth may be expected to stop and destruction of a considerable proportion of bacterial cells to take place during freezing. Another drop in the bacterial population takes place when the temperature decreases from 0°F to subzero temperatures. Several factors affect death by cold: the kind of microorganism, the state of the bacteria, whether they are vegetative cells or spores; the speed and temperature of freezing; and others. These relationships have been discussed in Chapter II.

Survival of part of the bacterial population must be expected.

Bacterial survivors of public health significance have been demonstrated after months of freezer storage. These survivors may resume multiplication upon thawing.

## Defrosting Zone

Foods not only freeze below 32°F, they also defrost below that temperature.

### General Quality Aspects

Fanelli and Gunderson (1961), who made a study of defrost temperature of frozen fruit pies, frozen meat pies, and frozen soups, sum up their findings by saying that defrost of any degree adversely affects the quality of frozen foods; that the observed loss in quality which is due to various factors is even operative when the numbers of microorganisms are low; and that unless the products are held continuously in the frozen condition, chemical and physical changes take place which cannot be reversed and possibly are not halted when the products are refrozen.

The deterioration in quality of frozen foods at fluctuating temperatures below 32°F may be due to the fact that these temperatures encompass the range of the actual defrost temperature of the product. Alternate partial thawing and refreezing may cause changes in cell tissue, enzyme systems, and microbial flora which result in loss of quality.

The effect of psychrophilic bacteria and their enzymes on the physical characteristics of the frozen product has been said to be a built-in indicator of defrost. Once the enzymes of psychrophilic bacteria are produced and liberated in the frozen product, lowering the temperature will not stop quality deterioration. In a very short time, enzymes of these bacteria can break down carbohydrates, protein, and fat with resultant protein digestion, fat rancidity, and acids from carbohydrate breakdown.

One of the problems with precooked frozen foods is the number of opportunities for defrost to occur, namely, during storage by the manufacturer, transportation and marketing, and on the consumers' premises. There is no way of estimating the amount of defrost due to poor care. Studies conducted on temperatures of frozen food cabinets in retail markets show that the temperature of the cabinet does not necessarily reflect the temperature inside the carton of food.

### Microbial Aspects

Defrost characteristics of frozen foods and interplay of bacterial populations have been discussed by Peterson et al. (1962). Temperatures between 0 and 31°F were observed. It was found that the changes in bacterial population varied greatly and were affected by these important factors: the length of time the product was held in the defrosted state, the refreezing procedure, the temperature attained by the defrosted product, and the kinds and numbers of bacteria initially present. Fourteen different products were studied, including dessert pies, meat pot pies, and soups. The items defrosted well below the freezing point of water, and defrost temperatures as low as 15.2°F ($-9.3$°C) were observed. In general, these products became organoleptically objectionable some time before they were bacteriologically unacceptable. The psychrophilic bacteria multiplied most actively and suppressed the staphylococci.

If defrosting is continued to the point that free water is available and if the temperatures are appropriate, multiplication of bacterial survivors is resumed. Which ones of the microorganisms present will multiply and to what extent depends on many factors such as types and number of microorganisms and their relationship with each other, the food substrate, ambient temperatures at which thawing takes place, and time.

Special danger exists in connection with food items which usually carry a flora of organisms capable of causing foodborne illnesses when these items require long thawing because of their bulk. Although it is fortunate that the lag period of bacteria surviving freezing and freezer storage is usually a long one (Hucker and David, 1957), it is also true that the opportunities are often present because of the long defrosting times which are required in case of large-bulk food materials.

One example is frozen turkey. Turkeys are notorious carriers of salmonellae, and large turkeys thaw extremely slowly, the thawing time being influenced by the size of the turkey and by ambient temperatures. Defrosting in the refrigerator takes 3 to 4 times as long as defrosting at room temperature. Therefore, in spite of the dangers from salmonellae, turkey is frequently defrosted by "leaving it out." Moragne and Longrée (1961) found that when large turkeys are defrosted at kitchen temperatures, the skin of the birds remained over 40°F for an average of 11 hours, and the leg meat for 7 hours. The body cavity was the last portion to defrost (Table 34).

Another example of frozen food items that may contain salmonellae are frozen eggs. Allowing large batches of frozen egg to thaw at high ambient temperatures may invite trouble. Winter and Wrinkle (1949) have shown that even in eggs defrosted at temperatures as low as 55°F for 24 hours, bacterial counts increased.

Table 34. Total Time (in hours) Necessary for Some Selected Parts of a Turkey to Pass through Certain Temperature Ranges, as Influenced by Various Conditions of Defrosting [Adapted from Moragne and Longrée (1961)]

| Thermocouple position | At refrigerator temperature | | | | | | At room temperature | | | | | | | |
| | Bag | | | No bag | | | Bag | | | | No bag | | | |
| | 0–27°F. | 28–32°F. | 33°F. and above | 0–27°F. | 28–32°F. | 33°F. and above | 0–27°F. | 28–40°F. | 41–50°F. | 51°F. and above | 0–27°F. | 28–40°F. | 41–50°F. | 51°F. and above |
|---|---|---|---|---|---|---|---|---|---|---|---|---|---|---|
| **8-lb turkey** | | | | | | | | | | | | | | |
| Inner thigh | 39.83 | 9.0 | —[a] | 19.66 | 10.5 | —[a] | 9.16 | 3.83 | none | none | 8.5 | 1.66 | none | none |
| Breast skin | 4.33 | 31.16 | 13.33 | 4.08 | 14.74 | 12.0 | .83 | .66 | 4.33 | 6.66 | .16 | 3.58 | 5.08 | 1.5 |
| Leg skin | 7.08 | 17.41 | 24.0 | 3.33 | 12.0 | 11.66 | .91 | 1.83 | 7.08 | 2.91 | .08 | 2.58 | 6.16 | 1.41 |
| Leg ½ in. | 18.0 | 16.41 | 14.41 | 11.75 | 16.0 | 2.5 | 3.25 | 2.75 | 4.75 | .58 | 1.16 | 4.41 | 4.58 | none |
| Breast 1 in. | 26.75 | 19.0 | 3.08 | 12.08 | 15.83 | 3.25 | 3.66 | 7.41 | 1.75 | none | 4.0 | 5.41 | .75 | none |
| Inner breast | 24.75 | 21.75 | 2.33 | 19.75 | 10.25 | none | 11.16 | 3.91 | none | none | 5.83 | 5.58 | none | none |
| Cavity | 43.33 | 3.16 | none | 23.5 | 6.5 | none | 9.16 | 3.66 | none | none | 9.58 | .58 | none | none |
| **14-lb. turkey** | | | | | | | | | | | | | | |
| Inner thigh | 40.5 | 14.33 | —[a] | 21.5 | 20.0 | —[a] | 15.0 | 1.0 | none | none | 9.41 | 1.75 | none | none |
| Breast skin | 8.25 | 10.0 | 29.66 | 13.0 | 15.5 | 6.0 | .16 | 1.58 | 9.91 | 4.41 | .33 | 2.25 | 6.33 | 2.83 |
| Leg skin | 6.66 | 7.5 | 33.75 | 2.0 | 12.08 | 20.0 | .16 | 3.66 | 7.91 | 4.33 | .25 | 1.41 | 5.58 | 4.41 |
| Leg ½ in. | 10.0 | 20.41 | 17.41 | 18.0 | 9.0 | 5.0 | 2.08 | 6.83 | 6.33 | .75 | 2.5 | 4.58 | 3.41 | 1.16 |
| Breast 1 in. | 25.5 | 22.66 | none | 15.0 | 15.25 | 5.0 | 6.16 | 6.33 | 3.66 | none | 6.0 | 4.5 | 1.25 | none |
| Inner breast | 48.0 | 5.66 | 1.5 | 29.0 | 5.0 | .16 | 13.66 | 2.33 | none | none | 10.0 | 1.66 | none | none |
| Cavity | 42.25 | 6.08 | none | 31.5 | none | none | 15.49 | .5 | none | none | 11.75 | none | none | none |
| **20-lb turkey** | | | | | | | | | | | | | | |
| Inner thigh | 62.83 | 9.41 | —[a] | 44.25 | 13.58 | —[a] | 16.41 | 1.75 | none | none | 15.33 | 1.5 | none | none |
| Breast skin | 15.5 | 36.25 | 18.5 | 10.5 | 32.5 | 14.83 | 1.75 | 3.25 | 5.75 | 7.41 | .5 | 2.58 | 12.08 | 2.0 |
| Leg skin | 7.58 | 24.83 | 39.66 | 2.33 | 5.91 | 49.75 | 2.91 | 3.0 | 3.66 | 7.83 | .08 | 2.25 | 7.5 | 7.16 |
| Leg ½ in. | 26.0 | 34.5 | 11.41 | 12.75 | 20.58 | 24.41 | 1.91 | 4.5 | 5.16 | 6.58 | 3.5 | 6.0 | 7.33 | none |
| Breast 1 in. | 38.25 | 29.25 | 5.25 | 27.5 | 21.75 | 8.58 | 9.0 | 6.5 | 2.66 | none | 8.83 | 7.25 | .75 | none |
| Inner breast | 58.25 | 14.0 | none | 39.5 | 9.75 | 8.58 | 17.25 | .91 | none | none | 14.41 | 2.41 | none | none |
| Cavity | 64.33 | 7.91 | none | 47.5 | 10.33 | none | 16.25 | 1.91 | none | none | 14.0 | 2.83 | none | none |

Precooked frozen foods are of interest in this connection. Husse-mann (1951) studied the bacteriologic flora of some selected frozen precooked items as they reached the kitchen and followed the results during subsequent kitchen procedures. Total counts of bacteria were determined and analyses were made for *Staphylococcus aureus* as well as for bacteria of possible enteric origin, the coliforms. The menu items investigated were frozen chicken a la king, beef stew, and assorted creamed seafood items. Staphylococci appeared to be present in the majority of samples. Even in a refrigerator at 43°F, continued multiplication of bacterial cells was observed in the chicken a la king and in the beef stew during thawing.

Data on the growth of naturally occurring mixed populations in precooked frozen foods during defrost, with special emphasis on staphylococci in competition, were presented by Peterson et al. (1962). Commercially prepared frozen chicken pies were stored at defrost temperatures for varying periods and then tested organoleptically and analyzed bacteriologically. The results showed that at 41°F the staphylococci failed to multiply, but the competitors multiplied to large numbers. At 68 and 99°F, the staphylococci did multiply but they were outnumbered by numerous competitors.

In another experiment, higher defrost temperatures were used in order to give the staphylococci a better chance to multiply. The pies were defrosted for 24 minutes in a 425°F oven. Under these conditions the internal temperatures quickly went up to 86°F and higher. The saprophytic bacteria developed to much higher numbers than the staphylococci. These results point to the fact that in a mixed population the staphylococci become suppressed, the repressive effect being definitely related to the proportion of staphylococci in the total population, to the total population level, and to the temperature of incubation.

While the presence of a mixed population seems at times to offer a certain degree of "protection" from staphylococcal growth, it should be remembered that the situation in freshly cooked, sterile foods may well be entirely different. When sterile foods are seeded with staphylococci, which may happen for example when a food handler's hands contaminate food items which have received a terminal heat treatment sufficient to eliminate other contaminants, the staphylococci reign the field alone; without competition the staphylococcal population may build up to extremely high numbers.

In a practical situation it is difficult to determine the danger point of bacterial multiplication in frozen food items during defrost. Therefore, the frozen food industry, eager to protect the quality and reputation of their products, has made it a practice to state on the package conditions and times suggested for defrosting. In general, these suggestions seem to be commendable.

Recommendations for defrosting involve these simple principles: that vegetables not be defrosted, before cooking, except corn on the cob; that fruit be defrosted in cold water or a refrigerator; that fruit juice concentrates not be defrosted before they are reconstituted; that poultry and large cuts of meat be defrosted in the refrigerator or, protected by a plastic covering, in cold water; that fish, shellfish, small parts of poultry, and small cuts of meat be thawed in the refrigerator or in cold water or that they be cooked from the frozen state unless breaded or covered with batter; that precooked frozen items be handled in accordance with specific instructions given by the manufacturer.

Some warnings are in order. When the manufacturer states "cold" water, he refers most probably to water of temperatures below 50°F. However, water which flows out of a faucet labeled "cold" is not necessarily below 50°F, and even if it is it must be kept flowing throughout the defrost operation to prevent a warmup. The reader is referred to the description of a food-associated outbreak of diarrhea and pharyngitis caused by a salad made from frozen shrimp thawed in "warm water" the night before the salad was prepared and served (Morbidity & Mortality Weekly Reports, 1965b). Another warning concerns frozen meat pies. It should be made clear that for frozen meat pies the end point of heating is sometimes given by the manufacturer as "browning of the crust," and that this end point does not guarantee freedom from viable food poisoning organisms. Ross and Thatcher (1958), who analyzed the bacterial flora of precooked frozen dinners and pies, point out that enterococci as well as staphylococci have been found to survive the heat treatment suggested by the manufacturer. Survival of staphylococci in baked frozen pies was also demonstrated by Canale-Perola and Ordal (1957). In light of these findings, it has been suggested that efforts be directed toward formulation of crusts which will brown slowly, because this would enable one to employ longer baking times. The problem of thermal destruction of pathogenic contaminants of menu items will be further discussed in Chapter XIII.

It should be remembered that the problem of low-temperature growth, survival, and death is a complex one and that many questions await solution. Borgstrom (1962) has called attention to the many unsolved problems in frozen food microbiology and has warned that too many hasty conclusions have been drawn with few efforts made to disentangle the different facets, namely, the micro-organisms, the media, the food, or the totality of all these. Until more is known about these facets, persons entrusted with the preparation and service of foods must consider all frozen foods which may be classified as "potentially hazardous foods," to be highly perishable items which are potentially dangerous, especially when they contain pathogens capable of causing foodborne illnesses. And finally, it must be remembered that defrosting has never been known to improve the organoleptic and bacteriological quality of a frozen precooked food item.

### Chilled (Refrigeration) Zone

Refrigeration is the process of removing heat, sensible and/or latent, from foods for the purpose of temporary preservation. As used in this presentation, the term "refrigeration" refers to chilling at above-freezing temperatures. And the term "refrigerator" refers to equipment which is used for the above-freezing storage of food items. Mechanical refrigeration has developed quickly since the turn of the century. The aim of refrigeration is to prevent micro-organisms from multiplying and, in the case of fresh foods, to retard loss of quality due to other causes such as enzyme action. Since microorganisms differ widely in their temperature requirements for optimum, minimum, and maximum growth, the temperature at which food is stored greatly affects the kind of spoilage which will take place. Spoilage due to microbial activity may occur at any temperature between 23 and 158°F, but the organisms of public health significance have narrower temperature ranges for growth. In quantity food service, temperatures ranging from 30 to 40°F are desirable for chilled storage of foods. At these temperatures the psychrophilic and psychrotropic bacteria find conditions favorable for growth and strongly compete with pathogens. The factors affecting growth of psychrophilic microorganisms in foods have been reviewed by Elliott and Michener (1965).

### Uncooked Foods

The purpose of chilling items such as fresh meats and poultry, fish, shellfish, dairy products, shell eggs, fruits, and vegetables is to retard their enzymatic activities and to prevent microorganisms from multiplying. This type of cold storage of fresh foods prolongs their shelf life considerably.

It is beyond the scope of this book to discuss the many aspects of chilled storage of fresh foods except those which are of significance from a public health point of view. It is for this reason that the discussion will be concentrated on some selected foods of animal origin.

## MEATS AND POULTRY

Chilling is a very important method of preserving meat and poultry and products made from them. The more promptly this chilling is applied in the packing and processing plants, and the more scrupulously it is maintained during transport to the consumer and on the consumer's premises, the less opportunity will be afforded for growth of mesophilic bacteria, among them the infectious and toxigenic types.

Storage temperatures for meats range from 30 to 36°F. For freshly packed beef the time limit for cold storage is about one month, the optimum length of time being dependent mainly upon the number of microorganisms present and the temperature and humidity of the storage. With an increase in storage temperature the relative humidity is usually lowered. For mutton, lamb, and pork, the storage time is less than a month, and for poultry a week or less. For veal, the average storage time is also very short, just a few days. For quantity food production use, poultry is usually marketed in the frozen state rather than the chilled; other preportioned meats are usually marketed in the frozen state also.

Carbon dioxide and ozone are sometimes used in addition to low temperature to discourage microbial activity during commercial storage of meats. Storage life in an atmosphere of $CO_2$ is prolonged with increasing concentration, but certain undesirable effects on the meat limit the amounts of gas that can be used. $CO_2$ hastens the loss of "bloom" or natural color through formation of metmyoglobin and methemoglobin. Recommendations for $CO_2$ concentration vary from 10 to 30 per cent for meats and up to 100 per cent for bacon. Ozone is used in a concentration of 2.5 to 3 parts per million.

Microorganisms which find the temperatures during cold storage to their liking are mostly the psychrophilic types such as *Pseudomonas, Achromobacter, Micrococcus, Streptococcus, Flavobacterium,* and *Proteus.* In meats stored at 40°F or below the microorganisms able to cause foodborne illnesses do not multiply; they may, however, resume growth when the temperature is raised above 40°F.

## FISH AND SHELLFISH

Fish and other seafoods are the flesh foods most susceptible to spoilage of many kinds, microbial, autolytic, oxidative, and others. Therefore, the requirements for chilling are that temperatures near

32°F be promptly applied and strictly maintained and that cold storage be of short duration. Even chilled seafood has short shelf life, as was discussed in Chapter VI. Some unavoidable contamination is to be expected in seafood. Therefore, when outside temperatures are high and when distances of transport are great, freezing may be a bacteriologically safer method than chilling by ice or mechanical refrigeration.

DAIRY PRODUCTS AND SHELL EGGS

Pasteurized milk and cream, cheese, butter, and shell eggs have excellent keeping quality under cold storage at approximately 40°F. Milk, cream, and cottage-type cheeses will keep for days; hard cheeses, butter, and shell eggs for weeks.

*Cooked Foods: Growth of Pathogens*

Cooked items such as partially prepared items, complete menu items prepared in advance, and leftovers, deserve careful attention in connection with refrigeration. The principles of effective chilling are straightforward, yet are frequently slighted in practice. Too often cooked foods are simply placed in a refrigerator with the thought that now they are cold and safe, no consideration being given to the temperature conditions actually prevailing in the food. It is not surprising, then, that hazards have arisen in connection with chilled cooked food items under conditions of quantity food service.

Paramount to efficient cooling is the rapid transfer to the surrounding air of the heat contained in the food. This transfer should achieve a temperature drop in the center of the food mass to a bacteriologically safe level within as brief a span of time as possible. If cooling is slow and the foods remain in the "danger zone" for hours, bacteria multiply.

Heat transfer in food materials is affected by numerous factors, some of which are difficult to control. Among these are the nature of food which determines its thermal conductivity, the area exposed to the coolant, and the temperature gradient between food and coolant. Cooling methods will be discussed in Chapter XIII.

As a first step to achieve efficient cooling applicable to conditions of quantity food preparation, these basic questions deserve attention: 1) What is a "bacteriologically safe" temperature level to which cooked food items should be cooled? 2) What are the cooling times of various foods when cooled by conventional methods under conditions of quantity food service, and how are these cooling times related to bacterial growth?

"Safe temperatures" are temperatures that are low enough to prevent multiplication of microorganisms capable of causing foodborne illnesses. Therefore, in a brief discussion, the minimum temperatures at which some common foodborne pathogens have been found to multiply in foods will be reviewed.

GROWTH OF STAPHYLOCOCCI

Early laboratory studies by Kelly and Dack (1936) have produced data which indicate that at temperatures as low as 46°F, toxigenic strains of *Staphylococcus aureus* multiplied, if slowly, in ham, tongue, and chicken sandwiches. Research results by Prescott and Geer (1936) have shown that refrigeration of foods at temperatures below 50°F prevented the formation of *Staphylococcus* toxin for long periods of cold storage.

Angelotti et al. (1961a) set up an experiment to study growth response of a mixture of two strains of *S. aureus* to temperatures between 40 and 50°F at 2° intervals, using three foods as media: custard, chicken a la king, and ham salad.

The incubation time was 5 days. In custard and chicken a la king the staphylococci grew at 44°F and above (Figs. 14 and 15). In ham salad the increase in numbers was insignificant at a temperature range of 40–50°F.

GROWTH OF SALMONELLAE

Angelotti et al. (1961a) inoculated custard, chicken a la king, and ham salad with mixed cultures of *Salmonella enteritidis, manhattan,* and *senftenberg,* and subjected them to temperatures of 40–50°F at 2° intervals for 5 days. In chicken a la king, multiplication occurred at 44°F and above (Fig. 15). No multiplication was observed in the other two foods at the temperatures studied.

It is apparent from these results that storage of highly perishable foods at 50°F does not preclude multiplication of these infectious organisms. Storage for prolonged periods may create hazardous conditions, especially if the foods are grossly contaminated at the start.

GROWTH OF FECAL STREPTOCOCCI

Angelotti et al. (1963) explored the response of *Streptococcus faecalis* to temperatures between 40 and 50°F using again the three menu items previously employed for their studies with staphylococci and salmonellae. This organism was able to multiply at a tempera-

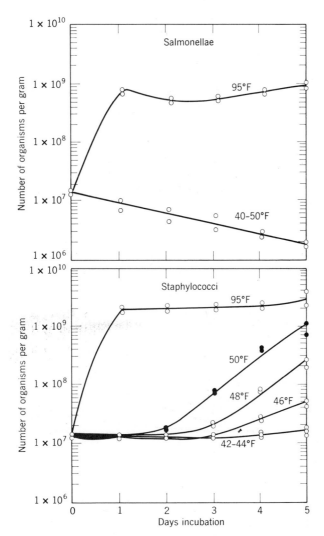

*Fig. 14. Growth of Salmonellae and Staphylococci in custard incubated at various temperatures.* Adapted from Angelotti, Foter, and Lewis (1961a).

ture as low as 42°F when suspended in custard (Fig. 16). In chicken a la king, the minimum temperature was 44°F, and in ham salad 50°F.

GROWTH OF CLOSTRIDIA

It has been demonstrated (Schmidt et al., 1961) that *Clostridium botulinum* Type E may grow and produce toxin at 38°F. At tempera-

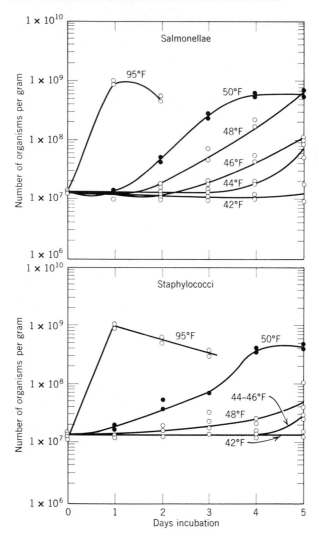

*Fig. 15. Growth of Salmonellae and Staphylococci in chicken a la king incubated at various temperatures.* Adapted from Angelotti, Foter, and Lewis (1961a).

tures near 50°F multiplication of Types A and B is possible.

It has been reported for the strains of *C. perfringens* studied that no multiplication took place in the temperature range of 5–15°C (41–59°F) (Hall and Angelotti, 1965). A summary of lowest temperatures reported for growth of some important pathogens is given in Table 35.

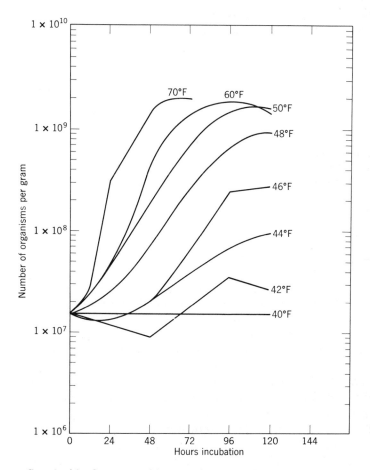

*Fig. 16.  Growth of fecal streptococci in custard at 40–70°F.* Adapted from Angelotti, Lewis, and Foter (1963).

## Cooked Foods: Cooling Times and Bacterial Growth

Research involving large pieces of meat and large batches of fluid foods has shown that cooling times are apt to be long and that bacterial populations may build up to large numbers during the cooling period, even under refrigeration.

Black and Lewis (1948) conducted a study observing the cooling rates and bacterial growth of hams, chickens, chicken broth, and custards cooled in several ways. These workers reported that, in general, cooling of the items was hastened and bacterial multiplication slowed by prompt chilling in a refrigerator. However, for the

Table 35. Summary of Lowest Temperatures Reported for Growth and Toxin Production by Food-Poisoning Bacteria[a]

| | Lowest reported temperature | | | |
|---|---|---|---|---|
| Type | Growth | | Toxin production[b] | |
| | °C | °F | °C | °F |
| *Staphylococcus aureus* | 6.7 | 44 | 18 | 64 |
| *Salmonella* | 6.7 | 44 | | |
| Fecal streptococci | 5.6 | 42 | | |
| *Clostridium botulinum* | | | | |
| Type A | 10 | 50 | 10 | 50 |
| Type B | 10 | 50 | 10 | 50 |
| Type C | 15 | 59 | 10 | 50 |
| Type E | 3.3 | 38 | 3.3 | 38 |
| *Clostridium perfringens* | 5.0 | 41 | | |

[a] These data have been compiled from different reports.
[b] Toxin production has not been reported in the absence of growth.

first 15–30 minutes, while the foods cooled from 180° to 150°F, the rate of heat loss was essentially the same in and out of the refrigerator. In general, the time in which foods remained in the temperature range 115° to 70°F was lessened by moving the food to the cooler before its internal temperature reached 115°F. The cooling curves of three hams are given in Figure 17.

Castellani et al. (1953) studied heat transfer in stuffed turkeys during heating and cooling. They found that when warm turkeys were chilled at 33°F the drop in the internal temperature of the turkeys was slow. The authors emphasize the fact that for several hours the temperatures in these turkeys were capable of supporting bacterial growth and that these hours must be added to the number of hours during which temperatures will again be favorable for multiplication during roasting. Heat penetration during cooking will be discussed in Chapter XIII.

Winter et al. (1954) inoculated different quantities of chicken salad with *Micrococcus pyogenes* var. *aureus* (*Staphylococcus aureus*). The controls were left uninoculated but were not sterilized. The salads were held for various lengths of time alternately at room temperature and in a refrigerator. The time required for cooling was found to be related to batch size and container shape. A difference of several hours was noted between the cooling times of salad of

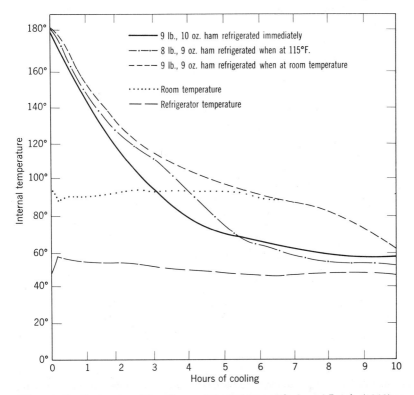

*Fig. 17. Cooling curves of three hams.* Adapted from Black and Lewis (1948).

large volume in a deep container as compared to the same volume when it was distributed into shallow pans. When the salads were kept below 50°F little increase in bacterial growth was noted, even after 72 hours; at temperatures above 50°F bacterial growth was rapid. Any change in environment resulted in a "lag" in increase or decrease of bacterial counts. This "lag," according to the authors, must be regarded as a potential danger when large quantities of warm food are refrigerated. It is interesting that in the controls, which were not inoculated, the bacterial counts were almost as high as in the inoculated samples.

Longrée and White (1955) determined cooling rates and bacterial growth in broth and white sauce prepared and chilled in large batches. Variables were type of container used for the storage of the food (tall, medium, and shallow); holding the food items at room temperature before refrigeration; batch size (2–8 gallons); and refrigerator

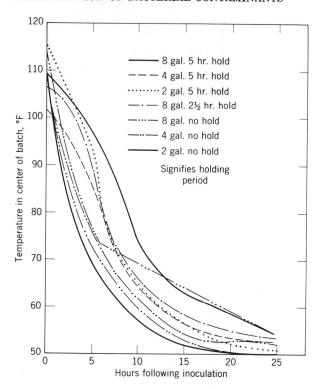

*Fig. 18. Cooling curves of different size batches of beef broth, with and without holding at room temperature. Refrigerator temperature was 47°F. Adapted from Longrée and White (1955).*

temperatures (42 and 47°F). The test organism was *Escherichia coli*. Extremely long cooling times were established for all batches. Some of the data are shown in Figure 18. The longer the cooling times, the higher were the bacterial counts (Fig. 19). Variables effecting the longer cooling times were: high viscosity of the food, large batch size, deep container, greater length of time that the food was held at room temperature preceding refrigeration, and higher refrigerator temperature.

It was shown that even 2-gallon batches did not cool fast enough to preclude bacterial multiplication. The use of shallow containers was shown to be very effective in speeding heat transfer in 4-gallon batches and in keeping bacterial counts low (Table 36).

The use of shallow containers is not practical for fluid foods, but it is applicable to solid and viscous semisolid items.

Table 36. Cooling Rates and Bacterial Counts of 4-Gallon Batches of White Sauce Inoculated with *Escherichia coli* and Refrigerated at 47°F in Containers of Same Volume but Different Shape [Adapted from Longrée and White (1955)]

| Shape of container | Temperature drop during initial cooling, °F 5-hr. period | 10-hr. period | Total cooling time to 60°F., hr. | Count per milliliter (log base of 10) |
|---|---|---|---|---|
| Shallow | 36 | 50 | 10.5 | 2.5 |
| Tall | 14 | 31 | 20 | 3.2 |
| Medium height | 15 | 34 | 20 | 5.4 |

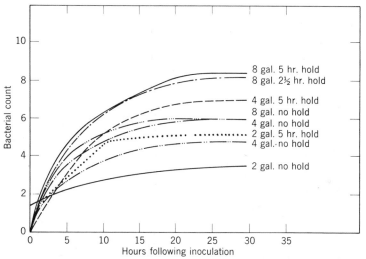

*Fig. 19. Bacterial counts (log values to base 10) of different size batches of beef broth with and without holding at room temperature. Refrigerator temperature was 47°F. Adapted from Longrée and White (1955).*

McDivitt and Hammer (1958) observed multiplication of a toxin-producing strain of *Micrococcus pyogenes* var. *aureus* (*Staphylococcus aureus*) related to the rate of heat loss in cornstarch pudding. The puddings were cooled in 9-quart (100-portion) lots using stockpots of two sizes, and as 3-quart lots in shallow pans, at room temperature and in a 40°F refrigerator. The results pointed toward a relationship between container size, area temperature, cooling rate, and bacterial development. Dividing the 100-portion lots into three parts and refrigerating them in shallow pans was the only method which did not allow extensive bacterial growth during cooling in the refrigerator.

The principles of control for chilled storage are aimed at preventing contaminants from multiplying in foods. Methods effectual in accomplishing rapid cooling will be discussed in Chapter XIII.

## Hazardous Temperature Zone

This zone includes the temperature range within which more or less extensive bacterial growth must be expected.

### Temperatures

In the older literature, the "danger zone" was, in general, spoken of as encompassing a narrower range than is now regarded as acceptable. At present, this zone covers the range of 45–140°F (U.S. PHS, Food Service Sanitation Manual, 1962). In establishing these terminal points, recent research findings on the multiplication of staphylococci, salmonellae, and fecal streptococci have been taken into account (Angelotti et al., 1961a, 1963). The fecal streptococci were shown to be capable of multiplying at relatively high temperatures, the extreme being 126°F (Fig. 21), whereas the salmonellae and staphylococci were seen to tolerate lower maximal temperatures for multiplication (Fig. 20).

The upper limit of the hazardous temperature zone, 140°F, gives a margin of safety. The lower one, 45°F, may seem a bit too high at first sight, but is acceptable for short storage since bacterial growth is very slow at temperatures at and below 45°F.

*Clostridium botulinum* Type E has been demonstrated to multiply and produce toxin at 38°F when several weeks of storage were allowed (Schmidt et al., 1961).

### Holding Time

It is difficult, if not impossible, to state the exact number of hours for which a specific food item can be safely held within the zone of bacterial multiplication. A number of factors affect this time such as the kind of organism, the physiological stage of the cells, the suitability of the food as substrate, and temperature. It is at present more or less agreed that the time for which a food may remain in the multiplication zone should not exceed 4 hours, and that 2 hours would give a wider margin of safety at the period of very active multiplication.

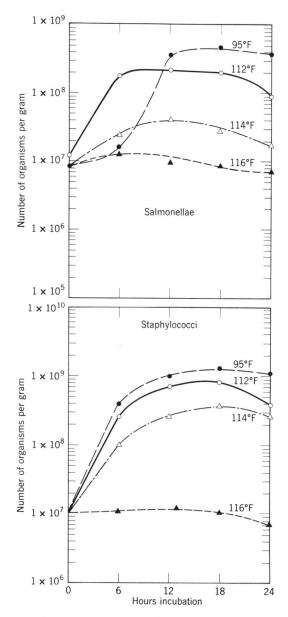

*Fig. 20. Growth of Salmonellae and Staphylococci in custard incubated at various temperatures.* Adapted from Angelotti, Foter, and Lewis (1961a).

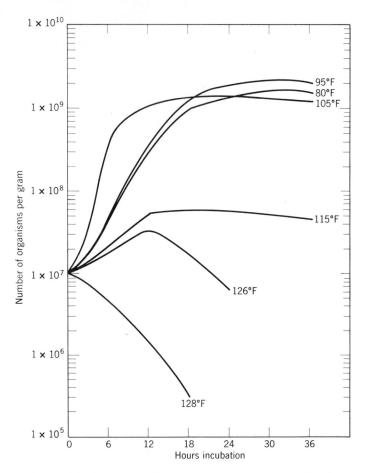

*Fig. 21. Growth of fecal streptococci in custard, temperature 80–128°F.* Adapted from Angelotti, Lewis, and Foter (1963).

## Improper Holding

There is no doubt that these maximum holding times of 2–4 hours are frequently exceeded under practical conditions of quantity food service, as the reports and analyses of food-poisoning outbreaks have brought out. Only a few typical examples can be given.

1) Sliced, cooked meat contaminated by a food handler and held in the kitchen from noon to the night meal
2) Ground meat patties shaped by hand, and held for "several hours" in the kitchen before cooking

3) Ham, boned, sliced, and held at kitchen temperatures for "several hours" before serving

4) Turkey, partially roasted, then held in the oven for "several hours," cooking being completed the next day

5) Large stuffed turkeys; heat could not penetrate to the center of the stuffing during roasting

6) Cream pies, brought to picnic grounds and subjected to warm temperatures for "long hours" before serving

7) Meat, chicken, turkey salads made from leftovers that had not caused trouble when served for the first time, but had subsequently been held at kitchen temperatures for "prolonged periods of time"

8) Poultry salad made from meat removed from the bones and refrigerated in large batches overnight before the meat was used

9) Poultry meat, removed from the bones and contaminated in the process, then held in a warm kitchen for "several hours"; then made into salads, casseroles, and creamed items

10) Pudding, pie filling, and pastry fillings held "several hours" in the bakeshop for cooling

11) Broth and gravy which were held overnight in the kitchen, or on the back of the stove

12) Shrimp defrosted overnight in warm water, made into a salad the next morning, then held in a large "refrigerated" vat in which the salad was held until served (at noon); shrimp did not cool below 65°F except for the layer in immediate contact with the surface of the vat

In brief, bacterial populations may build up to tremendous numbers if contamination is heavy, if the food is an excellent substrate for growth, if the temperature conditions are conducive to bacterial growth, and if several hours are available for multiplication. When toxigenic strains are involved, toxins may be released during this active growth and accumulate in the food in quantities sufficient to cause food poisoning.

## Automatic Ovens

Of special interest to homemakers, less so to the food service operator, are the bacteriological implications of holding menu items in automatic ovens.

Wiedeman et al. (1956) conducted studies on the effect of delayed cooking on bacterial growth in meat loaves. In part of the study, raw beef containing an uncontrolled bacterial flora was used; in others, the beef was inoculated with *Micrococcus pyogenes* var. *aureus* (*Staphylococcus aureus*), *Streptococcus faecalis*, and *Salmonella typhimurium*. Part of the loaves was held at room temperature and part in a prewarmed electric oven (heated to 150°F, then heat turned off). Growth proceeded slowly during the first 4 hours regardless of conditions of holding. However, after 8 hours considerable multiplication took place in the meat with the natural flora, a 10 to 100-fold increase being noted; in the inoculated loaves the staphylococci and streptococci increased as much as 100 to 1000-fold. Cooking the loaves to a terminal internal temperature of 160°F achieved complete kill of the streptococci and salmonellae, but not quite complete kill of the staphylococci. Of course, preformed toxins would not be eliminated by this heat treatment.

Wiedeman et al. (1957) made another study along similar lines, using chicken casseroles as the substrate. Holding times were 6–8 hours prior to cooking. Counts increased to high numbers during holding. Subsequent cooking killed the salmonellae, but did not completely eliminate the staphylococci and fecal streptococci.

Huppler et al. (1964) made a study of temperature and bacteriologic changes in casseroles held in a household oven for several hours before cooking. The data showed that freshly prepared, warm casseroles remained in the growth range of staphylococci during the entire holding period, but that thoroughly chilled casseroles could be held safely in electric ovens for 4–5 hours. This was not true, however, for gas automatic ovens, since the pilot light caused the items to warm quickly. In principle, holding foods for several hours in an oven should be discouraged.

In summary, the hazardous temperature or danger zone includes such a large range of temperatures that control measures encompass almost every activity of food preparation, storage, and service. It is important to understand and remember that the 2–4 hour maximum period for which a food may remain safely within the danger zone does not necessarily represent one continuous stretch of time; rather, warm periods are additive. What matters is the accumulated number of minutes for which a food item is subjected to warmth.

## Warming Zone

This zone encompasses temperatures which should prevent bacterial multiplication but would not necessarily kill the contaminants. The minimum temperature required for holding food in the warming zone is 140°F (U.S. PHS Food Service Sanitation Manual, 1962).

In light of available data, it seems that the minimum holding temperature of 140°F gives a comfortable margin of safety.

Many prepared menu items which are to be served hot are kept warm for prolonged periods of time before they are served. The bulk of a prepared item is usually held in the kitchen, small portions being transferred to "hot tables" or "warmers" as needed. Warming equipment is designed for "keeping warm" and is not to be looked upon and used as heating equipment. Therefore, menu items to be served hot should be of a temperature considerably higher than 140°F when placed in the warmer. That this is not always the case has been shown by Blaker (1962), whose data were discussed earlier.

An effort should be made to place only hot food on steam or electric tables and into warmers. "Hot" food has a temperature of at least 140°F. The question of whether or not food temperatures of at least 140°F can be maintained in present-day warming equipment available in food service establishments will be discussed in Chapter XIII. Problems in connection with hot vending will also be discussed there.

"Delayed service cookery" of meat has been recommended. The method involves long holding in warming equipment.

The microbiological aspects of delayed service cookery of loin cuts of beef were included in a study by Funk et al. (1966), whose other objectives were to compare heat penetration rates and culinary quality of roasts cooked by the delayed service method and the conventional dry heat method. The delayed service method requires that the meat be first browned at high temperatures and then transferred to a temperature-controlled cabinet at 140°F until needed. This method had been recommended for use when oven space was to be made available for other uses. Funk et al. (1966) roasted 10-kg (22 lb) loin cuts at 399°F oven temperature when using the delayed roasting method, and at 300°F when using the conventional method. All roasts were cooked to an internal temperature of 125.6°F. An average of 109 (90–120) minutes was required for delayed service roasts and 141 (120–160) minutes for the conventional roasts. The internal temperature of the roasts continued to rise after removal from the oven; a rise to 155°F was noted in the delayed service roasts, and to 144°F in the conventional roasts. In the delayed service roasts which were placed in the warmer upon completion of the roasting period, the internal temperature dropped to 133°F within the 6-hour holding period; no further temperature variations were recorded for the remainder of an 18-hour holding period. Microbiological analyses were made of all roasts cooked by the delayed service method, and of two roasts injected in the center with 8 ml of a culture of $1 \times 10^9$ cells/ml of *Salmonella senftenberg*, then cooked by the delayed service method and held for 18 hours in the warmer. In the non-injected roasts, counts of 0–183 per gram were obtained. In the *Salmonella*-injected roasts, no survivors were found under the conditions of this experiment. However, it should be noted that the internal temperature of 133°F is considerably below the holding temperature of 140°F required by the U.S. Public Health Service.

## Cooking Zone

### Temperatures

In this zone no multiplication of bacteria should take place in any part of the food; in fact, vegetative bacterial cells are expected to be destroyed in the cooking process. The question remains whether the heating used in lightly cooked menu items is always sufficient to destroy heat-tolerant strains of pathogens, especially when these are present in excessive numbers and are shielded by the protective qualities which some food materials possess. To the food technologist or the food service operator, death of a bacterium means that it has been rendered unable to reproduce.

The heat resistance of bacterial cells differs greatly. It is partly influenced by the characteristics of the particular microorganisms involved and partly by environmental conditions. Even within a population of bacterial cells, variation in heat resistance may occur. Death by heat is a complex process not fully understood.

Some of the factors that influence the heat resistance of cells are, besides the strain of organisms: the initial concentration of the cells—the higher the concentration, the higher the resistance to heat; the previous history and age of the contaminant—higher resistance being found in cells that grew in a medium to their liking and at a favorable temperature; and physiological age of the cells—higher resistance to heat being found in cells during the phase of maximum stationary growth.

The presence of certain protective substances such as proteins, fats, and a number of colloidal substances diminishes the lethal effect of the heat treatment on bacterial contaminants.

Cooking temperatures range from very mild to intense. Some examples of menu items given light heat treatments on purpose are: soft scrambled eggs where part of the egg usually remains under-coagulated, rare roasts, meat patties, meat loaf, oyster stew, and hollandaise. A few examples of menu items which are sometimes undercooked through carelessness, lack of time, or lack of knowledge of heat penetration are: warmed-over leftovers; fried patties and cakes, such as crab cakes; and meringued pies.

Heat used in quantity food preparation is essentially dry, moist, or a combination of both. Examples of dry heat are: broiling, frying, baking, and roasting; of moist heat: steaming and boiling; of combination dry-moist: braising and stewing. Actually, in all these forms of heating, the bacteria present in the food are subjected to moist heat some or all of the time, with the exception of the outside of items cooked by dry heat and items practically devoid of moisture.

## Thermal Death of Bacteria in Foods

To cause thermal destruction of pathogens in food preparation, it is desirable to apply heat sufficient to kill the bacteria without interfering with the culinary and nutritive quality of the menu item, by either long or intense heat treatment. Fortunately, both temperature and time affect thermal death. Heating a food to a lower temperature and holding it there for a long time may have the same lethal effect as heating it to a higher terminal temperature for a brief period. In determining thermal death times in the bacteriological laboratory, precautions can be taken and calculations can be made to eliminate errors produced by the fact that time will elapse before the coolest portion of the food has warmed up to the temperature whose effect is to be tested, and by the fact that some cells may die during the time necessary for heat to penetrate into the center of the food sample containing the bacteria. Very small food samples are exposed in tubes to a temperature-controlled bath, usually oil. The exposure time is corrected as follows: corrected exposure time = total time in bath − thermal lag time + lethality due to time of come-up and come-down.

When thermal death of bacteria is determined in a bulk of food, however, cognizance must be taken of the fact that the food warms up gradually and thermal death takes place gradually also, beginning at the instant when the minimum destructive temperature is reached and proceeding from then on. Since this time–temperature effect is an important factor which affects thermal death, it must be taken into consideration when evaluating thermal death data that have been collected under such conditions.

Resistance to heat and thermal death of the pathogens capable of causing foodborne illnesses has been discussed in Chapter IV. The reader will find it profitable to again review the work done by

Angelotti and co-workers (1961a,b; 1963), involving staphylococci, salmonellae, and fecal streptococci, and by Hall and Angelotti (1965) on *Clostridium perfringens*.

### MENU ITEMS USUALLY HEATED TO 180°F OR ABOVE

Heating foods to the boiling suffices to kill the majority of vegetative cells of pathogens capable of causing gastroenteric illness but does not necessarily kill bacterial spores. Heating foods to temperatures at or near boiling should eliminate *Staphylococcus aureus*, the salmonellae, the fecal streptococci and the vegetative cells of the clostridia; also, spores of the non-heat-resistant strains of *C. perfringens*. The spores of *C. botulinum* Types A and B are capable of enduring several hours of boiling; the spores of Type E are inactivated below boiling. The spores of *C. perfringens* vary in heat resistance with strain, some surviving high temperatures such as applied in boiling and roasting. A certain degree of heating may actually activate the spores to germinate.

Many menu items reach temperatures near 212°F before the stage

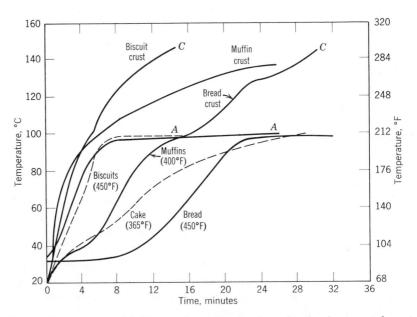

*Fig. 22. Temperature of baking products. Temperatures for the A curves taken at center of the baking products; those for the C curves with thermocouples just within the crusts; for baking powder biscuit crust, 1 mm; muffin side wall, 2 mm; bread top crust, 2 mm.* Adapted from Lowe (1955).

of doneness is reached, even though the method of their preparation and cooking equipment used may vary.

*Breads, cakes, cookies* and similar baked items have been shown to reach temperatures near 212°F (Fig. 22). Knight and Coppock (1957) studied the influence of the baking process on the destruction of heat-resistant salmonellae in certain baked products containing egg albumin and found that an inoculum of $10^9$ cells per gram of mixings was destroyed with a wide margin of safety in all baked products including angel cup cakes and layer cakes.

Hussemann and Tanner (1947) reported that staphylococci in sponge cake batter were killed when a temperature of 75.2°C (167°F) was reached; this temperature is well below the usual terminal temperature attained in this type of cake.

Breads, cakes, and cookies may be regarded as bacteriologically safe at the end of the baking period. However, after cream fillings or toppings are added, the picture changes completely. Cream fillings and toppings of bakery products are excellent media for bacterial growth and have been indicted many times as the cause of gastroenteric episodes. Sometimes bakers rebake cream-filled products to destroy contaminants possibly added with the filling.

*Soups, broths, and gravies* are usually boiled and the destruction of the vegetative cells of pathogens should be assured by this heat treatment. Spores of *Clostridium perfringens* are not necessarily killed. Items made from meat, or containing meat, have been repeatedly shown to contain spores of this pathogen which may have been survivors; some strains of this organism are extremely heat resistant.

Recontamination of cooked items may, of course, also occur in consequence of handling, or of adding contaminated ingredients. For example, gravies have been shown to have become recontaminated with salmonellae introduced with chopped giblets which had picked up the pathogens when in contact with contaminated chopping boards, and when the gravy was not reheated after the addition of the giblets. The records of gastroenteric outbreaks attest to the fact that an opportunity for extensive multiplication of the contaminants was afforded by holding contaminated gravies at lukewarm temperatures. Recontamination of meat with *Clostridium perfringens* probably occurs frequently.

From *broiled meats and roasts,* surface contaminants in the vegetative stage of growth should be eliminated in the process of broiling, frying, and roasting. Spores of *C. perfringens* may resist death by roasting (Morbidity and Mortality, 1965a).

Among the menu items which are usually broiled is bacon. Thatcher et al. (1962) studied the effect of broiling on bacterial and toxin destruction in bacon grilled at 401°F for 6 and 12 minutes. The authors report 190°F as the approximate terminal temperature that was reached in the bacon. However, it is not clear from the description whether this was the temperature reached by the bacon at the crisp or at the flaccid stage, or whether it represents an average of both. Staphylococci were destroyed at each treatment. After the lighter heat treatment, the somewhat flaccid stage, small amounts of toxin were found; no toxins were detected after the longer cooking period. Grilled bacon has an excellent record in connection with foodborne gastroenteric outbreaks.

Among the bulkier meats, poultry is usually heated to internal temperatures above 180°F, because most persons like poultry well done. The terminal temperature varies somewhat with the site at which the temperature is taken; it lies within the range of 185–195°F.

Hussemann and Wallace (1951) cooked parts of chickens which were known to have viable cells of *Salmonella typhimurium* in their bloodstream, collected heat penetration data, and analyzed the cooked meats for survivors. Some of the data are presented in Table 37 and in Figures 23 and 24. A very great reduction in inoculum was achieved by broiling to terminal internal temperatures of 93–96°C (199–205°F); and by roasting to internal temperatures above 80°C (176°F) in the breast and leg, and to 100°C (212°F) in the shallow parts of the carcass. An exceptional situation might arise when exceedingly high numbers of contaminants are involved.

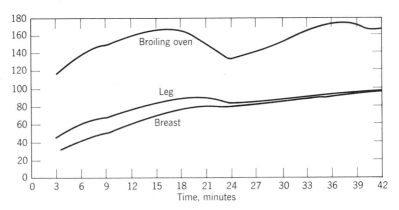

*Fig. 23.   Rate of heat penetration at the breast and at the leg of chicken during broiling (average of 16 determinations).* Adapted from Hussemann and Wallace (1951).

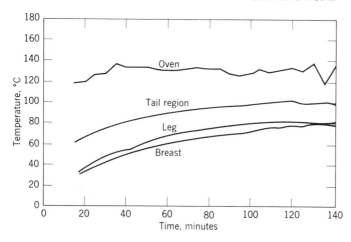

*Fig. 24. Rate of heat penetration of the breast, leg, and tail region of chicken during roasting (average of eight determinations).* Adapted from Hussemann and Wallace (1951).

Hussemann and Buyske (1954) investigated the thermal time–temperature relationships of *S. typhimurium* in chicken muscle and concluded that the organisms appeared to survive higher temperatures in chicken muscle than when broth was used as the menstruum. The salmonellae survived a 5-minute exposure to 90°C (194°F) but were destroyed after 15 minutes. The inoculum was very high in this study, and this may partially explain the high temperatures and the long heating needed to kill the contaminants.

The present trend is to heat pork roasts to end points below 180°F. In the past, the recommendation was to heat pork to an internal temperature of 180–185°F. Working with loin roasts, Carlin et al. (1965) found that roasts heated to 170°F were juicier than those heated to 185°F and cooking losses were lower. At the 170°F end point, *Trichinella spiralis* is no longer viable.

*Stews* allowed to simmer or boil should become devoid of living vegetative bacterial cells. As was stated for gravy, heat-resistant spores of *Clostridium perfringens* may survive the heat treatment given these menu items.

In *meat pies*, the temperatures attained have been found to vary greatly. Kereluk and Gunderson (1961) studied thermal death of bacteria during baking of chicken pies inoculated with *Staphylococcus aureus*, *Streptococcus faecalis*, *Escherichia coli*, and *Bacillus subtilis*. The pies which reached 214°F were practically sterile; there was a maximum of 0.1% survival of non-spore-forming bacteria, *S.*

Table 37. Number of Viable Salmonella in Chicken Tissue Before and After Broiling[a]
[Adapted from Hussemann and Wallace (1951)]

| Tissue | Before broiling | | After broiling | | |
| --- | --- | --- | --- | --- | --- |
| | Salmonella per gram | Number of samples | Salmonella per gram | Number of samples | Per cent reduction |
| Breast | $3.75 \times 10^9$ $(1.0 \times 10^8 - 2.9 \times 10^{10})$ | 13 | $9.05 \times 10^7$ $(0 - 1.37 \times 10^9)$ | 10 | 97.59 |
| Leg | $2.7 \times 10^9$ $(1.0 \times 10^8 - 2.0 \times 10^{10})$ | 12 | $3.8 \times 10^7$ $(0 - 1.8 \times 10^8)$ | 8 | 98.59 |
| Tail region | $3.15 \times 10^9$ $(1.0 \times 10^8 - 2.48 \times 10^{10})$ | 11 | $5.6 \times 10^6$ $(0 - 4.21 \times 10^8)$ | 10 | 99.82 |
| Liver | $1.1 \times 10^9$ $(9.0 \times 10^7 - 6.23 \times 10^9)$ | 15 | $1.24 \times 10^8$ $(0 - 5.26 \times 10^8)$ | 13 | 88.73 |

[a] Samples plated on SS agar after 24 hours at 37° C in tetrathionate broth.

*faecalis* surviving in the greatest numbers. The spore-forming *B. subtilis* showed a 0.35% survival. The baking time needed to reach this internal temperature was 40 minutes at 425°F oven temperature.

*Omelets* are usually cooked on top of the stove. Gibbons and Moore (1944) prepared omelets from reconstituted dried eggs containing salmonellae and cooked these items for 4–5 minutes to a terminal temperature of 94–98°C (201–209°F); they found no survivors.

*Souffles* are cooked in the oven. Time–temperature relationship data of souffles were collected by Longrée et al. (1962a), who used formulas and procedures applicable to quantity food preparation. Variables were batch size and use of water bath in baking. The authors found that the average temperature at doneness was 195.5°F and that the cooking times were long. Some of the heating curves are shown in Figure 25.

*Hard-cooked eggs* were studied by Licciardello et al. (1965). The authors determined the destruction of salmonellae in eggs of various sizes. Four serotypes of *Salmonella* were employed: *S. senftenberg* 775W, which is extremely heat-resistant, *S. derby*, *S. newport*, and *S. typhimurium*. Thermal resistance was determined on these organisms suspended in egg yolk, using miniature thermal death time tubes. Also, the rates of heat penetration during cooking into shell

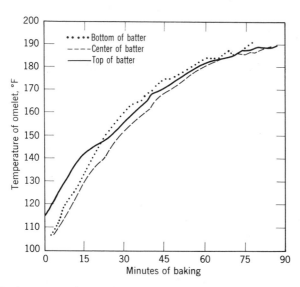

*Fig. 25. Heating curves of a souffle (large batch) baked in a water bath at 350°F. Recordings of three thermocouples initially positioned near the bottom, in the vertical center, and near the top of the batter.* Adapted from Longrée, White, and Sison (1962a).

eggs were determined; two methods of cooking shell eggs were used (Tables 38 and 39). By integrating the thermal resistance and heat penetration data, the authors calculated the theoretical cooking times that would be required to destroy the salmonellae (Table 40). By comparing these data with cooking times recommended for eggs in cookery under household and institutional conditions, the authors found that the cooking times recommended exceed the calculated times which are necessary to destroy salmonellae. On the basis of these data, therefore, hard-cooked eggs may be regarded as being safe from salmonellae.

For *cooked salad dressing*, Kintner and Mangel (1953) found that cooking dried egg in the dressing to a temperature of 183–186°F (84.9–85.6°C) rendered the product free from staphylococci and salmonellae.

*Desserts* other than cakes and cookies, which were discussed earlier, are a very diversified group. Many desserts are made with egg and do not tolerate intense or prolonged heat treatment without undesirable changes in culinary quality. It is not surprising, then, that much research in connection with thermal death has been de-

Table 38. Heat Penetration into Eggs of Various Sizes Placed in Boiling Water [Adapted from Licciardello, Nickerson, and Goldblith (1965)]

| Time, min. | Temperature, °F | | | |
| --- | --- | --- | --- | --- |
| | Small egg | Medium egg | Large egg | Jumbo egg |
| 0 | 44.5 | 45 | 46 | 47 |
| 1 | 84.0 | 75 | — | — |
| 2 | 105 | — | 82 | 82 |
| 3 | 122 | — | — | — |
| 4 | 139 | 104.5 | 103.5 | 102 |
| 5 | 150 | 119 | 118 | 115 |
| 6 | 161[a] | 134 | 132 | 127 |
| 7 | 155.5 | 144 | 142 | 137 |
| 8 | 148 | 154 | 152 | 146 |
| 9 | 142 | 163[a] | 160[a] | 155 |
| 10 | 129 | 158 | 156 | 163[a] |
| 11 | — | 147 | 144 | 160 |
| 12 | — | 135 | 132.5 | 150 |
| 13 | | 121 | | 142 |
| 14 | | | | 132 |

[a] End of cooking period.

Table 39. Heat Penetration into Eggs of Various Sizes Placed in Water at 68°F, Brought to a Boil, and then Simmered [Adapted from Licciardello, Nickerson, and Goldblith (1965)]

| Time min. | Temperature, °F | | |
|---|---|---|---|
| | Medium egg | Large egg | Jumbo egg |
| 0 | 48 | 43 | 45 |
| 3 | 61 | — | — |
| 4 | — | 57.5 | — |
| 5 | — | — | 52 |
| 6 | 80 | 70 | — |
| 8 | — | — | 61.5 |
| 9 | 109 | 92 | — |
| 10 | 118 | — | — |
| 11 | 128 | — | 78 |
| 12 | 137 | 111 | — |
| 13 | 148 | 123 | — |
| 14 | 158 | 135 | 100 |
| 15 | 168[a] | 146 | 109.5 |
| 16 | 163 | 158.5[a] | 119 |
| 17 | 153 | 154 | 129 |
| 18 | 142 | 145 | 137.5 |
| 19 | 131 | 132.5 | 147 |
| 20 | | | 156 |
| 21 | | | 164[a] |
| 22 | | | 155.5 |
| 23 | | | 146.5 |
| 24 | | | 137 |

[a] End of cooking period.

Table 40. Calculated Cooking Times for Eggs of Various Sizes to Obtain Nine Log Cycle Reduction of Two Species of *Salmonella* [Adapted from Licciardello, Nickerson, and Goldblith (1965)]

| Cooking method | Egg size | Minutes required to destroy: | |
|---|---|---|---|
| | | *S. senftenberg* 775 W | *S. typhimurium* |
| Placed in boiling water | Small | 5.6 | 4.5 |
| | Medium | 8.4 | 7.2 |
| | Large | 8.7 | 7.3 |
| | Jumbo | 9.4 | 7.8 |
| Placed in 68° F water, brought to a boil and simmered | Medium | 14.1 | 12.6 |
| | Large | 16.0 | 14.8 |
| | Jumbo | 20.6 | 18.8 |

voted to desserts such as custards, pie fillings, puddings, and pastry fillings.

Bakery custards were studied by Cathcart et al. (1942). The mixtures were inoculated with salmonellae and *Staphylococcus aureus*. The inoculum was killed when the custard mixture was brought to a boil after adding the egg–starch mixture to the liquid base. However, custards and puddings made by accepted methods are not boiled, the heating is usually terminated as soon as the mixture has "sufficiently thickened" (see Chapter XIII).

Kintner and Mangel (1953) investigated the survival of staphylococci and salmonellae in puddings and custards prepared with experimentally inoculated dried egg. Killing was achieved between 91 and 93°C (195.8–199°F) but not at the minimum temperatures required for the egg to coagulate.

Time–temperature relationships in oven-baked custards made with whole egg solids and prepared in quantity were studied by Longrée et al. (1961). Two variables, among others, were oven temperature and depth to which the pan was filled. The data showed that heating times were long and temperatures at doneness near 190°F. Although no bacteriological analyses were made, the time–temperature relationship indicated that all the custards received heat treatments which should suffice to kill salmonellae.

MENU ITEMS USUALLY HEATED TO TEMPERATURES BELOW 180°F

Among the *broiled and fried meats*, steaks, chops, cutlets, and other small cuts are likely to be contaminated on the surface. However, they are exposed to very high temperatures when broiled, pan broiled, and fried. Therefore, this treatment should eliminate vegetative cells clinging to the outside, even in cuts cooked to the rare stage.

However, in ground, chopped, or otherwise comminuted meats such as hamburger, ham patties, fishcakes, and the like, surface heating does not necessarily eliminate contaminants, which are apt to include pathogens of human source because of the handling these items have received.

Moragne et al. (1962) reported that oven-cooked patties made from fresh, raw beef, heated to an internal temperature as low as 145°F, were judged "acceptable" in doneness; yet these items would probably not have been rendered bacteriologically safe by the heat treatment they received. The authors point out that doneness in this case was not a criterion for bacteriological safety.

Bernarde (1957) studied penetration of heat into commercially prepared precooked frozen crab cakes of initial internal temperature of 19–23°F and found that when the directions given on the wrapper were followed in heating these cakes, very low terminal temperatures were achieved and that the heat treatment left much to be desired from a public health point of view.

Menu items made from cooked ingredients and reheated in deep fat are also apt to be lightly heated. This was proven for croquettes, for example. Deskins and Hussemann (1954) prepared ham croquettes from uncooked cured ham and heated them for 2 minutes in deep fat of 376°F to a deep golden brown color. It was found that the internal temperature in the finished product varied from 133 to 145°F, and that although browning reduced the bacterial counts, the products contained survivors. The number of survivors depended on the bacterial load present previous to browning. Some of the results are presented in Table 41.

*Beef and lamb roasts* may be cooked to varying internal temperatures, 125–140°F for rare, 160°F for medium, and 170°F for well-done. In unboned roast, danger from staphylococci and salmonellae is remote, the outside being exposed to high heat, the inside being practically sterile. However, the possibility exists that spores of heat-resistant *Clostridium perfringens* will survive the roasting process.

Sylvester and Green (1961) studied the effect of different types of cooking on artificially contaminated meat roasts. The organisms used were *C. welchii (perfringens)*, *Salmonella typhimurium*, and *Staphylococcus*. The roasts reached an internal temperature of 150°F; salmonellae and staphylococci were killed, but *C. welchii (perfringens)* survived. From the data it is not clear whether or not the roasts remained at the terminal temperature of 150°F for a prolonged period of time.

Funk et al. (1966) studied the fate of *Salmonella senftenberg* injected into loin cuts of 10-kg cuts of beef roasted at 399°F to an internal temperature of 125.6°F and then held for 18 hours in a 140°F warmer. The maximum internal temperature reached in the center of the roasts during their history of roasting plus warm holding was 152.6°F, recorded 1 hour after placing the roasts in the 140°F warmer. The lowest temperature attained in the roast during the 18 hour hold in the warmer was 132.8°F. There were no survivors under the conditions of this experiment.

For boned rolled roasts, chances for inside contamination from hands, knives and cutting surfaces are afforded. Survival of contaminants may well be expected when the roasts are heated to the

Table 41. Effect of Cookery on the Bacterial Content of Ham Loaves and Ham Croquettes[a] (Inoculum was *Micrococcus pyogenes* var. *aureus* 196) [Adapted from Deskins and Hussemann (1954)]

| Product | Type of ham used | Inoculum, cells/g. | Uninoculated mixture | | Inoculated mixture | | Cooked product | |
|---|---|---|---|---|---|---|---|---|
| | | | Total bacteria,[b] cells/g. | Micrococci,[b] cells/g. | Total bacteria,[b] cells/g. | Micrococci,[b] cells/g. | Total bacteria,[b] cells/g. | Micrococci,[b] cells/g. |
| Ham loaf[c] | Uncooked cured | — | 400 | 600 | — | — | 15 | 15 |
| Ham loaf[d] | Uncooked cured | 60 | 100,000 | 48,500 | 94,000 | 45,000 | 2,400 | 220 |
| Ham loaf[d] | Uncooked cured | 6,000 | 210,000 | 75,000 | 230,000 | 85,000 | 2,100 | 250 |
| Ham loaf[d] | Cooked cured | 6,000 | 200 | 85 | 6,100 | 6,800 | 130 | 65 |
| Croquettes[d] | Uncooked cured | 6,000 | 280,000 | 73,000 | 300,000 | 89,000 | 37,500 | 27,000 |

a Internal temperature of cooked ham loaves: 80° C (176°F). Mean internal temperature of cooked ham croquettes: 59.3°C (139°F); range: 56–63°C (133–145°F).

b Numerical results reported in accordance with method outlined by Jensen (1945).

c Each figure represents the mean value of 15 trials.

d Each figure represents the mean value of 8 trials.

rare stage. Bacteria in the vegetative stage could be expected to survive, and certainly spores of *C. perfringens*.

*Veal* is usually cooked to the "done" stage.

*Ham* and other cured pork pose a problem because of the handling they undergo with certain methods of processing. Micrococci have been frequently associated with the interior of hams which are cured by pumping brine into them. Deskins and Hussemann (1954) found center slices of hams more contaminated than end slices. These few examples point toward the hazard from internal contamination of cured pork. McDivitt and Hussemann (1957) made a study of micrococci in hams and reported that micrococci predominated in uncooked rolled hams. Cooking boned hams at an oven temperature of 300°F to an internal temperature of 77°C (170.6°F) was not sufficient to eliminate micrococci, according to these authors. Ham seems to exhibit a particularly protective action, making the micrococci quite resistant to the effect of heat.

Fresh pork roasts may contain live *Trichinella spiralis* unless the meat is heated to at least 137°F internal temperature. In the Food Service Sanitation Manual of the U.S. Public Health Service (1962) is stated that "pork and pork products which have not been specially treated to destroy trichinae shall be thoroughly cooked to heat all parts of the meat to at least 150°F." Since pink pork is not liked by most consumers, pork is routinely cooked to internal temperatures of 180°F at which temperature it should be bacteriologically safe also. At present, the trend is to reduce the temperature to 170°F to avoid dryness of the finished product (Carlin et al., 1965). According to Bowers and Goertz (1966), pork chops skillet-braised and oven-braised to internal temperatures of 170°F were more acceptable than comparable chops heated to 185°F. Holmes et al. (1966) found for broiled pork chops that with higher terminal temperatures, juiciness scores and moisture were lower; tenderness scores were unaffected.

*Stuffed roasted turkey* is of special interest because the turkey and/or the turkey stuffing (dressing) are very frequently indicted as the causes of foodborne gastroenteric episodes.

Stuffed turkey was studied by Castellani et al. (1953), who introduced an inoculum of *Staphylococcus aureus* and *Salmonella pullorum* mixed with *Streptococcus faecalis* into the stuffing of turkeys of 10–23 pounds weight before roasting the birds at 300°F.

The organisms multiplied in the stuffing during the initial part of the cooking. When an internal temperature of 160°F was reached, no viable organisms were detected. A post-oven temperature rise of 5–10°F was observed. The authors recommend that to allow for a margin of safety, a minimum internal temperature of 165°F should be attained in the center of the stuffed bird. These authors warn that for turkeys over 18 pounds there is little if any margin of safety (Fig. 26). They also question the wisdom of using a thigh temperature of 190°F as reliable measure of safety, because they found that the center of the stuffing in turkeys roasted from room temperature had not always reached 165°F by the time the thigh had reached a temperature of 190°F. When the thigh temperature reached 200°F the center of the stuffing reached sufficiently high

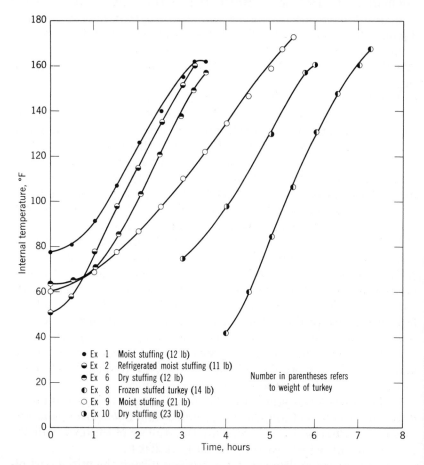

*Fig. 26. Record of temperature rise in the center of stuffed turkeys roasted at 300°F. The disconnected, uppermost portions of the curves represent the post-oven temperature rise observed when the roasted bird is held at room temperature.* Adapted from Castellani, Clarke, Gibson, and Meisner (1953).

temperatures to kill the pathogens studied. The danger exists that the meat may be "overdone" and tough at that point.

Rogers and Gunderson (1958) studied survival of salmonellae and staphylococci in stuffed turkeys during roasting and produced data which showed that an internal temperature of at least 160°F was required to kill the inoculum (Fig. 27). A terminal temperature of 165°F was suggested to allow for a margin of safety. To reach an internal temperature of 165°F longer roasting times were required for frozen than for nonfrozen birds. At present no data are available on survival of fecal streptococci and clostridia in roasted stuffed turkeys.

Hoke et al. (1965) published a report on their investigation dealing with the effectiveness of end point temperatures of 195°F in the breast of roasted turkeys to determine doneness and heat penetration into the center of the stuffing. Large Bronze turkeys of dressed weight of 16–23.5 pounds (Lot 1) and Beltsville Small White turkeys of dressed weight 13.4–16.1 pounds (Lot 2) were used; oven temperature was 325°F. For Lot 1 (large turkeys) the temperature of the stuffing increased from 34°F at the start to a range of 165–189°F by the end of roasting. For Lot 2 (small turkeys) the temperature of the stuffing increased from 30°F to a range from 154–191°F (Fig. 28). Stuffing below 165°F had a post-oven temperature raise of approxi-

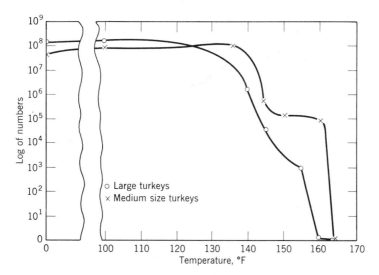

*Fig. 27. Survival of Micrococcus pyogenes var. aureus in the stuffing during the roasting of medium and large frozen stuffed turkeys.* Adapted from Rogers and Gunderson (1958).

mately 10° during a 20-minute holding period immediately following the removal of the birds from the oven. It was concluded that roasting to 195°F in the breast plus a 20-minute holding period outside the oven would ensure that the desired terminal temperature of 165°F would be reached in the center of the stuffing. The meat was not considered overcooked when a terminal temperature of 195°F (breast) was used.

Castellani et al. (1953) showed that heat transfer in frozen stuffed turkey is very slow and that adequate temperatures are not reached in the center of the stuffing. In fact, in one instance the stuffing of turkey roasted to a thigh temperature of 200°F reached only 90°F. In conclusion, it seems advisable to adhere to the sensible rule to roast turkeys in the unstuffed state. First, the roasting time is shorter. Hoke et al. (1965) lists the total roasting times for stuffed birds of 16–23.5 pounds dressed weight as 6½–7½ hours, whereas according to the National Turkey Federation Handbook (1964) the roasting times for unstuffed turkeys of comparable weight and

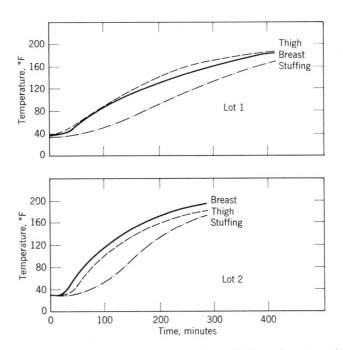

Fig. 28. Average heat penetration into breast, inner thigh, and stuffing of turkeys roasted at 325°F to a temperature of 195°F in the breast. Adapted from Hoke, Gilpin, and Dawson (1965).

roasted at the same oven temperature (325°F) is only 3¾–5½ hours. Second, labor time is saved. Third, the finished products look neat and are easy to portion and serve. Above all, the bacteriological risks of not achieving thermal death of contaminants present in the inside of the stuffed bird are eliminated.

Stuffing baked separately in shallow pans is quickly penetrated by heat, is portioned easily, and cools fast as a leftover. To prepare turkey unstuffed is thus a highly commendable practice. Another method to assure fast heat penetration is to bone the turkey and cook the cut-up parts rather than the turkey as a whole.

*Meat, turkey, and fish loaves* and similar items are of particular interest because proteinaceous ingredients when comminuted are known to often harbor bacteria in high numbers. Contaminants may also be contributed by the binding ingredients like flour and breadcrumbs.

Deskins and Hussemann (1954) investigated the effect of cooking on thermal death of *Staphylococcus aureus* in ground ham mixtures. Ham loaves were baked in a 350°F oven to an internal temperature of 80°C (176°F). The finished product was not sterile, but counts were low (Table 41).

Beloian and Schlosser (1963) studied the heat penetration into salmon loaf inoculated with a heat-resistant strain of *Salmonella senftenberg*. Under the conditions of the experiment, lethality was achieved at a terminal temperature of 160°F.

Longrée et al. (1963) studied the time–temperature relationships of beef, turkey, and salmon loaves under conditions of quantity food preparation. Variables included: oven temperature, use of a water bath, depth of mixture in pan, and terminal temperature to which the loaves were baked. Beef loaves and salmon loaves baked to a terminal temperature of 155°F were acceptable in culinary quality. It is therefore questionable whether such loaves would receive heat treatments sufficient to eliminate even vegetative cells of possible pathogens. Higher terminal temperatures were required to render the turkey loaves acceptable to the judges. These results point out the fact that "doneness" on a culinary basis is not necessarily a satisfactory end point from a bacteriological point of view.

Whether *meat pies, poultry pies, and casseroles* made with proteinaceous solid ingredients reach internal temperatures sufficient to kill pathogenic contaminants depends on many factors. The nature of the food is one. In general, heat transfer is slow into mixtures consisting of proteinaceous solids held together in starchy sauces. The depth of the material in the pan is another factor, and so are initial temperatures of the materials to be heated. Two other important factors are oven temperature and time of heating.

Individual meat pies were inoculated with salmonellae by Miller and Ramsden (1955) and baked at various oven temperatures. In 4-ounce pies, when heating was rapid and oven temperatures above 400°F, the crust was browned before the interior of the pies got sufficiently hot to kill the inoculum; the interior temperature of the fillings reached only 47.2°C (117°F). At oven temperatures near 320°F applied for one hour, kill was effected and an internal temperature of 86.6°C (188°F) was reached; however, the pie crust was not acceptable because of sogginess. Application of an intermediate oven temperature of 380°F also achieved kill and resulted in an acceptable crust. The internal temperature reached under these conditions was not stated by the authors.

Wiedeman et al. (1957) baked three chicken casseroles inoculated with one strain each of *Micrococcus pyogenes* var. *aureus*, *Streptococcus faecalis*, and *Salmonella typhimurium*, at 350°F for 40 minutes. The terminal internal temperature of the casseroles at the end of baking was 135°F and the temperature rose after removal from the oven to 145°F. Although the numbers of vegetative cells were reduced considerably during cooking, the mixtures were not sterile. The streptococci were most resistant to the heat treatment, the salmonellae least.

Thermal destruction of *Staphylococcus aureus*, *Streptococcus faecalis*, *Escherichia coli*, and *Bacillus subtilis* in baking artificially contaminated chicken pies was studied by Kereluk and Gunderson (1961). Only one species of bacteria was inoculated into each pie. The contaminated pies were frozen, then baked in a 425°F oven for 20, 30, or 40 minutes. The pies baked for 20 minutes to an internal temperature of 124°F had a "just thawed" appearance; in these pies the non-spore formers exhibited survival rates of 14–100%, and the spore former a survival rate of 150% or higher, indicating possible multiplication. In the pies baked for 30 minutes to 170°F, survival ranged from 0 to 3.6%, *S. faecalis* surviving in the greatest numbers. In the pies baked for 40 minutes to 214°F survival of non-spore formers was negligible, the highest percentage (0.1%) being found for *S. faecalis;* of the spore former *B. subtilis*, 0.35% survived. The data pertaining to *S. faecalis* are presented in Table 42. These data indicate that the heat treatment applied to a terminal temperature of 170°F was just about as effectual as the heat treatment applied to a terminal temperature of 214°F.

Table 42. Effect of Various Baking Periods at 425°F on the Survival of *Streptococcus faecalis* in Chicken Meat Pies[a] [Adapted from Kereluk and Gunderson (1961)]

| Before baking | Bacteriological sampling immediately after baking | Bacteriological sampling 10 min. after baking | Bacteriological sampling 20 min. after baking |
|---|---|---|---|
| | 40-minute baking period[b] | | |
| 460,000,000 | 290 | <10 | |
| 330,000,000 | <10 | <10 | |
| 330,000,000 | <10 | <10 | |
| 330,000,000 | <10 | <10 | |
| 260,000,000 | <10 | <10 | |
| 130,000,000 | <10 | <10 | |
| 49,000,000 | <10 | <10 | |
| 33,000,000 | <10 | <10 | |
| | 30-minute baking period[c] | | |
| 330,000,000 | 24,000,000 | <10 | |
| 240,000,000 | 79,000 | 220,000 | 45 |
| 170,000,000 | 7,900,000 | <10 | <10 |
| 130,000,000 | 1,300,000 | <10 | <10 |
| | 20-minute baking period[d] | | |
| 490,000,000 | 350,000,000 | 170,000 | 350,000,000 |
| 170,000,000 | 49,000,000 | 33,000,000 | 17,000,000 |
| 130,000,000 | 49,000,000 | 46,000,000 | 110,000,000 |
| 130,000,000 | 33,000,000 | 79,000,000 | 79,000,000 |
| 130,000,000 | 49,000,000 | 33,000,000 | 33,000,000 |
| 130,000,000 | 11,000,000 | | 17,000,000 |

[a] Figures are number of bacteria per gram as determined by the MPN method. Average temperature attained: [b] 214°F; [c] 170°F; and [d] 124°F.

Hussemann (1951) studied the effect of heating on the bacteriologic flora of chicken a la king, beef stew, and creamed seafood. These foods were heated from refrigerator temperatures to 85°C (185°F) in a double boiler, not in an oven. The heat treatment reduced the number of bacterial cells, including micrococci, but did not eradicate any type completely from a food in which it had been shown to be present originally.

In oven heating, "bubbling at the top" is not a sure sign that the pie or casserole has reached the boiling point in the center. In fact, items that are "run under the broiler" have been shown to be cool in the center when tested with a thermometer. Longer heating times at a moderate oven temperature would therefore be more effective in achieving heat penetration into the center without burning the top. The use of a thermometer is encouraged, especially for deep pies and casseroles. The terminal temperature should be at least 165–170°F.

*Creamed menu items* have been indicted many times as the offending food in gastroenteric outbreaks. Creamed meat, poultry, fish, shellfish, and eggs are potentially dangerous for several reasons: their proteinaceous nature and near neutral pH; the handling which the solid ingredients usually receive before they are incorporated into the sauce; and, last not least, the temperatures prevailing in the combined mixture.

The temperature of the base, a "cream" or white sauce, will vary with the method of preparation and batch size. Longrée et al. (1953) found that when scalded milk (188–194°F) was used in the preparation of the sauces, the temperatures of the finished products ranged from 166 to 180°F; such a product would be practically sterile. However, when the solid ingredients are combined with the sauce, the temperature of the resulting mixture will decrease, the extent of the decrease depending on the temperature of the solid ingredients. If the temperature does not fall below 140°F no multiplication of pathogenic contaminants needs to be expected. However, danger arises when the temperature falls below 140°F and lingers within the temperature zone favorable to multiplication.

To achieve thermal death of contaminants, reheating the combined mixture to appropriate temperatures is required. Knowledge and skill are necessary to do this without interfering with some culinary quality characteristics of the items heated. To aid heat transfer, a certain degree of agitation is required, and this may break up solid ingredients. Also, curdling upon harsh heat treatment may be a problem in creamed menu items.

Studies on *soft-cooked shell eggs* were made by Rettger et al. (1916), who inoculated eggs with *Salmonella pullorum*, then boiled the eggs for periods up to 4 minutes. Viable salmonellae were recovered from some of the eggs which received the maximum heat treatment. Survival of salmonellae in 25% of eggs inoculated with *S. pullorum* was also reported by Stafseth et al. (1952).

*Scrambled eggs* cooked to a soft stage of doneness are of special interest. In quantity food preparation, frozen rather than fresh eggs are largely used as an ingredient in these menu items. In the future, dried eggs may be expected to be used in ever-increasing amounts. In connection with these ingredients, thermal destruction of salmonellae is of interest.

Information on the bacteriological safety in scrambled eggs made with whole egg solids is limited. Gibbons and Moore (1944) inoculated whole egg solids with *S. bareilly*, *S. oranienburg*, and *S. typhimurium*. The eggs were reconstituted and used in preparing "scrambles" cooked on top of the stove. The batch containing the first contaminant was cooked to a maximum temperature of 68°C (154°F). Batches containing the other two contaminants were cooked to a maximum temperature of 82°C (180°F). No salmonellae organisms could be detected in the products after cooking.

Solowey and Calesnick (1948) inoculated reconstituted egg with *S. oranienburg*, *S. pullorum*, and a heat-resistant strain of *S. senftenberg*. Some of the inoculated batches were immediately scrambled, and some were held at room temperature and at refrigerator temperature before cooking. All "scrambles" were cooked to a moderately soft stage. Salmonellae were recovered from the "scrambles" at all ranges of the time–temperature interval. These results prove that when scrambled eggs are cooked to a soft, underdone stage, survival of salmonellae must be expected.

Scrambled eggs cooked to an internal temperature of 180°F are of dry consistency (Longrée et al., 1962b).

*Fried and poached eggs* are among the items often cooked to a soft, underdone stage. Survival of *Salmonella pullorum* in fried and poached eggs was studied by Stafseth et al. (1952). Survival was favored by brief heating. The data showed that survival must be expected under heat treatments usually applied in frying and poaching eggs. Heat penetration data were not collected.

*Hollandaise* receives an exceedingly light heat treatment. In fact, bacteria are likely to multiply in the sauce while it is held warm. Many food-poisoning outbreaks have been traced to this highly perishable item. To safeguard against excessive bacterial multiplication, hollandaise should not be held longer that 3 hours and desirably for briefer periods than that. If the holding time has reached the maximum limit of a 3-hour hold, the batch must be discarded. To guard against a bacteriological risk and financial loss, hollandaise sauce ought to be made in batches small enough to ensure use within an hour.

*Stirred (soft) custards* receive light heat treatments in their preparation. Such custards have been indicted many times as the food item in food-poisoning outbreaks, the causative organism being frequently *Salmonella* contributed by the eggs. Use of whole egg solids has, at least up to the present, been limited to items which tolerate "thorough" cooking. Soft custard was one item invariably included in the listing of menu items for which the use of whole egg solids was not recommended.

To determine the effect of certain quantity preparation procedures on the extent of heating which soft custards receive, Miller et al. (1961a,b) undertook two studies. In the first (1961a), a bain-marie water bath was used as the source of heat. Variables were batch size of custard, amount of egg in the formula, initial temperature of the milk before the egg was added, method of combining the ingredients, and interval of agitation. In general, the factor which was effective in producing temperatures just above 170°F within the custards was a short interval between agitations. In the second study (1961b), a steam-jacketed kettle was used as the source of heat and steam pressure was made a variable also. Higher terminal temperatures, near 180°F, were reached with this source of heat; at high steam pressures the custards curdled, however. Longer heating times were achieved when the egg was added along with the thickening agent (2-step method) instead of waiting until the starch had thickened (3-step method); the latter method is, at present, the conventional one.

*Puddings* were studied by Kintner and Mangel (1953), who prepared puddings with reconstituted dried eggs which had been inoculated with *Salmonella typhimurium, S. enteritidis, S. pullorum,* and *S. anatum;* and with a toxigenic strain of *Staphylococcus aureus.* The reconstituted dried egg was added to the thickened milk–starch–sugar mixture at 198–208°F, and cooked for ½ minute; the terminal temperature ranging from 172 to 187°F. *S. aureus* survived in chocolate pudding, and *S. pullorum, S. oranienburg,* and *S. enteritidis* in vanilla pudding. Survival was detected for the staphylococci after a 4-hour holding period at room temperature, whereas a 24-hour holding period was required to demonstrate the presence of the salmonellae. Survival could not be demonstrated in any of the puddings held for 24 hours at refrigerator temperature. The authors found that cooking stirred custards made with egg containing salmonellae and staphylococci to 196–199°F, sterilized the product. The total cooking time was 3–6 minutes. These terminal temperatures, 196 and 199°F, seem unusually high and perhaps not entirely applicable to quantity food preparation.

*Cream fillings* were studied by Hussemann and Tanner (1947). The authors used the thermal death tube method to determine the thermal death times for *S. aureus* in cream filling and found that the organism was killed by 8 minutes (lag time of 142 sec.) exposure at 149°F; by less than 4 minutes (lag time of 148 sec.) exposure at 167°F; and by less than 3 minutes (lag time of 151 sec.) exposure at

185°F. The average pH of these fillings was 6.48. The organisms survived an exposure of 30 minutes (lag time of 130 sec.) at 131°F. Cream filling prepared by accepted technique was found to be a sterile product, and it appeared that during its preparation the milk, flour, and sugar were maintained at above 149°F for much longer than 8 minutes, found in thermal death tube experiments to be necessary to kill the staphylococci; after the egg was added to the hot mixture the temperature remained above 167°F for a sufficient length of time to render the product free of staphylococci; at no time did the mixture boil.

*Meringued pies* in quantity food preparation are usually made using frozen egg whites in the meringues. Frozen egg whites have been shown to be contaminated with salmonellae and to have caused foodborne infections when used in meringues that were not sufficiently heated to destroy the contaminants. The terminal temperatures attained in meringued pies and survival of *Streptococcus faecalis* and *Escherichia coli* have been studied by Mallman et al. (1963). These authors varied the conditions of preparation as follows: the meringues were placed on cold (39°F) and hot (158°F) or warm (122°F) fillings; the pies were baked at 3 oven temperatures—325, 350 and 400°F—and the pies were baked for varying lengths of time, 8–24 minutes. Some of the data are presented in Table 43. The temperatures of filling and interface of the cold-filled pies remained considerably lower than the temperatures of their hot-filled counterparts. Meringues placed on cold fillings contained viable contaminants after baking under any conditions of the experiment. The safeness and servability of meringues cooked on hot and warm fillings were similar. Meringues baked at 400°F were either unsafe or they were unservable because they were dark, tough, and shrunken.

When the meringues were placed on hot fillings and the pies baked at 350 or 325°F for 16–20 minutes, or at 325°F for 24 minutes, the internal temperatures reached were sufficiently high to destroy the inoculum; these meringues were all palatable. Felt et al. (1956) also found that higher interface temperatures were reached when meringues were placed on hot (158°F) rather than cold (50°F) fillings. The interface temperature tended to be higher when the pies were baked for a longer period at the low (325°F) temperature than when baked for a shorter period at the medium (375°F) and high (425°F) oven temperatures.

*Leftover items* may have a varied history. It is sound thinking to assume that leftovers are apt to become contaminated with human pathogens because of the handling they receive. Additional danger,

**Table 43. Averages[a] of Temperature of Filling, Interface, and Meringue at End of Baking [Adapted from Mallman, Aldrich, Downs and Houghtby (1963)]**

| | Temperature at end of baking, °F | | | | | | |
|---|---|---|---|---|---|---|---|
| | 350°F. oven | | | 325°F. oven | | | |
| Part of pie | 12 min. | 16 min. | 20 min. | 12 min. | 16 min. | 20 min. | 24 min. |
| Hot Filling | | | | | | | |
| Filling | 144 | 165 | 181 | | | | |
| Interface | 147 | 162 | 176 | | | | |
| Meringue | 169 | 187 | 198 | | | | |
| Warm Filling | | | | | | | |
| Filling | | | | 142 | 149 | 160 | 174 |
| Interface | | | | 136 | 145 | 156 | 165 |
| Meringue | | | | 151 | 162 | 167 | 178 |
| Cold Filling | | | | | | | |
| Filling | | | | 113 | 133 | 122 | 151 |
| Interface | | | | 104 | 113 | 122 | 131 |
| Meringue | | | | 135 | 142 | 154 | 151 |

[a] Of four replications.

that of multiplication, may arise during long cooling periods. Precautions must therefore be taken to prevent additional multiplication of contaminants during rewarming before service.

Reheating practices vary and so do the thoroughness of the heating process and the temperatures attained. Blaker (1962) studied the temperatures of foods held in warming equipment and determined the temperatures of the items before they were placed in the warming equipment. She made the interesting observation that the temperatures of menu items prepared from precooked and cooled ingredients reheated just prior to serving time ranged from 82 to 140°F; these temperatures fall within the danger zone of bacterial multiplication.

The same author also observed that the end points of cooking for items reheated in the oven was usually determined by the cook on the basis of the degree of brownness, not internal temperature attained and that brownness was a poor criterion of internal temperature, especially if the items were at refrigerator temperature when placed in the oven. The author warned that such items when placed in a warmer might well become subjected to prolonged exposure at unsafe temperatures during the production period. The reader should again be reminded that the time periods for which food is held within the danger zone are cumulative regardless of whether the food was held in the oven (at supposedly hot, and safe, temperatures) or in the refrigerator (at supposedly cold, and safe, temperatures).

## Microwave Heating

Dessel et al. (1960) made a quantitative comparison of the destruction by electronic and conventional cooking of several bacterial species artificially inoculated into foods. Baked custards were inoculated with *Serratia marcescens, Staphylococcus aureus,* and *Bacillus cereus;* scrambled eggs with *S. aureus* and *B. cereus;* and ground beef patties with *Salmonella typhosa.* An electronic range, and two conventional ovens—electric and gas—were used. The results showed (Table 44) that cooking in the electronic range was at least as effective in destroying vegetative cells as conventional cooking and that spores were not eliminated with either method.

Woodburn et al. (1962) determined the destruction of salmonellae and staphylococci in precooked poultry products by heat treatment before freezing. The test organisms were *Salmonella senftenberg, S. typhimurium,* and *Staphylococcus aureus.* Internal temperatures necessary to considerably reduce the number of cells in the food heated in the microwave oven ranged from 176°F to 181°F, at a cooking time of 90 seconds. However, this heat treatment was inadequate to consistently reduce the inoculum to safe levels. To do this, a heating time of 120 seconds had to be applied with internal terminal temperatures of 196–203°F. A similar degree of destruction was achieved by heating the foods in a boiling water bath to internal temperatures of 178–192°F.

Reviewing the literature of survival and thermal death of food-poisoning organisms in bulky foods during the cooking processes, one is amazed by the discrepancies in results which no doubt are in part due to differences in the heat resistance of the organisms, but also to many other factors, such as the nature of the food, its composition, pH, and viscosity; the quantity of inoculum; previous history of inoculum; and rate of heating. From the data available, it seems that to destroy the vegetative cells of the common pathogens causing foodborne illnesses, temperatures of at least 165–170°F should be attained at that site of contamination which is the slowest one to heat and therefore the last to attain these temperatures.

Table 44. Effect of Electronic vs. Conventional Cookery on Bacteria Inoculated into Baked Custard, Scrambled Eggs, and Ground Beef Patties [Adapted from Dessel, Bowersox, and Jeter (1960)]

| | Number of samples | Cooking times | | Mean colony count per gram or milliliter | | |
| --- | --- | --- | --- | --- | --- | --- |
| Inoculation | | Range | Mean | Raw sample | Inoculated organism | Other organisms |
| **Baked Custard** | | | | | | |
| *S. marcescens* | | | | | | |
| Raw custard | 24 | — | — | a | — | — |
| Electronic range[b] | 12 | 3 min. 58 sec. to 4 min. 50 sec. | 4 min. 16½ sec. | — | negative | 108 |
| Conventional oven[c] | 12 | 34–39 min. | 36 min. 30 sec. | — | negative | 108 |
| *S. aureus* | | | | | | |
| Raw custard | 3 | — | — | $8.2 \times 10^6$ | — | — |
| Electronic range[b] | 4 | 4 min. 17 sec. to 4 min. 27 sec. | 4 min. 19 sec. | — | negative | 150 |
| Conventional oven[c] | 4 | 33 min. | 33 min. | — | 25 | 88 |
| *B. cereus* | | | | | | |
| Raw custard | 2 | — | — | $2.4 \times 10^4$ | — | — |
| Electronic range[b] | 8 | 4 min. 27 sec. to 5 min. 17 sec. | 4 min. 51 sec. | — | 62 | d |
| Conventional oven[c] | 8 | 31 min. to 34 min. 15 sec. | 32 min. 57 sec. | — | 25 | d |
| **Scrambled Eggs** | | | | | | |
| *S. aureus* | | | | | | |
| Raw egg | 3 | — | — | $3.9 \times 10^6$ | — | — |
| Electronic range[e] | 8 | 35 sec.—40 sec. | 37½ sec. | — | negative | 50 |
| Conventional stove[f] | 8 | 1 min. 10 sec. to 3 min. 10 sec. | 1 min. 39 sec. | — | 12 | 63 |
| *B. cereus* | | | | | | |
| Raw egg | 3 | — | — | $4.2 \times 10^5$ | — | — |
| Electronic range[e] | 4 | 35 sec. | 35 sec. | — | 540 | d |
| Conventional stove[f] | 4 | 1 min. 12 sec. | 1 min. 12 sec. | — | 985 | d |

Ground Beef Patties

| *S. typhosa* | | | | | | |
|---|---|---|---|---|---|---|
| Raw ground beef | 10 | — | — | $4.9 \times 10^5$ | — | — |
| Electronic range[g] | 16 | (1) 2 min. 25 sec. (2) 3 min. 35 sec. | (1) 2 min. 25 sec. (2) 3 min. 35 sec. | — | negative | 5 |
| Conventional broiler[h] | 16 | 7 min. 30 sec. | 7 min. 30 sec. | — | negative | negative |

[a] Trial experiment; exact colony count not made (too numerous to count accurately).
[b] Bottom-shelf position, high frequency.
[c] Shelf slightly above middle of oven; temperature, 350°F.
[d] Not identified.
[e] Bottom-shelf position, low frequency.
[f] Thermostatically controlled surface unit at 160°F.
[g] Top-shelf position, low frequency. Magnetron and browning units operated simultaneously. (1) indicates time of magnetron unit operation; (2) indicates time browning unit operated.
[h] Conventional electric broiler; meat placed 4–5 inches below broiler coils.

The elimination of *Clostridium perfringens* is a problem, since this organism is a spore former. Heating to a terminal temperature of 165–170°F would not eliminate the spores of this ubiquitous contaminant. The potential hazard from this organism would be particularly great in areas where heat-resistant strains prevail.

Another problem is that of preformed toxins. For example, heat-resistant toxins formed by *Staphylococcus aureus* would not be inactivated by heating to 165–170°F or, for that matter, by heating to boiling.

It is obvious from the above presentation that although many menu items receive in routine preparation an amount of heat sufficient to destroy the majority of cells of pathogens which are capable of causing foodborne illnesses, other items are given insufficient heat treatment, routinely or arbitrarily. These items will be further discussed in Chapter XIII and appropriate control measures will be suggested.

## References

Angelotti, R., M. J. Foter, and K. H. Lewis. (1961a). "Time–temperature Effects On Salmonellae and Staphylococci in Foods. I. Behavior in Refrigerated Foods. II. Behavior at Warm Holding Temperatures." *Amer. Jour. Publ. Hlth.*, *51*(1): 76–83, 83–88.

Angelotti, R., M. J. Foter, and K. H. Lewis. (1961b). "Time–temperature Effects on Salmonellae and Staphylococci. III. Thermal Death Time Studies." *Appl. Micr.*, *9*(4): 308–315.

Angelotti, Robert, Keith H. Lewis, and Milton J. Foter. (1963). "Time–temperature Effects on Fecal Streptococci in Foods. II. Behavior in Refrigerated Foods and At Warm-Holding Temperatures." *Jour. Milk & Food Tech.*, *26*(9): 296–301.

Beloian, A., and G. C. Schlosser. (1963). "Adequacy of Cooking Procedures For The Destruction of Salmonellae." *Amer. Jour. Publ. Hlth., and the Nations Hlth.*, *53:* 782–791.

Bernarde, M. A. (1957). "Heat Penetration Into Precooked Frozen Crab Cakes." *Jour. Milk & Food Tech.*, *20:* 307–311.

Billings, M. N., A. M. Briant, K. Longrée, and K. H. Harris. (1952). "Cream Pie Fillings Prepared in Multiples of An Eight-Pie Batch." *Jour. Amer. Dietet. Assoc.*, *28*(3): 228–230.

Black, Lois Carolyn, and Martha Nelson Lewis. (1948). "Effect on Bacterial Growth By Various Methods of Cooling Cooked Foods." *Jour. Amer. Dietet. Assoc.*, *24:* 399–404.

Blaker, Gertrude. (1962). "Holding Hot Foods Before They Come to the Steam Table." Unpublished paper presented at the 90th Annual Meeting of the American Public Health Association, Miami Beach, Florida. October.

Borgstrom, Georg. (1962). "Unsolved Problems in Frozen Food Microbiology."

*In:* Proceedings. Low Temperature Microbiology Symposium. 1961. Campbell Soup Company. pp. 197–251.

Bowers, J. R., and G. E. Goertz. (1966). "Effect of Internal Temperature on Eating Quality of Pork Chops. I. Skillet and Oven-Braising." *Jour. Amer. Dietet. Assoc., 48*(2): 116–120.

Canale-Perola, E., and Z. J. Ordal. (1957). "A Survey of the Bacteriological Quality of Frozen Poultry Pies." *Food Tech., 11*(11): 578–582.

Carlin, A. F., D. M. Bloemer, and Donald K. Hotchkiss. (1965). "Relation of Oven Temperature and Final Internal Temperature to Quality of Pork Loin Roasts." *Jour. Home Ec., 57*(6): 442–446.

Castellani, A. G., Ruth R. Clarke, Margaret I. Gibson, and D. F. Meisner. (1953). "Roasting Time and Temperature Required to Kill Food Poisoning Microorganisms Introduced Experimentally Into Stuffing in Turkeys." *Food Res., 18*(2): 131–138.

Cathcart, W. H., Albert Merz, and R. E. Ryberg. (1942). "Staphylococcus and Salmonella Control in Foods. IV. Effect of Cooking Bakery Custards." *Food Res., 7*(1): 100–103.

Deskins, B. B., and D. L. Hussemann. (1954). "Effect of Cooking on Bacterial Count of Ground Ham Mixtures." *Jour. Amer. Dietet. Assoc., 30*(12): 1245–1249.

Dessel, Marydale M., Edna M. Bowersox, and Wayburn S. Jeter. (1960). "Bacteria in Electronically Cooked Foods." *Jour. Amer. Dietet. Assoc., 37*(3): 230–233.

Elliott, R. P., and H. D. Michener. (1965). "Factors Affecting The Growth of Psychrophilic Microorganisms In Foods." A Review. USDA Agric. Res. Serv. Techn. Bull. No. 1320.

Fanelli, M. J., and M. F. Gunderson. (1961). "Defrost of Prepared Frozen Foods. I. Defrost Temperatures of Frozen Fruit Pies, Frozen Meat Pies and Frozen Soups." *Food Tech., 15*(10): 419–422.

Felt, S. A., K. Longrée, and A. M. Briant. (1956). "Instability of Meringued Pies." *Jour. Amer. Dietet. Assoc., 32:* 710–715.

Funk, Kaye, P. J. Aldrich, and T. F. Irmiter. (1966). "Delayed Service Cookery of Loin Cuts of Beef." *Jour. Amer. Dietet. Assoc., 48*(3): 210–215.

Gibbons, N. E., and R. L. Moore. (1944). "Dried Whole Egg Powder. III. The Effect of Drying, Storage and Cookery on the Salmonella Content." *Cand. Jour. Res., 22F:* 58–62.

Hall, Herbert, and Robert Angelotti. (1965). "*Clostridium perfringens* in Meat and Meat Products." *Appl. Micr., 13*(3): 352–357.

Hoke, I. M., G. L. Gilpin, and E. H. Dawson. (1965). "Heat Penetration Quality and Yield of Turkeys Roasted to an Internal Breast Temperature of 195°F." *Jour. Home Ec., 57*(3): 188–191.

Holmes, Z. A., J. R. Bowers, and G. E. Goertz. (1966). "Effect of Internal Temperature on Eating Quality of Pork Chops. II. Broiling." *Jour. Amer. Dietet. Assoc., 48*(2): 121–123.

Hucker, G. J., and E. R. David. (1957). "The Effect of Alternate Freezing and Thawing on the Total Flora of Frozen Chicken Pies." *Food Tech., 11*(7): 354–356.

Huppler, P. P., C. Helgeson, and M. E. McDivitt. (1964). "Bacteriological Implications of Holding Casseroles in Automatic Ovens." *Jour. Home Ec., 56:* 748.

Hussemann, Dorothy L. (1951). "Effect of Cooking on the Bacteriologic Flora of Selected Frozen Precooked Foods." *Jour. Amer. Dietet. Assoc.*, *27*: 855–858.
Hussemann, D. L., and F. W. Tanner. (1947). "Relation of Certain Cooking Procedures to *Staphylococcus* Food Poisoning." *Amer. Jour. Publ. Hlth.*, *37*: 1407–1414.
Husseman, D. L., and J. K. Buyske. (1954). "Thermal Death Time–Temperature Relationships of *Salmonella typhimurium* in Chicken Muscle." *Food Res.*, *19*: 351–356.
Hussemann, D. L., and M. A. Wallace. (1951). "Studies on the Possibility of the Transmission of *Salmonella* by Cooked Fowl." *Food Res.*, *16*: 89–96.
Jensen, L. B. (1945). *The Microbiology of Meat*. 2nd ed. Garrard Press, Champaign, Ill.
Kelly, F. G., and G. M. Dack. (1936). "Experimental *Staphylococcus* Food Poisoning. A Study of the Growth of a Food Poisoning *Staphylococcus* and The Production of an Enterotoxic Substance in Bread and Meat." *Amer. Jour. Publ. Hlth.*, *26*: 1077–1082.
Kereluk, Karl, and M. F. Gunderson. (1961). "Survival of Bacteria in Artificially Contaminated Frozen Meat Pies After Baking." *Appl. Micr.*, *9*(1): 6–10.
Kintner, Treva C., and M. Mangel. (1953). "Survival of Staphylococci and Salmonellae in Puddings and Custards Prepared With Experimentally Inoculated Dried Egg." *Food Res.*, *18*: 492–496.
Knight, R. A., and J. B. M. Coppock. (1957). "The Influence of the Baking Process on the Destruction of Salmonellae in Certain Baked Products Containing Egg Albumen." *Roy. Soc. Prom. Hlth. Jour.*, *77*: 528–532.
Licciardello, J. L., J. T. R. Nickerson, and S. A. Goldblith. (1965). "Destruction of Salmonellae in Hard-boiled Eggs." *Amer. Jour. Publ. Hlth.*, *55*(10): 1622–1628.
Longrée, Karla. (1953). "Viscosity of White Sauces Prepared in Quantity." *Jour. Amer. Dietet. Assoc.*, *29*(10): 997–1003.
Longrée, Karla, Martha Jooste, and James C. White. (1961). "Time–Temperature Relationships in Custards Prepared in Quantity With Whole Egg Solids. III. Baked in Large Batches." *Jour. Amer. Dietet. Assoc.*, *38*(2): 147–151.
Longrée, Karla, and James C. White. (1955). "Cooling Rates and Bacterial Growth in Food Prepared and Stored in Quantity." *Jour. Amer. Dietet. Assoc.*, *31*(2): 124–132.
Longrée, Karla, James C. White, and Beatriz Y. Sison. (1962a). "Time–Temperature Relationships of Souffles: Baked Foamy Omelets Made With Whole Egg Solids." *Jour. Amer. Dietet. Assoc. 41*(2): 107–110.
Longrée, Karla, James C. White, Beatriz Y. Sison, and Kathleen Cutlar. (1962b). "Scrambled Eggs Made With Whole Egg Solids: Time–temperature Relationships." *Jour. Amer. Dietet. Assoc., 41*(3): 213–216.
Longrée, Karla, Lenora Moragne, Betty A. Bell, and James C. White. (1963). "Time–Temperature Studies of Baked Loaves, Meat, Fish, Poultry." *Jour. Amer. Dietet. Assoc., 42*(6): 500–504.
Lowe, Belle. (1955). *Experimental Cookery, From the Chemical and Physical Standpoint*. 4th ed. John Wiley & Sons, New York.
Mallman, W. L., P. J. Aldrich, Doris M. Downs, and G. Houghtby.(1963). "Safeness and Servability of Meringued Pie." *Jour. Amer. Dietet. Assoc., 43*(1): 43–47.
McDivitt, M. E., and M. L. Hammer. (1958). "Cooling Rate and Bacterial

Growth in Cornstarch Pudding." *Jour. Amer. Dietet. Assoc.*, *34*(11): 1190–1194.

McDivitt, M. E., and D. L. Hussemann. (1957). "Growth of Micrococci in Cooked Ham." *Jour. Amer. Dietet. Assoc.*, *33*(3): 238–242.

Michener, H. D., and R. P. Elliott. "Minimum Growth Temperature for Food-poisoning, Fecal Indicator and Psychrophilic Microorganisms." *Advances in Food Research*, *13:* 349–396. 1964.

Miller, A. A., and F. Ramsden. (1955). "Contamination of Meat Pies by *Salmonella* in Relation to Baking and Handling Procedures." *Jour. Appl. Bact.*, *18*(3): 565–580.

Miller, Cathrine, Karla Longrée, and James C. White. (1961a,b) "Time-Temperature Relationships of Custards Made With Whole Egg Solids. I. In the Bain Marie. II. In the Steam Jacketed Kettle." *Jour. Amer. Dietet. Assoc.*, *38*(1): 43–48; 49–53.

Moragne, Lenora, and Karla Longrée. (1961). "Defrosting Times of Frozen Turkeys." *Hosp. Mgt.*, *92*(1): 64–67.

Moragne, Lenora, Karla Longrée, Nancy Lawrence Fuller, and James C. White. (1962). "Time–Temperature Relationships of Beef Patties Made With Whole Egg Solids." *Jour. Milk & Food Tech.*, *25*(9): 274–276.

Morbidity and Mortality Weekly Reports, U.S. Department of Health, Education and Welfare. (1965a). *Public Health Service, 14*(25), June 26.

Morbidity and Mortality Weekly Reports, U.S. Department of Health, Education and Welfare. (1965b). *Public Health Service, 14*(41): October 16.

National Turkey Federation Turkey Handbook. (1964). National Turkey Federation, Mount Morris, Illinois.

Peterson, A., J. J. Black, and M. F. Gunderson. (1962). "Staphylococci in Competition. I. Growth of Naturally Occurring Mixed Populations in Precooked Frozen Foods During Defrost." *Appl. Micr.*, *10*(1): 16–22.

Prescott, S. C., and L. P. Geer. (1936). "Observations on Food Poisoning Organisms Under Refrigeration Conditions." *Refrig. Eng.*, *32:* 211–212; 282–283.

Rettger, L. F., T. G. Hull, and W. S. Sturges. (1916). "Feeding Experiments with *Bact. pullorum.* The Toxicity of Infected Eggs." *Jour. Exper. Med.*, *23:* 475–489.

Rogers, R. E., and M. F. Gunderson. (1958). "Roasting of Frozen Stuffed Turkeys. I. Survival of *Salmonella pullorum* in Inoculated Stuffing. II. Survival of *Micrococcus pyogenes var. aureus* in Inoculated Stuffing." *Food Res.*, *23*(1): 87–95; 96–102.

Ross, A. D., and F. S. Thatcher. (1958). "Bacteriological Content of Marketed Precooked Frozen Foods in Relation to Public Health." *Food Tech.*, *12*(7): 369–371.

Schmidt, C. F., R. V. Lechowich, and J. F. Folinazzo. (1961). "Growth and Toxin Production of Type E. *Clostridium botulinum* below 40°F." *Jour. Food Sci.*, *26*(6): 626–630.

Solowey, M., and E. J. Calesnick. (1948). "Survival of *Salmonella* in Reconstituted Egg Powder Subjected to Holding and Scrambling." *Food Res.*, *13:* 216–226.

Stafseth, H. J., M. M. Cooper, and A. M. Wallbank. (1952). "Survival of *Salmonella pullorum* On the Skin of Human Beings and In Eggs During Storage and Various Methods of Cooking." *Jour. Milk & Food Tech.*, *15:* 70–73.

Sylvester, P. K., and J. Green. (1961). "The Effect of Different Types of Cooking On Artificially Infected Meat." *Med. Jour. of Australia*, *2*(19): 765.

Thatcher, F.S., J. Robinson, and I. Erdman. (1962). "The'Vacuum Pack' Method of Packaging Foods in Relation to the Formation of the Botulinum and Staphylococcal Toxins." *Jour. Appl. Bact.*, *25*(1): 120–124.

U.S. Department of Health, Education and Welfare, Public Health Service. (1962). "Food Service Sanitation Manual." PHS Publication No. 934, Washington, D.C.

Wiedeman, K., M. A. Watson, H. Mayfield, and W. G. Walter. (1956). "Effect of Delayed Cooking on Bacteria in Meat Loaf." *Jour. Amer. Dietet. Assoc.*, *32*(10): 935–940.

Wiedeman, K., M. A. Watson, J. Neill, and W. G. Walter. (1957). "Effect of Holding Time on Bacteria in Chicken Casserole." *Jour. Amer. Dietet. Assoc.*, *33*(1): 37–41.

Winter, A. R., and C. Wrinkle. (1949). "Proper Defrosting Methods Keep Bacterial Counts Low in Frozen Egg Products." *U.S. Egg and Poultry Mag.*, *3:* 28–31, 44. March.

Winter, A. R., H. H. Weiser, and M. Lewis. (1954). "The Control of Bacteria in Chicken Salad." *Appl. Micr.*, *1*(6): 278–281.

Woodburn, M., M. Bennion, and G. E. Vail. (1962). "Destruction of Salmonellae and Staphylococci in Precooked Poultry Products by Heat Treatment Before Freezing." *Food Tech.*, *16*(6): 98–100.

## Additional Readings

Anderson, O. E. *Refrigeration in America.* Princeton Univ. Press, Princeton, New Jersey. 1953.

Anellis, A., M. M. Rayman, and J. Lubas. "Heat Resistance of *Salmonella* Species in Liquid Whole Egg. II. Salmonella Problems." *In:* Quartermaster Food and Container Institute for the Armed Forces. "Stability of Dehydrated Eggs." pp. 83–86. 1954.

Ball, C. O., and F. C. W. Olson. *Sterilization in Food Technology.* McGraw-Hill Book Co., New York. 1957.

Bate-Smith, E. C., and T. E. Morris (ed.) *Food Science—Theory, Practice and Calculations.* A symposium on quality and preservation of foods. Cambridge Univ. Press, London and New York. 1952.

Beckett, M. B., J. S. Wyman, and W. W. Joy. "An Epidemic of *Salmonella typhimurium* Traced to Frozen Egg Whites." *Student Med.*, *9:* 142. 1960.

Cameron, E. J. "Report on Microbiological Methods." *Jour. Assoc. Off. Agr. Chem.*, *23:* 607–608.

Canada, J. J., and D. H. Strong. "Effects of Animal Alimentary Passage on the Heat Resistance of *Clostridium perfringens.*" *Appl. Micr.*, *13*(5): 788–792.

Collee, J. G., J. A. Knowlden, and B. C. Hobbs. "Studies on the Growth, Sporulation and Carriage of *Clostridium welchii* with Special Reference to Food Poisoning Strains." *Jour. Appl. Bact.*, *24:* 326–339.

Dack, G. M., O. Woolpert, I. Noble, and E. Halliday. "Experimental Study of Possible Routes of Contamination of Cakes With Food Poisoning Staphylococci." *Jour. Prevent. Med.*, *5:* 391. 1931.

Dack, G. M. *Food Poisoning.* 3rd ed. Univ. Chicago Press, Chicago, Illinois. 1956.

Dawson, E. "Heat Penetration, Quality and Yield of Turkeys Roasted to an

Internal Temperature of 195°F." *Jour. Home Ec.*, *57*(3): 188-191. March, 1965.

Esselen, W., and A. S. Levine. "Bacterial Food Poisoning and Its Control." A Review. Bulletin No. 493, College Agr., Univ. Mass., Amherst, Mass. 1957.

Foter, M. J. "Time-Temperature Relationships in Food Sanitation." *The Cornell Hotel and Rest. Admin. Quarterly*, *4*(1): 58-62. 1963.

Gall, B. O. M. "Microwave Heating." *The Cornell Hotel and Restaurant Administration Quarterly*, *4*(1): 79-82. 1963.

Ott, Thomas M., Hamed M. El-Bisi, and W. B. Esselen. "Thermal Destruction of *Streptococcus faecalis* in Prepared Frozen Foods." *Jour. Food Sci.*, *26*(1): 1-10. 1961.

Straka, R. P., and Frances M. Combes. "Survival and Multiplication of *Micrococcus pyogenes var. aureus* in Creamed Chicken Under Various Holding, Storage and Defrosting Conditions." *Food Res.*, *17*(5): 448-455. 1952.

Stritar, J., G. M. Dack, and F. G. Jungewalter. "The Control of Staphylococci in Custard-Filled Puffs and Eclairs." *Food Res.*, *1*: 237-246. 1936.

Tanner, F. W., P. R. Beamer, and J. C. Ricker. "Further Studies on the Development of *Clostridium botulinum* in Refrigerated Foods." *Food Res.*, *5*: 323-333. 1940.

Webster, R. C., and W. B. Esselen. "Thermal Resistance of Food Poisoning Organisms in Poultry Stuffing." *Jour. Milk & Food Tech.*, *19*: 209-212. 1956.

# CHAPTER XIII

# TIME-TEMPERATURE CONTROL: PRINCIPLES RELATING TO, AND MEASURES DIRECTED AT, PREVENTING MULTIPLICATION OF CONTAMINANTS IN INGREDIENTS AND MENU ITEMS

As was demonstrated with the aid of research data presented in Chapter XII, there are many opportunities for food items prepared in quantity to be subjected to conditions under which bacterial multiplication is possible due to favorable temperatures.

Time–temperature control is the most powerful measure which a food service manager can apply in the control of bacterial multiplication in the storage, preparation, and service of food.

The control measures discussed below are designed to retard the multiplication of bacterial contaminants through the application of cold and/or heat and to reduce or eliminate contaminants by heating.

## Frozen Foods

In frozen foods, no multiplication of bacteria should be possible. Frozen foods must be freezer-stored at 0°F. At temperatures between 32 and 19°F, certain food spoilage bacteria, the psychrophilic or cold-loving ones, may multiply. Although these are not pathogenic, they mar or ruin the quality of the frozen product. Bacteria capable of causing foodborne illnesses are able to survive freezing and freezer storage and may resume growth when the food thaws.

## Purchased Items

RECOMMENDATIONS

Purchase only the amount of the food item which can be used in the immediate future. The quantity ordered depends on such factors as: the inventory on hand, present needs, amount of freezer space available, and frequency of delivery. In general, rapid turnover is preferable over long holding; less than 1 month being a desirable holding time with 3 months being the maximum acceptable time. After this length of time the quality of the food may deteriorate; the degree of deterioration will vary with the nature of the food frozen.

Specify transit conditions; frozen foods should be held at 0°F or lower during the entire period.

When receiving frozen foods, have the necessary freezer space ready; check for signs of mishandling. If there is suspicion of defrost, the delivery should be refused.

Store frozen foods promptly at 0°F.

## Cooked Items Frozen on the Premises

Food service operators who freeze precooked items on the premises must inform themselves about the principles of freezing and the sanitary hazards connected with the operations (Tressler and Evers 1957). The food service manager may find helpful information available in Extension Bulletins, leaflets, etc. Most of the sanitary hazards connected with freezing are identical with those applicable to commercial freezing of precooked frozen items (Chapter VII, Part III). Certainly, foods to be frozen must be of excellent quality, and should not be overcooked to avoid cell and tissue breakdown. Good sanitary practices must be used in producing and handling the food at all times. Low temperatures cannot be expected to nullify the effects of poor sanitation. The hazard in products of this type lies in contamination with pathogens and possibly toxin production in consequence of extensive bacterial multiplication in the foods to be frozen, and again when frozen foods are mishandled during and after defrost.

The packaging must also conform to high sanitary standards, and rapid heat transfer must be insured for fast freezing. Storage at 0°F or lower is recommended. No frozen food improves in quality with storage. The freezer must not become a catch-all for leftovers.

RECOMMENDATIONS

Start with raw material of excellent quality.

Keep working surfaces and equipment in sanitary condition by cleaning and sanitizing these at 2-hour intervals.

Have employees exercise strict personal hygiene, including periodic handwashing (two-hour intervals are suggested), and meticulous handwashing after visit to the toilet.

Exercise scrupulous general kitchen sanitation.

Maintain strict time–temperature control by ensuring that the ingredients and/or menu items do not remain in the hazardous temperature zone (45–140°F) more than 2 hours.

Remember that the period of 2 hours for which food may "safely" remain at hazardous temperatures is a composite of every minute of warm holding, not necessarily one continuous 2-hour span of time; and that hazardous temperatures may prevail during handling as well as cooling.

Be cognizant of the fact that many frozen foods which need to be cooked again before being served receive minimum heat treatment before they are frozen, and that bacterial survivors may remain.

Prevent recontamination of the food during cooling and packaging.

Use appropriate moisture-proof, sanitary containers. A good quality container or wrapping material is moisture-vapor resistant, does not impart a flavor of its own, and is sanitary and durable.

Freeze food in small (shallow) batches for fast heat transfer, since the typical institutional freezer is not efficient for freezing bulky items.

### Defrosting Foods

In the Food Service Sanitation Manual (U.S. PHS, 1962) it is stated that frozen foods must be stored at such temperatures as to remain frozen, except when being thawed for preparation or use. Furthermore, it is required that potentially hazardous foods be thawed at refrigerator temperatures of 45°F or below or under cold running water. As part of the cooking process, foods may be quick-thawed, and other methods are permitted if they are satisfactory to the health authority.

The main principles underlying these recommendations are that unless defrosting is absolute necessary it should be omitted and that the utmost precautions should be taken to assure that potentially hazardous foods do not unduly warm up during the defrosting process.

It should always be remembered that if defrosting is continued to the point that the ice crystals have been converted to free water, and if temperatures are above 45°F, bacterial multiplication is possible.

It is important to use all defrosted items promptly. Holding defrosted items under refrigeration more than a day may lead to a buildup of cold-loving bacteria. Even pathogenic contaminants, if present in large numbers, may multiply to dangerously high populations (Miller, 1965).

Refreezing of defrosted items is not recommended in principle. The frozen food industry has wisely protected the quality of its products by discouraging this practice since the culinary as well as the microbiological quality usually suffers in defrosting.

GUIDELINES

It is the responsibility of the food service manager or dietitian to set up detailed guidelines concerning defrosting procedures which should include these major points:

1) Type of food, whether it should be defrosted or not
2) Place
3) Equipment
4) Details of defrosting procedures:
    a) Length of time (approximate)
    b) Protection against contamination during period of defrost
    c) Protection against chances of warmup beyond the point where bacterial multiplication can be resumed (above 45°F)

RECOMMENDATIONS

*Fresh Frozen Foods Served Unheated. Fruit juice concentrates:* Reconstitute from frozen state and chill at once. *Fresh fruit:* Defrost in original container in the refrigerator, or in a tightly sealed moisture-proof container in cold running water.

*Fresh Frozen Foods to be Heated. Fruits:* Defrost just enough for convenience in handling; defrost in a refrigerator or in a tightly sealed moisture-proof container in cold running water. If the fruit must be thawed at room temperature it should be kept in the original closed container. Prolonged warming will cause mushiness of the fruit and may allow microbial multiplication in mildly acid fruits.

*Vegetables:* Do not defrost before cooking, except corn on the cob.

*Fish, shellfish, meats (small cuts), and poultry (small cuts):* Do not defrost unless breaded or covered with batter. If defrosting is necessary, place item in refrigerator or, enclosed in tightly sealed moisture-proof bag, in cold running water.

*Whole turkeys, large roasts, frozen egg:* Defrost in a refrigerator or, provided that the item is protected by a tightly sealed moisture-proof container, in cold running water.

**Precooked Frozen Foods.** The manufacturers' directions will state whether an item requires defrosting.

## Chilling Cooked Foods

For cooked foods the purpose of chilling is to prevent microbial multiplication. The chilling of uncooked foods may extend to other purposes also. For items prepared in the food service establishment chilling is used to protect items prepared in advance to be used later as ingredients, complete menu items, and leftovers.

Items prepared outside the food service establishment which need chilling may include canned goods which have been opened and otherwise packaged perishables, frozen foods destined to defrost, and items received in a partially prepared or fully prepared state which await further preparation and/or service.

For items sold through vending machines, refrigeration must be applied to readily perishable items which are to be served cold.

### Refrigeration Needs

The refrigeration needs of a food service operation depend on many managerial factors (West et al., 1965; Kotschevar and Terrell, 1961). Certainly no perishable foods classified as potentially hazardous should be stored at room temperatures because of lack of refrigeration, although this is all too frequently done. When setting up refrigeration requirements, space must be allowed for defrosting of frozen items.

In order to be used effectively, refrigerators should be placed near the appropriate preparation centers. At present, salad centers usually have refrigeration units nearby. For green, gelatin, and many other types of salad the benefit of refrigeration is obvious, since visible deterioration is prevented. Not obvious to the eye is the need for refrigeration in connection with ingredients and menu items which are vulnerable to warmth because of their capacity to serve as media for multiplication of bacterial pathogens. Food handlers who are expected to keep potentially hazardous foods out of the danger zone of bacterial multiplication should be provided with adequate refrigeration nearby and readily accessible to them.

### Temperature Required for Chilling Cooked Food

In the U.S. Public Health Service Food Service Sanitation Manual (1962) is stated that "all potentially hazardous foods shall be maintained at *safe* temperatures (45°F or below . . .), except during necessary periods of preparation and service." These recommendations take into account the lowest temperatures reported for growth and toxin production of food-poisoning bacteria and of pathogens causing foodborne infections and intoxications.

The food should cool rapidly; the center of the food mass should reach 45°F within a time span of 2–4 hours. This cannot be achieved unless the refrigerator temperature is 40°F or lower.

## Length of Storage

Gathering of data pertaining to the multiplication of foodborne pathogens at low temperatures resulted in the recommendation that a temperature of 45°F is safe for short periods, but that for longer storage, lower temperatures are desirable. The maximum lengths of storage suggested by Foter (1963) for readily perishable cooked food are given in Table 45. The temperatures and times presented therein are based on results of studies conducted on salmonellae and staphylococci (Angelotti et al., 1959) and are also in accordance with the lower growth limits of the fecal streptococci (Angelotti et al., 1963) and *Clostridium perfringens* (Smith, 1962).

These recommendations presuppose that the refrigerator temperatures in question are strictly maintained and that deviations toward the warm side are excluded. Moreover, these recommendations do not include the time required to cool warm food items to the specific storage temperatures. These cooling times should not exceed 2–4 hours; however, they frequently do under conditions of quantity food service. In well-managed food service operations, highly perishable cooked foods are used within a day of preparation and refrigerator storage.

Table 45. Maximum Length of Storage at Temperatures Preventing Growth of Salmonellae and Staphylococci in Readily Perishable Cooked Foods [Data from Foter (1963)]

| Length of storage without growth, days | Storage temperature, °F |
|---|---|
| 1 | 50 |
| 2 | 48 |
| 3 | 46 |
| 4 | 44 |
| 5+ | 42 |
| 5+ | 40 |

In summary: Perishable cooked foods should be cooled to 45°F or below within a period of 2–4 hours and stored at 40°F or below for as brief a period as possible. The storage times stated in Table 45 should not be exceeded. The food temperature should be maintained at or below 45°F. at all times.

## Refrigerators for Chilling Cooked Food

### SANITARY FEATURES

The cleanability of materials used for walls, ceilings, floors, and shelves and construction features should be considered. Floor drains are a sanitary hazard. It is beyond the scope of this book to discuss the component parts and principles of refrigeration. An informative discussion of refrigeration and refrigerators which should prove helpful to the food service manager has been presented by Frolich (1964) and by West, Wood, and Harger (1965).

Certain principles pertaining to refrigerators and their use apply to all types of walk-in and reach-in refrigerators: the *temperature* through appropriate refrigeration units is reduced to a predetermined level; the *air flow* is usually controlled; and the *moisture content* of the air (relative humidity) is sometimes controlled. Actually, these three factors are interdependent.

### TEMPERATURES

The colder the refrigerator air, the faster food will cool. The temperature of a refrigerator used for the cooling and storage of cooked foods should be kept as low as is feasible without causing the food to freeze; the maximum temperature should not exceed 40°F.

Before adjusting the temperature of a refrigerator, experimentation is necessary to determine its temperature conditions over a number of days, including those of peak production and those of no production. These points should be kept in mind:

1) Ascertain the warmest area, or areas, and the coldest area, or areas, where food is stored; check the temperature there; never place the thermometer on a wall.

2) Record temperatures frequently throughout the testing days, and possibly nights; this way one should find the lowest as well as the highest temperatures that are likely to occur; it is important to include periods when the refrigerator carries a typical "full load" and a small load.

The results may look like these:

1) The warmest and coldest areas are similar; this indicates good

ventilation throughout the refrigerator. Controls should be tentatively set to allow for a maximum of 40°F and a minimum of 32°F or above and checks made to find out whether these temperatures are maintained at times of a capacity warm load. If at capacity load the refrigerator temperatures do not rise, all is well.

2) The warmest and coldest areas are quite dissimilar even when the load is light and cold: adjustment will be difficult, because poor circulation is probably the cause of this discrepancy. Refrigerators with poor circulation respond poorly to a large load, especially when the load is warm. When using such a refrigerator, it is essential that the load be precooled before it is introduced. If possible, a refrigeration system with adequate circulation should be provided.

3) The warmest and coldest areas are similar when the food load is light and cold, and the circulation seems adequate; after food is introduced there are peaks of unduly high temperature rises in the warmest as well as the coolest areas. The controls should be set as low as possible without risking the danger of freezing the food. If the temperature at peak load rises above 40°F and lingers there for hours, the capacity of the refrigerator obviously does not meet the requirements of the load. In this case, precooling the warm food outside the refrigerator may solve the problem. Precooling methods will be discussed below.

Longrée and White (1955) continuously recorded for six working days the temperature fluctuations in six locations within a walk-in refrigerator equipped with a forced air unit. The cooler was used for the storage of cooked foods. The lowest temperature recorded during this period was 39°F, the highest 55°F (Fig. 29). Two distinct temperature peaks were observed: one following the close of the noon meal, the other following the night meal. At night, the employees rushed, and much of the food placed in the cooler came from the steam table and other warming equipment. At noon, some effort was made to precool some items. This may explain the somewhat lower peak temperatures following the lunch hour. The graph shows clearly that: 1) The load of warm food had a tremendous effect on the temperatures prevailing in the refrigerator. 2) The refrigerator temperatures decreased very slowly; in fact, temperatures continued to drop until high noon of the following day. 3) Opening and closing of the refrigerator door during the busy morning hours had little if any effect on the temperatures.

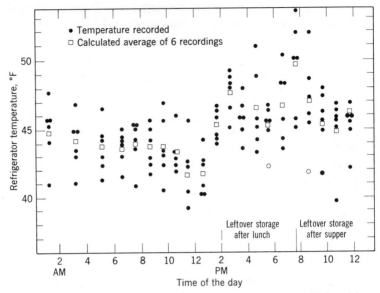

*Fig. 29. Diurnal and nocturnal fluctuation of air temperature in walk-in refrigerator, minimum temperature 39°F. Temperature was recorded continuously for six 24-hour periods.* Adapted from Longrée and White (1955).

## AIR FLOW

Refrigeration works by the removal of heat. Circulation plays a very important role in the removal of the blanket of warm air and in supplying cold air to the food to be cooled. The effect of forced air was demonstrated by Moragne et al. (1959a) for a 55-cubic foot reach-in refrigerator in which loads of 8, 16, and 32 gallons were cooled from 140° to 80°F. The effect of forced air on the temperature of the refrigerator air and the cooling time of the sauce is shown in Tables 46 and 47. In this particular refrigerator a ceiling-type

**Table 46. Effect of Total Load and the Effect of Forced Air on the Temperature Range of the Refrigerator Air[a] [Adapted from Moragne, Longrée, and White (1959a)]**

| Total load, gal. | Number of stock pots | Size of batch, gal | Air temperature, °F | |
|---|---|---|---|---|
| | | | Fan on | Fan off |
| 8 | 8 | 1 | 32–42 | 63–65 |
| 16 | 8 | 2 | 32–41 | 64–75 |
| 32 | 8 | 4 | 30–52 | 68–85 |

[a] Sauce was cooled from 140° to 80° F.

Table 47. Effect of Forced Air on the Total Cooling Time of White Sauce[a] [Adapted from Moragne, Longrée, and White (1959a)]

| Total load, gal. | Number of stock pots | Size of batch, gal. | Total cooling time | | | |
|---|---|---|---|---|---|---|
| | | | Fan on | | Fan off | |
| | | | hr. | min. | hr. | min. |
| 8 | 8 | 1 | 2 | 26 | 3 | 55 |
| 16 | 8 | 2 | 4 | 43 | 9 | 21 |
| 32 | 8 | 4 | 7 | 45 | 16 | 46 |

[a] Sauce was cooled from 140° to 80°F.

forced air evaporator was used, and since air is taken in and discharged at the ceiling, the various sections varied greatly in temperatures.

More efficient circulation of air is provided when the air intake is near the ceiling and the exit is near the floor, below the bottom shelf.

HUMIDITY

The relative humidity of the refrigerator has an effect on moisture changes in the food stored. If the relative humidity of the air is lower than that of the stored items, moisture will be drawn from them and the food surfaces may take on a dry appearance. If the relative humidity of the air is higher than that of the food, the food will pick up moisture and sliming and bacterial deterioration will result.

Since cooked items stored in a refrigerator range in relative humidity from high to low, it follows that losses or gains in moisture must be prevented by covering each item.

## Heat Transfer Problems in Foods

In principle, refrigeration should remove the heat from foods at a rate that effects cooling to safe temperatures within a span of time sufficiently brief to prevent bacterial multiplication in the foods cooled. The methodology applied will vary with the nature of the food cooled, the quantity of the food cooled, and with the cooling facilities.

SOLID FOODS

Solid foods are, in general, difficult to cool. Solid foods cool by conduction and this is a slow process. Variation in heat transfer is affected, among other factors, by the composition of the food, its geometry, and its bulk.

Research data on heat transfer in solid foods are scarce. Therefore, cooling times are largely anticipated on the basis of experience rather than scientific knowledge. Recently, an apparatus which makes possible rapid and accurate determination of certain thermal properties of solid foods was described by Dickerson (1965).

### FLUID FOODS

The viscosity of fluid food plays an important role in heat transfer. In low-viscosity items, convection currents help to continually mix the fluid as long as a temperature difference exists within a batch. In high-viscosity items, cooling takes place largely by conduction, a relatively slow process of heat transfer. As a food becomes more viscous while cooling, as many foods do, the convection currents are increasingly suppressed and conduction cooling takes over gradually.

Fatty and starchy foods are slow to cool. As the temperatures decrease, a dense film forms at the wall of the container surrounded by the coolant, be this air or water; this film constitutes a barrier to heat transfer.

## Cooling Procedures Pertaining to the Quantity of Food Cooled

The quantity of warm food to be cooled may prolong cooling times in several ways: the total warm load may be too large for the particular refrigerator to handle, or the individual batch may be too large, even if the refrigerator maintains the desired low temperature, or a combination of these conditions may exist.

### CONTROL OF TOTAL LOAD

The size of the total load of warm food which may be placed in a refrigerator without raising the temperature of the refrigerator air to an extent which makes rapid cooling of the food to 45°F impossible must be established by the food manager. Frequent checks of the refrigerator temperature in a manner described previously in this chapter are necessary to do this.

Overloading can be remedied by using another refrigerator to accommodate the excess load or decreasing the temperature of the food before the load is introduced into the refrigerator.

Data showing the effects of total load and of initial temperature on the temperature range prevailing in a refrigerator and the cooling time of the food were reported by Moragne et al. (1959a). These

Table 48. Effect of Placing White Sauce in the Refrigerator at Two Initial Temperatures on the Temperature Range of the Refrigerator Air[a] [Adapted from Moragne, Longrée, and White (1959a)]

| Total load, gal. | Number of stock pots | Size of batch, gal. | Air temperature, °F | |
|---|---|---|---|---|
| | | | Sauce at 140°F | Sauce at 80°F |
| 8 | 8 | 1 | 32–41 | 33–44 |
| 16 | 8 | 2 | 32–39 | 33–41 |
| 32 | 8 | 4 | 31–51 | 31–41 |

[a] Sauces were cooled to 60°F.

Table 49. Effect of Total Load and Effect of Placing the Sauce in the Refrigerator at Two Initial Temperatures on the Total Cooling Time of White Sauce[a] [Adapted from Moragne, Longrée, and White (1959a)]

| Total load, gal. | Number of stock pots | Size of batch, gal. | Total cooling time | | | |
|---|---|---|---|---|---|---|
| | | | 140° to 60°F | | 80° to 60°F | |
| | | | hr. | min. | hr. | min. |
| 8 | 8 | 1 | 3 | 57 | 2 | 33 |
| 16 | 8 | 2 | 7 | 11 | 2 | 51 |
| 32 | 8 | 4 | 11 | 20 | 5 | 7 |

data are presented in Tables 48 and 49. Methods of precooling foods outside the refrigerator will be discussed later.

CONTROL OF DEPTH OR SIZE OF BATCH

Even if the total load is sufficiently small or sufficiently cool or both, and thus will not cause a rise in the temperature of the refrigerator air above the desirable low level, batch depth or size must be controlled whenever warm food is introduced into a refrigerator (as was discussed in Chapter XII) to assure that the food will cool from 140° to 45°F within 2–4 hours.

*Solid Foods* lend themselves well to being cooled in shallow layers. A few examples should suffice: meats can be sliced, poultry sliced or divided into smaller pieces, fish placed in shallow layers, and so forth; salads, such as potato and poultry placed in shallow pans and refrigerated, cool faster than when cooled in deep containers. They can be refrigerated either without precooling or following precooling on ice.

*Semisolid Foods* must be handled according to the judgment of the food manager; some semisolid items would be treated like solid foods, others like fluid ones.

*Fluid Foods* are difficult and impractical to handle in shallow containers. Regular stock pots are more suitable and less liable to spill the food. Since the cooling surface cannot be increased vertically, it must be extended horizontally; this means that a large batch must be broken up in several small ones, of 2 gallons or even less. The smaller the batches are, the faster will cooling proceed.

For food which has been effectively precooled to a low temperature, separation into small batches may be eliminated. Precooling to 60°F or lower is desirable; the process should not take longer than one hour.

### Precooling Methods

Precooling methods should be efficient. If the methods are slow, more harm than benefit may result. Ideally, the combined cooling from 140° to 45°F outside and inside the refrigerator should be achieved with a maximum 4 hours, preferably within 2 hours.

#### USING ROOM TEMPERATURE

Precooling in the kitchen, at room temperature, is a deplorable, yet all too popular, practice. This method is unacceptable from a sanitation point of view, because the process is slow and temperature conditions favorable to bacterial multiplication are likely to be created. Furthermore, recontamination may occur easily when food is left for hours in a place as busy as a kitchen.

At best, temporary holding at room temperature may be applied to hot foods (above 140°F) provided the batches are small and the holding times are brief, and provided the food is protected from contamination. These conditions usually cannot be fulfilled and dangerous conditions are created whenever potentially hazardous foods are allowed to precool on kitchen floors or other warm and unsuitable places. Research data are available to prove the dangers of this practice (Black and Lewis, 1948; Lewis et al., 1953; Longrée and White, 1955; McDivitt and Hammer, 1958; Miller and Smull, 1955).

#### USING LOW-TEMPERATURE COOLANTS

Low-temperature coolants which can be applied are ice, cold water, and cold air.

It is the responsibility of the food service manager or dietitian to set up the appropriate procedures and to see to it that they are carried out. It will take some experimentation on the part of the person in charge of food preparation to work out procedures to fit the refrigeration situation of his food service operation. If the refrigeration space available for the storage of cooked foods is such that refrigerators get easily overloaded and unduly warmed up when average or large loads are introduced, precooling must be carried to lower temperatures than would be necessary if refrigeration space were adequate.

Experimentation would also be necessary to determine the approximate cooling times for specific quantities of specific foods cooling in specific containers, because all these factors affect cooling times. Experimentation should be accurate and results reproducible. A reliable thermometer should be used and measurements made in the warmest part of the food mass. The combined cooling times outside the refrigerator and inside should, if at all possible, be shorter than 4 hours.

Therefore, the specifications set up for precooling should state:

1) Type of food
2) Type of container
3) Amount placed in each container
4) Type of covering used
5) Length of time for which the food should be precooled, terminal temperature to be achieved in the warmest part of the food mass, and approximate location of the warmest part
6) Treatment following precooling

For solid foods ice is a very practical coolant. The foods to be cooled should be placed in shallow layers in shallow pans or trays and covered as protection against contamination.

Some semisolid foods may lend themselves to precooling like a solid food item; others would have to be treated like fluid foods. The food service manager will need to make that decision.

For fluid foods, cold running water can be successfully used in precooling even when batch size is large. A prerequisite to successful cooling is that the water be actually cold, say 40°F or lower. In some areas the so-called cold water is not as cold as is necessary for an effective cooling job. The importance of water temperature in precooling has been demonstrated by Moragne et al. (1959b), who found that the cooling times of the foods were prolonged one and a half times when the water temperature was increased from 35° to 42°F; and that at a summer water temperature of 70°F the food rarely cooled to below 75°F and cooling proceeded at an extremely slow pace.

Steam-jacketed kettles can be constructed to be used as cooling kettles. Some manufacturers of steam-jacketed kettles make such equipment available. Cooling kettles should be designed and constructed in such a way that the coolant circulates all around the kettle. Special baffles installed between kettle and jacket are effective in directing the flow of the coolant. Finally, provision should be made for slowly agitating the food during cooling. Agitation will be discussed at a later time in detail.

Stock pots containing food to be precooled can be placed in sinks, in converted bains-marie, or in other water baths supplied with cold running water. Under practical conditions of food service, sinks are usually used for various other purposes in food preparation; therefore, danger exists that sooner or later the stock pot containing the food will end on the kitchen floor and cooling will become an illusion. The food would now become subjected to increased chances for contamination.

In contrast to a much used kitchen sink, a bain-marie converted to a water bath and supplied with cold water at a fast rate of flow is a very desirable piece of equipment to use (Moragne et al., 1959b). Preferably, all cooling equipment should be installed in a separate cooling room maintained at a low temperature. Foods precooled should be agitated, at least at certain intervals, say every 15–20 minutes.

USING AGITATION

Agitation is known to be a powerful tool in hastening heat transfer in fluid materials, including foods. Agitation is used extensively in heating of foods. The food-processing industry uses agitation in cooling processes also. Unfortunately, the food service industry has not made much use of agitation in cooling, probably because of force of habit to "simply refrigerate" or because of lack of suitable equipment to do the job.

To show the application of agitation in the precooling of fluid foods, some research data will now be presented.

*Manual Agitation.* The beneficial effect of manual agitation on cooling times of white sauce was studied by Moragne et al. (1959b). White sauces were cooled in stock pots immersed in cold running water in a bain-marie water bath. Of the implements compared for effectiveness a wire whip proved most efficient; however, this whip was not employed for whipping, but rather to remove the cooled portion of food away from the container wall, using a complete circle agitation technique. Intervals of agitation were 15 and 30 minutes. The two intervals achieved similar reductions in cooling time, approximating one-half the time required by the batches cooled without the use of agitation.

However, helpful as manual agitation may be, it cannot be expected to be very effective when applied to a large food mass.

Manual agitation with kitchen utensils such as whips, spoons, spatulas, and similar implements is not very effective in removing the layers of cold food which tend to build up on the inside wall of the vessel containing the food, and which interfere with the transfer of heat into the surrounding coolant. Agitation by hand increases labor cost. Also, agitation may be forgotten because of more pressing demands on employees. After all, an employee who fails to apply agitation in certain heating processes sees and smells the consequences of his negligence, whereas nothing so startling will happen when he omits agitation during cooling, for no one sees or smells the activity of food-poisoning bacteria.

*Mechanical Agitation.* Mechanical agitation has the advantage over manual agitation of being more efficient and more predictable.

The effect of mechanical agitation on cooling of puddings was studied by McDivitt and Hammer (1958), who used an electric mixer at slow speed. The coolant in this case was therefore air of room temperature. The cooling times of the agitation batches were reduced as compared with those of unagitated ones. The 9-quart batches of pudding cooled from 142° to 77°F in 1¾-hour period of stirring.

Cooling effects of an agitator consisting of a cold tube which contained refrigerated water was studied by Longrée et al. (1960) and Moragne et al. (1961) using white sauce and pudding as foods. Cooling times were reduced to one-half or one-third of the time required by non-agitated batches.

The efficacy of the agitator was further improved by applying a scraper-lifter attachment as described by Moragne et al. (1963). The foods cooled were custards and puddings. Using this gadget, the cooling times of the foods were approximately one-sixth of the time needed to cool comparable batches in the conventional manner, namely, under refrigeration (Table 50).

A difficulty encountered with fatty foods in tube cooling was solidification of the fat on the surface of the tube. An entirely different approach was tried; agitation was applied to foods while they were cooling in a refrigerator (Longrée et al., 1963a). The

Table 50. Cooling Times of 4-Gallon Batches of Custard and Pudding Agitated with Plain Cold Tube and with Scraper-Lifter Modification of Tube [Adapted from Longrée (1964)]

| | Cooling time from 140° to 60°F | | |
|---|---|---|---|
| Food | Not agitated,[a] hr. | Agitated with cold tube,[b] hr. | Agitated with cold tube plus scraper-lifter,[b] hr. |
| Custard | 10.7 | 4.5 | 1.6 |
| Pudding | 11.1 | 5.0 | 1.7 |

[a] Refrigerated at 370°F, not agitated.
[b] At 6 rpm.

Table 51. Average Cooling Times of 4-Gallon Batches of Custard and Pudding when Scraper-Agitated under Refrigeration at 37°F [Adapted from Longrée (1964)]

| Rate of agitation | Total cooling time,[a] hr. |
|---|---|
| Custard | |
| Zero | 10.7 |
| 16 rpm | 3.8 |
| 38 rpm | 3.5 |
| Pudding | |
| Zero | 11.1 |
| 16 rpm | 4.0 |
| 38 rpm | 3.8 |

[a] From 140° to 50°F.

refrigerator air served as the coolant, and the agitator used was a scraper type gadget. Use was made of the fact that properly designed scrapers are highly efficient in removing films from cooling surfaces and markedly improve the rates of heat transfer of viscous materials (Ackley, 1960). Some of the results are shown in Tables 51 and 52.

There is a danger when using agitation of creating undesirable changes in the consistency of the foods; such changes may pertain to viscosity, to breaking up of solid ingredients, and the like. Therefore, it is essential that the rate of agitation be kept as low as is absolutely essential to achieve the desired degree of cooling. Nowrey et al.

Table 52. Average Cooling Times of 2-Gallon Batches of Soups and Entrees Scraper-Agitated under Refrigeration at 37°F [Adapted from Longrée, Moragne, and White (1963a)]

| Food | Total cooling times,[a] min. | |
|------|------------------|------------|
| | Not agitated | Agitated[b] |
| **Soups** | | |
| Chowders | 145 | 50 |
| Cream soups | 200 | 50 |
| Navy bean soup | 120 | 45 |
| Vegetable soup | 185 | 50 |
| **Entrees** | | |
| Chop suey | 140 | 45 |
| Meat and vegetable stew | 160 | 40 |

[a] From 140° to 50°F.
[b] At 38 rpm.

(unpublished) studied heat transfer in large agitated batches and found that rates of agitation below 10 rpm were sufficiently rapid. When purchasing a cooling kettle equipped with an agitator it is essential to specify that the agitator be capable of being operated at very slow speeds and be of the scraper type. The importance of appropriate construction features which allow the cooling water to completely circulate around the food has been pointed out earlier.

It is the responsibility of food service management to make its needs known to the manufacturers of equipment. If there is sufficient demand, the manufacturing industry will endeavor to fill these needs. The initiative, however, must come from the food service industry.

RECOMMENDATIONS

Provide appropriate and sufficient facilities for chilling.

Provide the facilities in locations where potentially hazardous food items are handled during preparation and service. Use these facilities. Do not hold food at kitchen temperature other than during actual manipulation.

Be sure that the air temperature of the refrigerator is at least 40°F, but not cold enough for the food to freeze. Check temperature frequently, especially at times of peak load and low load; make adjustment if indicated.

Make provisions which ensure that cooked items do not remain in the hazardous temperature range of 45–140°F for more than 2 hours; an absolute maximum being 4 hours. Remember that the safe temperature span is a composite of all the minutes for which the cooked food was exposed to bacteriologically hazardous temperatures.

To aid rapid cooling, do not introduce large food batches into the refrigerator. Solid foods should be divided into smaller units, or sliced; placed in shallow layers on trays precooled, if indicated, and refrigerated. Fluid foods should be refrigerated in 1–2-gallon batches. Cool meat and poultry separately from broth and gravy.

Precool foods to avoid overloading the refrigerator with warm food and to speed cooling. Solid foods are precooled on trays or shallow pans set on ice; fluid foods in stockpots immersed in cold running water; fluid food should be agitated at frequent and regular intervals. For large quantities, jacketed cooling kettles equipped with slow-speed scraper agitators and an efficient cooling system are appropriate.

Do not allow food to precool to room temperatures in the kitchen because cooling is very slow at the temperatures prevailing in the food preparation area. At 140°F the hazardous temperature zone is entered, and food must be cooled down rapidly to 45°F, using efficient procedures described above.

Use cooked food held in cold storage as soon as possible. It is a desirable practice to limit holding time to 24 hours.

Food should be protected from recontamination at all times.

### Cold Foods Prepared Outside the Food Service Establishment

As the number of food services, including hospital and school food services, which contract for food from outside grows, the sanitary hazards connected with lack of time–temperature control gain in importance.

The dangers lie in the fact that foods which should be kept under constant refrigeration are apt to be subjected for prolonged periods to temperatures at which bacterial growth may take place. Although specifications made by the food buyer may state strict time–temperature control during preparation and transit, this control is up to the vendor in the end. The reliability of the vendor can therefore not be overestimated.

### Cold Foods Dispensed from Vending Machines

Milk, ice cream, pastries, sandwiches, salads, and other potentially hazardous cold food items sold through vending machines are either purchased from local sources or prepared in a special vending commissary. Although it is the vending machine operator who is responsible for the sanitation of the product, and the machine, it is in the interest of the food service establishment where the machines are set up that the items dispensed be prepared under sanitary conditions and that strict time–temperature control be maintained throughout their preparation, transport, and holding in the machine. As has been pointed out by Tiedeman (1958), placing stacks of sandwiches prepared at room temperature in a cold compartment in the expectation that they will be cooled in a short time is no more than wishful thinking. Tiedeman (1958) reported that by "imbedding a thermocouple in the meat filling in the center of a cubical pack of 36 sandwiches made at 78°F and placed in a refrigerator at about 45°F, it was found that the center had not reached 50°F overnight, that is about 15 hours."

For low-temperature stored hazardous items transported to and sold through vending machines the U.S. Public Health Service recommends a temperature of 45°F or below, except for the actual time required to load or service the vending machine, and a maximum recovery period of 30 minutes following the servicing of the machine. The temperature of the vending machine should be thermostatically controlled. Controls should be available which ensure that in the case of mechanical trouble or power failure, no food will be dispensed until the machine has been serviced by the operator. PHS regulations demand that vending machines dispensing potentially hazardous foods be provided with thermometers which are accurate to within ±2°F within the warmest portion of the cold storage compartment. In this writer's opinion a temperature-recording device would be even more effective, since it would accurately determine the time–temperature conditions prevailing in the machine every minute of the day, every day of the week; and the record would be there for everyone to inspect.

Hazardous cold foods are frequently dispensed in conjunction with hot foods. An example is cream dispensed in conjunction with hot coffee. The regulations of the U.S. PHS (1965) require that

milk and fluid milk products . . . shall be pasteurized and shall be dispensed only in individual, original containers or from bulk containers into which such product was placed at the milk plant: *Provided,* That such products may be reconstituted automatically within the vending machine when (a) the powder or concentrate is made from a pasteurized milk or milk product and is from an approved source; (b) the mixing chambers or bowls and any food-contact surface downstream from such mixing units are maintained at safe temperatures; and (c) the product is reconstituted for immediate dispensing in individual unit servings.

PHS regulations further stipulate that

milk and fluid milk products used as an ingredient in hot liquid beverages dispensed from vending machines may be transferred to a multiuse machine canister at the machine location: *Provided,* That (a) the location offers adequate protection against dust, insects, and other contamination; (b) the milk or fluid milk product is transferred from a dairy-filled container of not to exceed one-half gallon capacity; (c) the entire contents of such dairy-filled container are used in the transfer; (d) unused portions removed from the machine are discarded to waste; and (e) the milk or fluid milk product is poured only into an empty canister which has been effectively cleaned and sanitized at the commissary: *Provided further,* That milk or fluid milk products shall not be used as an ingredient under the terms of this paragraph unless the temperature of the hot beverage at the point of mixing with the milk product is 160°F or higher.

## Handling and Holding Foods at Kitchen Temperature

During precooking operations, potentially hazardous foods are frequently held at kitchen temperatures for several hours. This is serious since the temperature range of 70–100°F is particularly favorable to bacterial multiplication of the pathogens capable of causing foodborne illnesses except that the optimum temperature range for growth of *Clostridium perfringens* lies higher, 112–116°F.

Exact timing of the holding of perishable food items may seem to be a difficult task. Actually it is not, provided thoughtful and purposeful management is put to work.

Control measures, although varying in the details of execution, do not vary in principles. Therefore, the food manager will have to use his resourcefulness in putting this all-important principle to work in a manner suitable to the specific setup of the food service operations to which he lends his services. The principles underlying the control measures pertain to food prepared on the premises as well as to food prepared outside the food service establishment.

*Recommendations (General)*

Reduce to a minimum the time during which the potentially hazardous foods, such as milk, meat, poultry, eggs, fish and items made with them, are held at kitchen temperatures.

Move operations which can be performed in an area other than the kitchen, to cool surroundings, if available.

Stagger preparation procedures as much as is feasible. Keep potentially hazardous foods cold (45°F) or hot (140°F) except for manipulations required. Especially items which have been ground, sliced, shaped, mixed or otherwise handled, are apt to be contaminated and should not be held at kitchen temperatures except for a brief period of time.

*Recommendations (Specific Hazardous Items)*

*Sandwiches* made with potentially hazardous ingredients (example: meat, poultry, egg, fish):

Use ingredients of excellent sanitary quality.

Prepare sandwiches from cold ingredients except butter which should be soft for spreading.

Maintain hands, working surfaces, equipment, and utensils in sanitary condition.

Work rapidly to minimize time during which ingredients and sandwiches remain at hazardous temperatures.

Stagger production: place finished sandwiches on shallow trays no more than approximately 3 or 4 inches high; refrigerate. Start a new batch.

*Salads* made with potentially hazardous ingredients:

Use ingredients of excellent sanitary quality. A minimum of handling is essential to keep them sanitary. For example, deboning poultry before cooking reduces the chances for contaminating the meat after it has been cooked.

Have ingredients chilled.

Maintain hands, working surfaces, equipment, and utensils in sanitary condition.

Incorporate part of the acid dressing into potentially hazardous ingredients immediately after these have been handled and, probably, contaminated (see Chapter XI).

Work rapidly and stagger production, thereby minimizing time for which ingredients remain at hazardous temperatures.

Chill promptly in shallow pans.

*Leftovers:*

Plan to have no or little food left over. Leftovers can be wasteful and are a bacteriological hazard. They are handled often and are thus subjected to many chances for contamination. Moreover, leftovers are usually subjected to various cycles of holding, cooling, and warming and are often held for many hours at temperatures at which bacteria may multiply.

Stagger menu item production of combination items involving proteinaceous ingredients such as poultry, meat, egg, fish, and seafood with cream sauces, gravies, and the like. Keep the hazardous ingredients refrigerated and add to hot sauces as needed.

Before storage reheat lukewarm leftovers to boiling, if possible, to destroy contaminants; precool and refrigerate. This rule applies in particular to items which come back from counters, patient floors, and the like.

Precool and refrigerate leftover items following the methods stated above under General Recommendations.

Use leftovers within a day.

## Foods Held in Warm-Holding Equipment

As recommended by the U.S. Public Health Service, the minimum temperature at which prepared hot food should be kept warm is 140°F (Food Service Sanitation Manual, 1962). Menu items which cannot tolerate holding at this temperature without serious damage to their culinary quality, for example hollandaise, should be made in small quantities to insure that they are consumed within a 2 or 3 hour period. If they are not used, they must be discarded.

Items placed in warming equipment should be at temperatures considerably above 140°F. Warm-holding equipment is principally designed to keep food warm rather than to heat it. The question of whether or not food temperatures of at least 140°F can be maintained in present-day warming equipment is an important one.

### Steam Tables

Blaker (1961) observed the temperatures at which hot foods were being held in four types of food service establishments, including a college pay cafeteria, a commercial cafeteria, an industrial cafeteria, and a table-service dining room. She surveyed the kind of heat-holding equipment being used and recorded visible quality changes in the foods held, changes in color and consistency, surface drying, scum formation, and the like. The types of the steam tables used included the "wet" as well as the electric "dry" kind. She found that the temperatures of foods brought to the steam table at 160°F or above remained well above 140°F for an extended holding period, 45 minutes or longer.

In separate laboratory studies, longer holding periods were applied to determine the effectiveness of the steam tables in maintaining temperatures. The menu items studied included cream soups, meats, potatoes, and "made" entrees and/or baked vegetables. It was found that if the foods were placed on the steam table at 170°F or above, their temperatures gradually declined, but seldom did they drop below 140°F within a 2-hour holding period, provided the steam was not turned off during holding.

It was found that the wet steam table was efficient in maintaining temperatures with minimum damage to the quality of the menu items studied. However, wet steam tables are often not operated at temperatures necessary to maintain safe temperatures in the foods because of a tendency of the steam to escape around the inserts. Blaker calls attention to the situation and recommends that methods should be investigated for sealing sectored surfaces. It seems that the buyers and users of such equipment should make their dissatisfaction known to the manufacturing industry, and insist on equipment which can be operated at the capacity necessary to produce safe temperatures without creating a nuisance to employees and guests.

## Other Warm-Holding Equipment

Blaker (1962) determined the temperatures of food items held warm in heat-holding equipment other than steam tables. The equipment included these types: electric holding cabinet, bain-marie, steam-jacketed kettle, top of range (solid grill top; open burner), and steamer. When such primary equipment was converted to keep food warm prior to being served, the following conditions were fulfilled: ovens and steam-jacketed kettles were turned off, solid grill top range units were turned low, and open burner range units were turned low or were turned off.

These important observations were made on the temperatures of items subjected to holding: items which had been prepared in one continuous cooking operation were at high temperatures, 170°F or above. However, those prepared from ingredients which had been precooked, then cooled, and finally reheated prior to being served were at low temperatures, 140°F or even lower.

In food prepared in one continuous operation and at approximate temperature of 170°F or above, and held in electric holding cabinets set at 175°F, the temperature rarely fell below 140°F during prolonged (1½ hours) holding. However, in cabinets set at 150°F the food temperatures often decreased to temperatures as low as 130°F.

In primary cooking equipment used as "makeshift" warm-holding equipment, food temperatures were observed to be fairly adequately maintained. The open-burner range was the least satisfactory primary equipment used for warm-holding because of severe changes in quality, whereas the solid grill top did a more satisfactory job in maintaining adequate temperatures without such severe quality changes.

In summary, the studies showed that both conventional heat-holding equipment and primary cooking equipment used for warm-holding were capable of keeping cooked food items at temperatures of 140°F and higher for a prolonged period of time, 1½ hours at least, provided the initial temperature of the food was at least 170°F. Therefore, a special effort must be made to reheat all precooked and cooled foods to 170°F before they are allowed to go into warm-holding equipment.

### RECOMMENDATIONS

Plan menu item production to: keep warm holding time at a minimum, insure bacteriological quality, and retain nutritive value as well as other culinary quality characteristics such as color, texture, and flavor.

Be sure the food is hot, preferably near 170°F, when it is placed in the warm-holding equipment. Do not use warm-holding equipment for heating lukewarm foods.

Maintain warm-holding equipment in good working condition. Check its heat-holding capacity periodically using a thermometer placed in the coolest portion of the batch at the beginning and close of warm-holding; perform this test on various types of foods prepared by different heating procedures; repeat the tests in order to obtain typical, average temperature values; food temperature should be maintained at 140°F or above during warm-holding.

### Hot Foods Dispensed from Vending Machines

The U.S. Public Health Service (1965) requires that readily perishable hot foods or ingredients be held at temperatures not lower than 140°F, and that vending machines be equipped with controls which insure that this temperature is maintained at all times, except for the period needed to service the machine. After servicing, a maximum recovery period of 30 minutes is allowed for the required temperature to be reestablished in the warm-holding cabinet.

Vending machines dispensing hot foods may be equipped with both a cooling and a heating unit, or with only a heating unit. Thermostatic controls should insure the maintenance of applicable temperatures which are 45°F or below and 140°F or above, except for the actual time required to load or service the machine. There should be controls which prevent the machines from dispensing potentially hazardous foods until serviced by the operator in the event of power failure or mechanical breakdown.

The U.S. Public Health Service (1965) demands that foods be held either at 45°F and below or at 140°F, and that the time required to heat food through the 45–140°F temperature zone should not exceed a maximum of 2 hours. The regulations also stipulate that in those hot vending machines which are not equipped with refrigerated storage, no time delay should be permitted after placing potentially hazardous foods in the machine.

It is recommended that hot food vending machines which are designed to heat food from 45° to 140°F should be equipped with automatic controls which render the machine incapable of dispensing potentially hazardous items in case the 2-hour span is exceeded.

According to PHS regulations, thermometers should be installed which register the temperature to an accuracy of ±2°F. They should be placed in the warmest part of the cold storage unit or the coldest part of the heated storage unit. As was stated earlier in this chapter, it is the opinion of this writer that a recording device would be extremely desirable since it would provide a continuous record of the time–temperature conditions prevailing in the various compartments of the machine which could be inspected by all interested.

## Cooking Foods

Many menu items, but not all, are heated sufficiently to render them free from pathogens if these should be present.

### End Point of Heating Adequate to Destroy Bacteria

At this time it is almost universally accepted that for all practical purposes, internal temperatures of 165–170°F achieved in food will be sufficient for the effective reduction in number, or even elimination, of non-spore-forming pathogens such as the salmonellae and staphylococci. The spores of *Clostridium perfringens* are not eliminated by such heat treatments; non-heat-resistant spores of this organism have been demonstrated to survive, at least in part, an exposure to 176°F for 10 minutes. The spores of heat-resistant strains of this organism may endure prolonged boiling, for as much as several hours. The response of the fecal streptococci in food to heating to terminal temperatures of 165–170°F is at this time not clarified.

The degree of heating applied in many routinely used cooking methods eliminates pathogenic contaminants and parasites such as trichinae from menu items, as was shown in Chapter XII. In thoroughly heated menu items, the pathogens might be killed, but bacterial toxins preformed in the food are not necessarily eliminated by this heating. Heating the spores of *C. perfringens* up to 176°F may simply heat-shock them, thus stimulating them to subsequent germination (Hall and Angelotti, 1965). Moreover, food sterilized by heating and subjected to recontamination would be an excellent medium for pathogens which are sensitive to microbial competitors, such as *Staphylococcus aureus.* Another frequent after-cooking contaminant of meat and gravy is the pathogen *C. perfringens.*

It is therefore evident that even thorough heating is not a cure-all, rather a supportive sanitary measure.

RECOMMENDATIONS

Items which do not suffer a decrease in culinary quality upon heating to high temperatures should be heated to 165–170°F; a thermometer should be used to check on the temperature reached.

In cases where heating to safe temperatures is not applicable the control measures directed at preventing bacterial contamination and bacterial multiplication can and must be effectively used.

## Items Given Mild Heat Treatments, Routinely or Arbitrarily

It was shown in Chapter XII that certain menu items are routinely or occasionally heated to temperature end points which would not insure the elimination of pathogens. Among these are bulky items such as stuffed turkeys and hams.

Under discussion will be those items which are apt to be contaminated with pathogens, and items which are potentially hazardous because of their composition and previous history or items which are hazardous for a combination of these reasons.

For the sake of discussing appropriate control measures, the food likely to receive mild heating to unsafe terminal temperatures is categorized as follows:

1) The item becomes less desirable or attractive or is completely ruined when heated to high temperatures; mild heating is applied by the cook on purpose.

2) The item is bulky and penetration of heat to the center is slow; unless an effort is made to ascertain the internal temperatures reached and a thermometer is used, the cook does not know whether the center has become hot, or lukewarm, or whatever; heating is haphazard.

3) The item is cold when heating is started and the heat source is intense (broiler, very hot oven); the cook uses as end point of heating the appearance of the outside; the center may become hot or just lukewarm; heating is haphazard.

4) Cold ingredients are incorporated into a warm base resulting in a lukewarm mixture; the combined mixture, unless pur-

posely reheated to a definite safe end point, may never get hot; heating is haphazard.

## MEATS COOKED TO THE RARE STAGE

Meats, especially beef, are frequently cooked to the rare stage, a terminal temperature of 125–140°F. The inside of roasts which have not been deboned or otherwise handled should not pose a sanitary problem. Rolled roasts, however, may be contaminated on the inside because of the handling they have received. If rareness is a desired quality characteristic, heat cannot be applied to eliminate the contaminants.

These contaminants may resume multiplication as soon as the meat has sufficiently cooled to make this possible and will continue this activity until the temperature has dropped to below 45°F.

### *Recommendations:*

Serve rolled roasts cooked to the rare stage, which are to be served hot, within a short period following the close of the cooking.

Keep the temperatures of these roasts as near 140°F as is feasible. At approximately 116°F rapid multiplication of *Clostridium perfringens* spores must be expected.

Slice rare rolled roasts to be served cold soon after the termination of cooking; cool the slices quickly to 45°F and keep meat at that temperature, or below, until served.

Treat products made from ground meat like rolled roasts since they must be expected to be contaminated all the way through. Meat loaf and meat patties have been shown to be acceptable when heated to a medium rate (140°F) stage and they are frequently served that way.

Cool gravy separately from meat.

## SHELLFISH

Oysters, clams, and mussels are usually lightly heated to preserve their culinary quality, and much seafood is eaten raw. Therefore, one must not rely on heating as an effective measure in the control of pathogenic contaminants.

### *Recommendations:*

Procure shellfish from sources approved by the State Shellfish Authority; if the source is outside the state, the source must be certified by the state of origin.

Keep shellfish cold, near 32°F, as long as feasible.

Stagger production for lightly heated menu items and reduce warm holding to a minimum.

Avoid having leftovers.

EGGS AND PRODUCTS MADE WITH EGG

Shell eggs, unless dirty and/or cracked, should be free from salmonellae and therefore may be given mild heat treatment in preparing boiled, poached, fried, and scrambled eggs, sauces, and other items requiring egg.

Up to the present, precautionary measures have been advised in the use of processed eggs. Unpasteurized frozen and dried egg may contain salmonellae. These products will, in the future, be processed after pasteurization to remove contaminants. Unpasteurized egg white should not be used in unheated items such as chiffon desserts. If unpasteurized processed egg products are used in products that are mildly heated, provisions must be made to ensure thorough heating without ruining the culinary quality of the product.

Recontamination of cooked products from uncooked eggs is a possibility often overlooked. Sources may be egg shells, egg dust consisting of unpasteurized powdered egg, and unwashed containers containing remnants of unpasteurized frozen or reconstituted dried egg.

*Scrambled Eggs* can be heated up to 180°F, or a dry stage, then remoistened through incorporation of a medium white sauce (USDA, 1959; Longrée et al., 1962); for 50 servings of egg use 1 quart of sauce. Also, baked scrambled eggs can be moistened by serving them with a creole sauce (USDA 1963).

*Hollandaise* is now fortunately excluded from the menu list of most institutions. It is a very hazardous item, consisting largely of egg and butter, slightly acidified with lemon juice. It is an excellent medium for bacterial growth, and does not tolerate high heat. Therefore, heating as a control measure is not applicable to this potentially dangerous sauce. As a control measure its holding time must be kept very brief, and when the specified time has gone by, the unused portion must be discarded. In the Food Service Sanitation Manual of the U.S. Public Health Service (1962) the recommendation is made that hollandaise and other sauces which must be held in the temperature range of 45–140°F must be prepared from fresh ingredients, made only with shell eggs if eggs are used, and must be discarded as waste within 3 hours after preparation. The Armed

Forces and some municipalities have set up even stricter requirements.

For *Custards, Cream Fillings, and Puddings* the procedures directed at making menu items safe whenever processed egg is used which is unpasteurized and may contain salmonellae, involve heating to safe terminal temperatures and/or prolonged heating. Not all procedures routinely used ensure that the egg is thoroughly cooked. In these potentially unsafe procedures the egg is added at the end of the cooking period, after the other ingredients have been cooked to doneness. This conventional and much used procedure for making custards, fillings, and puddings is the "three-step method." The milk is heated (no definite terminal temperature is usually given); the starch and sugar are added and the mixture cooked until it has thickened; finally the egg is incorporated, the end point of cooking being usually brief and uncertain. In the two-step method, developed by Billings et al. (1952), the egg is added early and higher temperatures as well as longer cooking times are assured. In this method, three-fourths of the milk, sugar, and salt are heated to 190–200°F and a suspension prepared from one-fourth of the milk, starch, and egg are added to the hot milk. This method is applicable to custards, fillings, and puddings. The studies on custards made by Miller et al. (1961a,b) showed that in a steam-jacketed kettle higher terminal temperatures were achieved than in a bain-marie, the terminal temperatures being 180° and 170°F, respectively. In the steam-jacketed kettle, the steam pressure had to be kept low to prevent scorching. Fillings cooked in a steam-jacketed kettle had terminal temperatures of 172–182°F (Billings et al., 1952).

*Fish or Poultry Loaves* in which processed egg is used should be placed in baking pans in batches of shallow depth, approximately 2½ inches, to assure heat penetration to the center (Longrée et al., 1963b). An excellent way to increase variety of uses for dried whole egg solids is to prepare a batch of *Hard-Cooked Egg* from reconstituted solids (12 ounces of solids to 1 quart of water), and to bake the egg in greased pans at 400°F until the mixture is set; when cool the egg can be cut into 1-inch squares, and used as an ingredient in main dishes ( University of the State of New York, 1959).

*Meringued Pies* are items which are often lightly heated in the interior portion because the cooks are interested in producing a pretty meringue. Brief heating at high oven temperature is dangerous, because this procedure results in undercooking of the lower portion of the meringue. An attractive and safe meringue may be produced by using a procedure worked out by Mallman and co-workers (1963): The meringue should be placed on a hot (approximately 158°F) filling, and the pie baked at 325°F for 24 minutes or at 350°F for 16 minutes.

### Recommendations:

*Shell eggs:* Use high quality, clean eggs with unbroken shells.

*Processed eggs:* Buy and use only pasteurized processed (frozen, dried) eggs.

When unpasteurized processed egg must be used, the following heating recommendation will be an aid to achieve either high terminal temperatures or long heating times at moderate temperatures. Both methods are effective in reducing or eliminating salmonellae in the cooking process. Menu items in which egg is used as a binder should be baked in shallow layers to insure complete heat penetration.

*Scrambled eggs:* Cook in oven or steamer to the dry stage; moisten with a medium white sauce for soft texture.

*Hollandaise:* Stagger production. Discard portion not used within 2 or 3 hours.

*Custards, cream fillings:* Use the two-step method of preparation as described in the text which involves that the egg is incorporated early in the cooking process and receives a thorough heat treatment.

*Meringued pies:* Place filling in shells while filling is hot (at least 158°F); use the hot-process method for preparing meringue which involves incorporating the sugar as a hot sirup; bake the pies at a moderate temperature, 325° or 350°F for 24 or 16 minutes, respectively.

#### TURKEY

The dangers of the practice of stuffing and roasting large turkeys have been discussed in Chapter XII.

The only control measure recommended is that large turkeys should not be stuffed for several reasons. (1) Bacteriological safety. The cavity of the turkey is apt to be contaminated with salmonellae; if the bird is roasted without stuffing, the heat penetrates easily into the cavity and kills the contaminants, whereas the temperatures prevailing in the stuffing during roasting may even allow bacterial multiplication. (2) Labor is saved. (3) The finished product looks neat and is easy to portion and serve. (4) Cooking time is short. (5) The cavity of the bird cannot possibly accommodate all the stuffing needed for the number of servings which the turkey itself provides;

therefore, additional dressing must be baked outside the turkey. (6) Heat penetration is fast in stuffing baked in pans. Even potentially hazardous stuffings, such as those made with giblets, oysters, etc., can be efficiently heat treated when baked in separate pans. The stuffing should be heated to 165–170°F.

*Recommendations:*
Do not stuff turkey.
Bake dressing in separate, shallow pans to an internal temperature of at least 165–170°F.

HAMS

Hams are available untenderized or tenderized, and may be labeled partially-cooked, fully-cooked, or ready-to-eat (see Chapter VI). The minimum heat treatment for the cooked hams required by USDA regulations is 148°F which is adequate to destroy trichinae, but not necessarily bacterial pathogens.

*Recommendation:*
Heat all hams to an internal temperature of 165–170°F.

*Cold Precooked Items Requiring Terminal Heating*

In this group are included the "made" dishes, meat, poultry and fish pies, casseroles, croquettes, meat cakes, fish cakes, and the like. Leftovers served hot and combination items made with leftovers, and served hot, belong here. The group includes precooked frozen foods such as meat pies and chicken pies.

The ingredients used in the preparation of these items are usually handled considerably in the course of their preparation, and adequate time–temperature control is often wanting. Use of leftovers may pose a special problem because of their history which may include long exposures to lukewarm temperatures during their previous preparation, holding, cooling, and subsequent rewarming. It is sound thinking to assume that all these items have been contaminated, probably with pathogens, before they are served.

The extent to which heating should be carried varies somewhat with the ingredients. Certainly, all menu items should attain internal temperatures of at least 165°F, and items made with meat should be brought to boiling.

In light of recent research data on *Clostridium perfringens* (Hall and Angelotti, 1965), it is necessary to require that all meats, especially beef, and menu items made with beef should be reheated to boiling if at all feasible. This precaution, however, is not effective toward heat-resistant strains. As has been reported earlier, a high percentage of meats must be expected to be contaminated with *C. perfringens.* Cooked meats and gravy may prove contaminated because of survival of heat-resistant spores or because of recontamination after cooking with the spores and vegetative cells of this organism. Therefore an additional safety measure is to prevent meat and gravy from remaining at temperatures which will permit rapid bacterial growth for longer than 2 hours.

To achieve the desired internal temperatures in the food without ruining the outside portion, it is often necessary to apply moderate temperatures and longer heating times. The internal temperatures should be checked in the coldest portion of the food with an accurate thermometer.

"Running under the broiler" is the worst way to reheat food, and "bubbling at the top" and "browning" are most unreliable criteria for determining the end point of heating required to kill pathogenic contaminants.

In a well-managed food service establishment where standardized quantities, procedures, equipment, and temperatures are used, it should not prove difficult to work out specific directions for the reheating of cold precooked menu items and frozen precooked items. Some experimentation on the part of the manager or dietitian will have to precede the setting up of appropriate workable directions which should result in a safe and otherwise acceptable product.

It may not prove feasible to achieve terminal temperatures of 165°F or above in items fried in deep fat (see Chapter XII), such as croquettes and crab cakes. Control measures applicable to all foods, but of specific aid here, are: provide and use only ingredients of the highest sanitary quality. Keep them cold until ready for heating. Prepare mixtures, cool if required, shape, bread, heat, and serve with a time span sufficiently brief to prevent bacterial multiplication; apply time–temperature control measures using your knowledge of bacterial growth and good judgment.

### Recommendations:

Items made with beef should be heated to boiling, if at all feasible.

All other items should be heated to at least 165–170°F internal temperature.

Items which are heated in deep fat may not reach internal temperatures sufficiently high to kill contaminants. Use every precaution to prevent contamination, and exercise strict time–

temperature control. Use high quality ingredients, *do not use leftovers*, minimize contamination from hands during shaping, keep shaped items cold until ready to heat, and heat in small quantities for immediate service.

## Creamed Items

When preparing cream soups and creamed entrees, danger exists that the cold solid ingredients when incorporated into the cream base may create temperature conditions in the combined mixture which are conducive to bacterial multiplication. The problem is greater in connection with entrees, than soups, heat transfer being rather easily achieved in soups. It is essential that the combined mixture be reheated at once. In cases where reheating to 165–170°F proves difficult because of poor heat transfer, the procedure of mixing the cream base and solid ingredients has to be staggered. It is absolutely essential that the temperature of food before it goes to the steam table be well above 140°F in order to have it remain at the required temperature (of 140°F) during the warm-holding period. It must be remembered that the solid ingredients incorporated into the cream base have frequently undergone considerable handling, deboning, cutting, cubing, etc. Therefore, if it was not reheated to at least 165°F and bacterial kill was not achieved, the mixture will harbor these contaminants. Holding at 140°F will prevent their multiplication, true, but the potential danger remains.

Leftover creamed items must be reheated to at least 165°F and then cooled rapidly to a safe temperature, 45°F or below; in many food service operations, it is required that leftovers of creamed food be discarded.

### Recommendations:

Have cream sauce as hot as possible.

Use only ingredients of excellent sanitary quality. *Do not use leftovers.*

Reheat the mixture to 165–170°F; in the coolest part of batch the temperature should never be below 140°F.

Stagger production unless you are sure you serve the entire batch. Creamed items are particularly poor risks as leftovers. Creamed leftovers, if any, should be discarded.

## References

Ackley, E. J. (1960). "Film Coefficients of Heat Transfer for Agitated Process Vessels." *Chem. Engin.*, *67:* 133.

Angelotti, R., E. Wilson, M. J. Foter, and K. H. Lewis. (1959). "Time–Temperature Effects on Salmonellae and Staphylococci in Foods. I. Behavior in Broth Cultures and Refrigerated Foods." Techn. Report F59-2, The Robert A. Taft Sanitary Engineering Center, Public Health Service, Department of Health, Education and Welfare.

Angelotti, R., K. H. Lewis, and M. J. Foter. (1963). "Time–Temperature Effects on Fecal Streptococci in Foods. I. Behavior in Refrigerated Foods and at Warm-Holding Temperatures." Jour. Milk & Food Tech., 26(9): 296–301.

Billings, M. N., A. N. Briant, K. Longrée, and K. W. Harris. (1952). "Cream Pie Fillings Prepared in Multiples of an Eight-Pie Batch." Jour. Amer. Dietet. Assoc., 28(3): 228–229.

Black, L. C., and M. N. Lewis. (1948). "Effect on Bacterial Growth of Various Methods of Cooling Cooked Foods." Jour. Amer. Dietet. Assoc., 24: 399.

Blaker, Gertrude. (1961). "Holding Temperatures and Food Quality." Jour. Amer. Diet. Assoc., 38(5): 450–454.

Blaker, Gertrude. (1962). "Holding Hot Foods Before They Come to the Steam Table." Unpublished paper presented at the 90th Annual Meeting of the American Public Health Association, Miami Beach, Fla. October.

Dickerson, R. W. (1965). "An Apparatus for the Measurement of Thermal Diffusivity of Foods." Food Tech., 19(5): 198–204.

Food Protection Committee of the Food and Nutrition Board. (1964). "An Evaluation of Public Health Hazards From Microbiological Contamination of Foods." National Academy of Sciences, National Research Council Publication 1195. Washington, D.C.

Foter, M. J. (1963). "The Time–Temperature Relationships in Food Sanitation." Cornell Hotel and Restaurant Administration Quarterly, 4: 58–62.

Frolich, Louise A. K. (1964). "Refrigeration as a Tool of the Food Service Industry." School Lunch Jour., 18(2): 17–29.

Hall, H. E., and R. Angelotti. (1965). "Clostridium perfringens in Meat and Meat Products." Appl. Micr., 13(3): 352–357.

Kotschevar, L. H., and M. E. Terrell. (1961). Food Service Planning: Layout and Equipment. John Wiley & Sons, New York, N.Y.

Lewis, M. N., H. H. Weiser, and A. R. Winter. (1953). "Bacterial Growth in Chicken Salad." Jour. Amer. Dietet. Assoc., 29(11): 1094–1099.

Longrée, Karla. (1964). "Cooling Fluid Food Under Agitation." Jour. Amer. Dietet. Assoc., 44(6): 477–479.

Longrée, K., and J. C. White. (1955). "Cooling Rates and Bacterial Growth in Food Prepared and Stored in Quantity. I. Broth and white sauce." Jour. Amer. Dietet. Assoc., 31: 124–132.

Longrée, K., L. Moragne, and J. C. White. (1960). "Cooling Starch-Thickened Food Items with Cold Tube Agitation." Jour. Milk & Food Tech., 23: 330.

Longrée, K., A. R. Willman, and M. Knickrehm. (1960). "Soups and Main Dishes For Your Community Meals." New York State College of Home Economics, Cornell University Miscellaneous Bulletin No. 35.

Longrée, K., J. C. White, B. Y. Sison, and K. Cutlar. (1962). "Scrambled Eggs Made with Whole Egg Solids." Jour. Amer. Dietet. Assoc., 41(3): 213–216.

Longrée, K., L. Moragne, and J. C. White. (1963a). "Cooling Menu Items by Agitation Under Refrigeration." Jour. Milk & Food Tech., 26: 317–322.

Longrée, Karla, L. Moragne, B. Bell, and J. C. White. (1963b). Time–Temperature Studies of Baked Loaves." Jour. Amer. Dietet. Assoc., 42(6): 500–504.

McDivitt, M. E., and M. L. Hammer. (1958). "Cooling Rates and Bacterial Growth in Cornstarch Pudding." *Jour. Amer. Dietet. Assoc., 34:* 1190–1194.

Mallman, W. L., P. J. Aldrich, Doris M. Downs, and G. Houghtby. (1963). "Safeness and Servability of Meringued Pie." *Jour. Amer. Dietet. Assoc., 43*(1): 43–47.

Miller, Cathrine, Karla Longrée, and James C. White. "Time–Temperature Relationships of Custards Made with Whole Egg Solids. I. In the Bain-Marie (1961a). II. In the Steam-Jacketed Kettle (1961b)." *Jour. Amer. Dietet. Assoc., 38*(1): 43–48; 49–53.

Miller, W. A. (1965). "Bacterial Counts of Prepackaged, Frozen and Unfrozen Pork and Veal Cutlets." *Jour. Milk & Food Tech., 28*(7): 217–219.

Miller, W. A., and M. L. Smull. (1955). "Efficiency of Cooling Practices in Preventing Growth of Micrococci." *Jour. Amer. Dietet. Assoc., 31*(5): 469–473.

Moragne, L., K. Longrée, and J. C. White. (1959a). "Heat Transfer in Refrigerated Foods." 33rd Annual Report, New York State Association of Milk Sanitarians. 5 pp. December.

Moragne, L., K. Longrée, and J. C. White. (1959b). "Heat Transfer in White Sauce Cooled in Flowing Water." *Jour. Amer. Dietet. Assoc., 35*(12): 1275–1285.

Moragne, L., K. Longrée, and J. C. White. (1960). "The Effect of Some Selected Factors on the Cooling of Food Under Refrigeration." *Jour. Milk & Food Tech., 23*(5): 142–150.

Moragne, L., K. Longrée, and J. C. White. (1961). "Cooling Custards and Puddings with Cold-tube Agitation." *Jour. Milk & Food Tech., 24*(7): 207–210.

Moragne, L., K. Longrée, and J. C. White. (1963). "Effect of a Scraper-Lifter Agitator on Cooling Time of Food." *Jour. Milk & Food Tech., 26*(6): 182–184.

Nowrey, J. E., K. Longrée, E. J. Race, and S. A. Wald. (unpublished). "Batch Cooling with Slow-Speed Scraper Agitator." *Food Tech.,* to be published.

Smith, Louis DS. (1962). "*Clostridium perfringens* Food Poisoning." *In:* Slanetz, L. W., et al. "Microbiological Quality of Foods." Proceedings of a Conference held at Franconia, New Hampshire, August 27–29, 1962. Academic Press, New York, N.Y.

Tiedeman, W. D. (1958). "Implications of New Developments in Food and Milk Processing—Packaging, Storing and Vending." *Amer. Jour. Publ. Hlth., 48*(7): 854–860.

Tressler, Donald K., and Clifford F. Evers. (1957). *The Freezing Preservation of Foods.* Volume II. "Freezing of Precooked and Prepared Foods." 3rd ed. Avi Publishing Co., Westport, Conn.

U.S.D.A. (1959). "School Lunch Recipes Using Dried Whole Egg Solids." AMS Bulletin 194. Washington, D.C.

U.S.D.A. (1963). "School Lunch Recipes Using Dried Whole Egg Solids." PA-437. Washington, D.C.

U.S. Department of Health, Education and Welfare, Public Health Service. (1962). "Food Service Sanitation Manual." PHS Publication No. 934, Washington, D.C.

U.S. Department of Health, Education and Welfare, Public Health Service. (1965). "The Vending of Foods and Beverages." A Sanitation Ordinance and Code. PHS Publication No. 546.

University of the State of New York. State Education Department. (1959).

"Hard-cooked Eggs Prepared from Dried Whole Egg Solids" (mimeo). Supplement No. 2 to Fact Sheet No. 16. Foods Distribution Unit, Albany 1, N.Y.

West, Bessie B., Levelle Wood, and Virginia Harger. (1965). *Food Service in Institutions*. 4th ed. John Wiley & Sons, New York, N.Y.

## Additional Readings

Newcomer, J. L., Edward W. Ramsey, and Harold D. Eaton. "Effect of Air Flow in a Refrigerator on Cooling Rate." *Jour. Amer. Dietet. Assoc.*, *40*(1): 39–40. 1962.

U.S. Department of Agriculture. "Food Storage Guide for Schools and Institutions." Agricultural Marketing Service. PA-403. November, 1959.

U.S. Department of Agriculture. "Quantity Recipes Using Dried Whole Egg Solids." PA-437. 1961.

U.S. Department of Agriculture. "Quantity Recipes for Type A School Lunches." PA-631. October 1965.

# CHAPTER XIV

# EDUCATING FOOD SERVICE PERSONNEL IN FOOD SANITATION

For a food sanitation training program to be effective, it should involve everyone, from top management down to the employee performing the seemingly lowest tasks.

Unfortunately, few food service establishments seem to have the benefit of a well-structured training program in sanitation for employees. In many localities the health authority does not have sufficient staff time to conduct classes in sanitation. In the food service establishment itself, qualified teachers may not be available. Even if they are available, these persons are usually so busy with other responsibilities that this "one more thing" cannot be shouldered.

This is an unfortunate situation since training employees in sanitation is absolutely essential to the success of a sanitation program. The new employee should become convinced of the importance of sanitation, a subject probably foreign to him. Therefore, he has to learn about the fundamentals: bacterial growth, foodborne illness, personal hygiene, temperature control, and so forth. He has to become imbued with the fact that he, the food handler, plays an important role in sanitation. He needs to understand and become trained in sanitary techniques in handling food. It is essential that he be informed on matters on sanitation as soon as he starts working.

In large institutions or other large food service operations, training courses in sanitation are usually conducted by professionally trained food service personnel. In small institutions and other small food service establishments, professionally trained managers are frequently not available.

In some areas, training courses for food service workers are avail-

369

able through the health departments and are taught by sanitarians. The various State and local health departments vary widely regarding this activity. In some states, municipalities, and localities, regular and intensive training programs are set up and carried out. In a few cities, the health authorities offer regularly a complete course in sanitary food handling which every food handler is required to complete. This is an excellent requirement.

### Education and Self-Evaluation for Top Management and Professional Food Service Personnel

Top management and professional food service personnel have a key position. If they are convinced of the importance of food sanitation and are eager to achieve and maintain high sanitary standards in their food service establishments, training in sanitation is an essential part of their total training program for employees.

The Food Service Sanitation Manual of the U.S. Public Health Service (1962) states that to enforce the regulations recommended, "at least once every six months, the health authority shall inspect each food service establishment . . . and shall make as many additional inspections and reinspections as are necessary for the enforcement of this ordinance."

A sample checklist suggested by the Public Health Service (1962) for inspection reports on the sanitation of food service establishments is shown in Table 53. Using this as a guide, the food service manager may prepare his own rating sheets to be used for more frequent and regular checking. An inspection as widely spaced as six months cannot have the desired results unless management is convinced of the importance of these regulations and gives them their unrelenting support. It is management who carries the legal and moral responsibility for serving wholesome food to the public.

The first step in developing or improving a training program in sanitation is self-evaluation of management. Self-evaluation, or self-inspection, programs have been conducted on municipal and state levels. One program for the city of New York, described by Trichter (1951), began through action of the Board of Health of that city. Since 1959 a course in food sanitation for supervisors or persons in charge of food preparation has been required by city law (New York City Health Code Section 87.07). By amendment the date of compliance was extended twice. The latest date for compliance was October 1, 1963, or within six months of the commencement of the food handler's employment. Proof must be given by persons in charge of food preparation that they have successfully completed the course in sanitation. The course involves attendance at classes twice weekly for six weeks. The Department may approve courses given by educational institutions, industry, and labor groups.*

Another example of self-inspection is the program described by Vester and Norton (1959) for Rocky Mount, North Carolina.

Self-evaluation on a statewide basis was described by Gibbs and Hansell (1964). The Georgia State Department of Health conducted a pilot study involving a number of food service establishments in that state, including school food service operations. The program was described as including training sessions with food service managers, use of a brochure on sanitary food handling, showing of slides, demonstrations of techniques, and explanations of a management analysis sanitation form, a rating sheet somewhat similar to the one shown in Table 53.

## Keeping Up on Developments in the Profession

It is a human trait to support causes in which one believes and to slight those which seem unimportant. Fortunately, matters on which one keeps well informed tend to gain in importance; this applies to the field of food sanitation. It is therefore desirable that management keep well informed on the various aspects related to the area of sanitation: developments in food processing, food microbiology, food service equipment, detergents and sanitizers, and the like. For instance, specific microbiological hazards are arising in connection with new food processing methods as well as with new methods of merchandizing prepared menu items. Examples of new processes are mild heating (pasteurizing) of meats and fish, aseptic packaging, freeze-drying, and irradiation. Examples of now increasingly popular methods of merchandizing are catering of prepared menu items and selling menu items through vending machines.

Management also needs to keep informed on current problems in food microbiology and epidemiology as they relate to food service. Advances are currently being made in the elucidation of the causes of foodborne illnesses previously classified as "unknown." Examples of illnesses which were not considered foodborne until recently are the enteric viruses (Berg, 1964; Eisenstein et al., 1963) and certain enteropathic strains of *Escherichia coli* (Riley, 1964). Mycotoxins—for example, the aflatoxins of *Aspergillus flavus* (Forgacs and Carll, 1962; Hartley et al., 1963; Wogan, 1965)—are under scrutiny, as food-poisoning substances. The role of *Clostridium perfringens* as a

* Written communication, New York City Department of Health.

**Table 53. Sample Checklist Suggested by the U.S. Public Health Service**

### INSPECTION REPORT
### FOOD SERVICE ESTABLISHMENTS

Permit No. _____
Type _____ NSD

| CITY, COUNTY OR DISTRICT | NAME OF ESTABLISHMENT | ADDRESS | OWNER OR OPERATOR |
|---|---|---|---|

Sir: Based on an inspection this day, the items marked below identify the violation in operation or facilities which must be corrected by the next routine inspection or such shorter period of time as may be specified in writing by the health authority. Failure to comply with this notice may result in immediate suspension of your permit (or down-grading of the establishment).* An opportunity for an appeal will be provided if a written request for a hearing is filed with the health authority within the period of time established in this notice for the correction of violations.

### SECTION B. FOOD
#### 1. FOOD SUPPLIES

| Item | | Specify: | Bakery products | Poultry and poultry products | Meat and meat products | Frozen desserts | Shellfish | Milk and milk products | Demerit points |
|---|---|---|---|---|---|---|---|---|---|
| 1 | Approved source | | | | | | | | 6 |
| 2 | Wholesome - not adulterated | | | | | | | | 6 |
| 3 | Not misbranded | | | | | | | | 2 |
| 4 | Original container; properly identified | | | | | | | | 2 |
| 5 | Approved dispenser | | | | | | | | |
| 6 | Fluid milk and fluid milk products pasteurized | | | | | | | | 6 |
| 7 | Low-acid and non-acid foods commercially canned | | | | | | | | 6 |

#### 2. FOOD PROTECTION

| Item | | Preparation | Storage | Display | Service | Transportation |
|---|---|---|---|---|---|---|
| 8 | Protected from contamination | | | | | 4 |
| 9 | Adequate facilities for maintaining food at hot | | | | | |

### SECTION D.  FOOD EQUIPMENT AND UTENSILS
#### 1. SANITARY DESIGN, CONSTRUCTION AND INSTALLATION OF EQUIPMENT AND UTENSILS

| Item | | Good repair; no cracks | No chips, pits or open seams | Cleanable; smooth | Approved material | No corrosion | Proper construction | Accessible for cleaning and inspection | Demerit points |
|---|---|---|---|---|---|---|---|---|---|
| 31 | Food-contact surfaces of equipment | | | | | | | | 2 |
| 32 | Utensils | | | | | | | | 2 |
| 33 | Non-food-contact surfaces of equipment | | | | | | | | 2 |
| 34 | Single-service articles of non-toxic materials | | | | | | | | 2 |
| 35 | Equipment properly installed | | | | | | | | 2 |
| 36 | Existing equipment capable of being cleaned, non-toxic, properly installed, and in good repair | | | | | | | | 2 |

#### 2. CLEANLINESS OF EQUIPMENT AND UTENSILS

| Item | | | Demerit points |
|---|---|---|---|
| 37 | Tableware clean to sight and touch | | |
| 38 | Kitchenware and food-contact surfaces of equipment clean to sight and touch | | 4 |
| 39 | Grills and similar cooking devices cleaned daily | | |
| 40 | Non-food-contact surfaces of equipment kept clean | | 2 |

| No. | Pts | Item |
|---|---|---|
| 10 | 2 | Suitable thermometers properly located |
| 11 | 2 | Perishable food at proper temperature |
| 12 | 6 | Potentially hazardous food at 45° F. or below, or 140° F. or above as required |
| 13 | 2 | Frozen food kept frozen; properly thawed |
| 14 | 4 | Handling of food minimized by use of suitable utensils |
| 15 | 6 | Hollandaise sauce of fresh ingredients; discarded after three hours |
| 16 | 6 | Food cooked to proper temperature |
| 17 | 2 | Fruits and vegetables washed thoroughly |
| 18 | 2 | Containers of food stored off floor on clean surfaces |
| 19 | 2 | No wet storage of packaged food |
| 20 | 2 | Display cases, counter protector devices or cabinets of approved type |
| 21 | 2 | Frozen dessert dippers properly stored |
| 22 | 2 | Sugar in closed dispensers or individual packages |
| 23 | 4 | Unwrapped and potentially hazardous food not re-served |
| 24 | 6 | Poisonous and toxic materials properly identified, colored, stored and used; poisonous polishes not present |
| 25 | 6 | Bactericides, cleaning and other compounds properly stored and non-toxic in use dilutions |

SECTION C. PERSONNEL
1. HEALTH AND DISEASE CONTROL

| No. | Pts | Item |
|---|---|---|
| 26 | 6 | Persons with boils, infected wounds, respiratory infections or other communicable disease properly restricted |
| 27 | 6 | Known or suspected communicable disease cases reported to health authority |

2. CLEANLINESS

| No. | Pts | Item |
|---|---|---|
| 28 | 6 | Hands washed and clean |
| 29 | 2 | Clean outer garments; proper hair restraints used |
| 30 | 4 | Good hygienic practices |

| No. | Pts | Item |
|---|---|---|
| 42 | 2 | Clean wiping cloths used; use properly restricted |
| 43 | 2 | Utensils and equipment pre-flushed, scraped or soaked |
| 44 | 4 | Tableware sanitized |
| 45 | 4 | Kitchenware and food-contact surfaces of equipment used for potentially hazardous food sanitized |
| 46 | 4 | Facilities for washing and sanitizing equipment and utensils approved, adequate, properly constructed, maintained and operated |
| 47 | 2 | Wash and sanitizing water clean |
| 48 | 2 | Wash water at proper temperature |
| 49 | 2 | Dish tables and drain boards provided, properly located and constructed |
| 50 | 2 | Adequate and suitable detergents used |
| 51 | 2 | Approved thermometers provided and used |
| 52 | 2 | Suitable dish baskets provided |
| 53 | 2 | Proper gauge cocks provided |
| 54 | 2 | Cleaned and cleaned and sanitized utensils and equipment properly stored and handled; utensils air-dried |
| 55 | 2 | Suitable facilities and areas provided for storing utensils and equipment |
| 56 | 2 | Single-service articles properly stored, dispensed and handled |
| 57 | 2 | Single-service articles used only once |
| 58 | 6 | Single-service articles used when approved washing and sanitizing facilities are not provided |

SECTION E. SANITARY FACILITIES AND CONTROLS
1. WATER SUPPLY

| No. | Pts | Item |
|---|---|---|
| 59 | 6 | From approved source; adequate; safe quality |
| 60 | 4 | Hot and cold running water provided |
| 61 | 6 | Transported water handled, stored; dispensed in a sanitary manner |
| 62 | 6 | Ice from approved source; made from potable water |
| 63 | 2 | Ice machines and facilities properly located, installed and maintained |
| 64 | 6 / 2 | Ice and ice handling utensils properly handled and stored; block ice rinsed |
| 65 | 4 | Ice-contact surfaces approved; proper material and construction |

* Applicable only where grading form of ordinance is in effect.

# Table 53 (continued)

| Item | | Demerit Points |
|---|---|---|
| | **2. SEWAGE DISPOSAL** | |
| 66 | Into public sewer, or approved private facilities | 6 |
| | **3. PLUMBING** | |
| 67 | Properly sized, installed and maintained | 2 |
| 68 | Non-potable water piping identified | 1 |
| 69 | No cross connections | 6 |
| 70 | No back siphonage possible | |
| 71 | Equipment properly drained | 2 |
| | **4. TOILET FACILITIES** | |
| 72 | Adequate, conveniently located, and accessible; properly designed and installed | 6 |
| 73 | Toilet rooms completely enclosed, and equipped with self-closing, tight-fitting doors; doors kept closed | 2 |
| 74 | Toilet rooms, fixtures and vestibules kept clean, in good repair, and free from odors | 2 |
| 75 | Toilet tissue and proper waste receptacles provided; waste receptacles emptied as necessary | 2 |
| | **5. HAND-WASHING FACILITIES** | |
| 76 | Lavatories provided, adequate, properly located and installed | 6 |
| 77 | Provided with hot and cold or tempered running water through proper fixtures | 4 |
| 78 | Suitable hand cleanser and sanitary towels or approved hand-drying devices provided | 2 |
| 79 | Waste receptacles provided for disposable towels | 2 |
| 80 | Lavatory facilities clean and in good repair | 2 |
| | **6. GARBAGE AND RUBBISH DISPOSAL** | |

| Item | | Demerit Points |
|---|---|---|
| | **SECTION F. OTHER FACILITIES** | |
| | **1. FLOORS, WALLS AND CEILINGS** | |
| 91 | Floors kept clean; no sawdust used | 2 |
| 92 | Floors easily cleanable construction, in good repair, smooth, non-absorbent; carpeting in good repair | 1 |
| 93 | Floor graded and floor drains, as required | 2 |
| 94 | Exterior walking and driving surfaces clean; drained | 2 |
| 95 | Exterior walking and driving surfaces properly surfaced | 1 |
| 96 | Mats and duck boards cleanable, removable and clean | 2 |
| 97 | Floors and wall junctures properly constructed | 2 |
| 98 | Walls, ceilings and attached equipment clean | 2 |
| 99 | Walls and ceilings properly constructed and in good repair; coverings properly attached | 1 |
| 100 | Walls of light color; washable to level of splash | 2 |
| | **2. LIGHTING** | |
| 101 | 20 foot-candles of light on working surfaces | |
| 102 | 10 foot-candles of light on food equipment, utensil-washing, hand-washing areas and toilet rooms | 2 |
| 103 | 5 foot-candles of light 30″ from floor in all other areas | 6 |
| 104 | Artificial light sources as required | 2 |
| | **3. VENTILATION** | |
| 105 | Rooms reasonably free from steam, condensation, smoke, etc. | 2 |
| 106 | Rooms and equipment vented to outside as required | 2 |
| 107 | Hoods properly designed; filters removable | 2 |
| 108 | Intake air ducts properly designed and maintained | 1 |

| # | Item | Score |
|---|------|-------|
| 81 | Stored in approved containers; adequate in number | 2 |
| 82 | Containers cleaned when empty; brushes provided | 2 |
| 83 | When not in continuous use, covered with tight fitting lids, or in protective storage inaccessible to vermin | 2 |
| 84 | Storage areas adequate; clean; no nuisances; proper facilities provided | 2 |
| 85 | Disposed of in an approved manner, at an approved frequency | 2 |
| 86 | Garbage rooms or enclosures properly constructed; outside storage at proper height above ground or on concrete slab | 2 |
| 87 | Food waste grinders and incinerators properly installed, constructed and operated; incinerators areas clean | 2 |
| | **7. VERMIN CONTROL** | |
| 88 | Presence of rodents, flies, roaches and vermin minimized | 4 |
| 89 | Outer openings protected against flying insects as required; rodent-proofed | 2 |
| 90 | Harborage and feeding of vermin prevented | 2 |

| # | Item | Score |
|---|------|-------|
| 109 | Systems comply with fire prevention requirements; no nuisance created | 2 |
| | **4. DRESSING ROOMS AND LOCKERS** | |
| 110 | Dressing rooms or areas as required; properly located | 1 |
| 111 | Adequate lockers or other suitable facilities | 1 |
| 112 | Dressing rooms, areas and lockers kept clean | 2 |
| | **5. HOUSEKEEPING** | |
| 113 | Establishment and property clean, and free of litter | 2 |
| 114 | No operations in living or sleeping quarters | 2 |
| 115 | Floors and walls cleaned after closing or between meals by dustless methods | 2 |
| 116 | Laundered clothes and napkins stored in clean place | 2 |
| 117 | Soiled linen and clothing stored in proper containers | 1 |
| 118 | No live birds or animals other than guide dogs | 2 |

DEMERIT SCORE OF THE ESTABLISHMENT _____

REMARKS _____

_____

_____

_____

Date _____          Health Authority _____

foodborne pathogen has recently been elucidated and control measures have been suggested (Hall and Angelotti, 1965). Also, the ability of *C. botulinum* Type E to multiply at temperatures below 40°F has recently been demonstrated (Schmidt et al., 1961).

In the equipment field, development regarding improved cooling equipment and warm-holding equipment should not only be watched but should be stimulated by requesting it. For example, there is a need for cooling kettles in which cooked food can be brought to safe temperatures rapidly using scraper-type agitators at low rates of speed, as was pointed out in Chapter XIII. Well-informed management has this responsibility: to make known their need for equipment appropriate for fast cooling, for efficient cold storage, and for efficient warm holding; to procure this equipment; and to train employees in using it.

To keep abreast of current developments in the food field, including sanitary aspects, is no easy task even for those who have the benefits of professional associations, professional journals, and attendance at professional meetings. Fortunately, the health authorities, from the federal level to the local, are eager to be of constructive assistance to the food service industry. For example, food service managers may take advantage of excellent training courses developed by the Public Health Service (Robert A. Taft Sanitary Engineering Center, Cincinnati, Ohio). Subject matter dealing with current problems in food service sanitation is presented by staff and invited guest lecturers, and an opportunity is afforded for a stimulating exchange of factual information and ideas.

The cooperation of State and local health authorities in self-evaluation programs of food service management was discussed earlier.

To develop a successful training program for employees, these points should be considered by management:

1) Knowing the fundamentals of sanitary practices acceptable to the health authority.
2) Supplying the new employee with background information which will enable him to understand the concept of sanitation. This information should be supplied as part of his orientation.
3) Teaching the employee the techniques of sanitary food handling; this instruction should start the day the employee begins work.
4) Supplying proper and adequate equipment, tools, and supplies.
5) Supplying supervision on the job.

6) Supplying refresher sessions in sanitation.

7) Giving recognition to the employee for information well learned and techniques well performed.

## Education and Training for Nonprofessional Food Service Personnel

The number of new food service employees who have to be trained is staggering because of a high turnover rate. Food service employees often come from lower socioeconomic levels and have not received formal training for the trade. Many of them are not easy to teach, have language difficulties, or read poorly. Consequently, they advance slowly, earn poorly, feel insecure and dissatisfied, and leave their jobs frequently to seek employment elsewhere.

Teaching sanitation to unskilled employees of a poor socioeconomic background is a hard task, and the concepts "cleanliness" and "sanitation" may prove difficult to convey. Yet the advantages of training unskilled food service employees are obvious. For management they are: chance of foodborne illness is reduced; labor turnover is reduced; supervision of employees is reduced; the working standards are improved; production is increased; and a larger supply of skilled employees is created for the particular food service as well as the food service industry as a whole.

There are also distinctive advantages for the employee: job satisfaction; chance for advancement; and greater sense of security which comes with recognition, advancement, and job satisfaction.

### The Instructor

A successful instructor knows his subject matter; is alerted to current changes in the food field relevant to sanitary aspects; has time and is willing to plan and prepare his lessons, including visual aids, in detail; is able to hold the attention of his trainee—or group of trainees—who is apt to be tired after a full day's work; is tactful yet frank in handling subjects touching on such intimate matters as personal hygiene; and always seeks ways of improving his teaching.

Qualified instructors may not be available in small hospitals, nursing homes, and school lunch operations. It is desirable that training courses be set up by the health authority for those establishments which at present do not have the benefit of such instruction.

In institutions which employ professionally trained managers who are qualified to be instructors, these persons are frequently overburdened with other duties. It seems that it is the responsibility of top management to relieve these persons of those duties which could be taken over by others and to free them for the important task of instructing employees in food sanitation. But it also seems that professionally trained managers might well take the initiative and make it known to top management that they wish to conduct a well-structured training program in sanitation and for what reasons. They should be prepared to suggest which duties could be taken on by someone else to free them for the teaching responsibility. Nothing succeeds like conviction, initiative, and perseverance. The need for delegating duties and responsibilities in dietary departments to nonprofessional personnel has been emphasized by the American Dietetic Association for years. A grant was established in 1959 by the W. K. Kellogg Foundation to establish a correspondence course for food service supervisors. According to Piper (1965), a significant number of food service supervisors have already completed a course. He warns that this course cannot possibly meet the total training needs and that more local post-high school short courses should be established.

It is hoped that with more responsibilities delegated to supervisors who have successfully completed such short courses, the professionally trained food service manager will be able to devote time to the important responsibility of instruction in food sanitation.

## Training Methods

The methods which are used include on-the-job training, conferences, lectures and discussions, demonstrations, and other use of visual aids such as posters, slides, and films. Programmed instruction using teaching machines is a new development in teaching employees. Combinations of these devices are possible and are frequently employed.

All teaching methods require that follow-up instruction take place and that supervision on the job be employed, to reemphasize what was learned.

### ON-THE-JOB TRAINING

On-the-job training is probably the most frequently used method today in food service establishments. Its success depends on how carefully the program is planned and executed.

The most knowledgeable teachers are just good enough for this important job. Unfortunately, the on-the-job trainee is all too frequently simply assigned to another employee who shows him "how to do it." Faulty and bacteriologically unacceptable methods are perpetuated in this manner.

Lukowski and Eshbach (1963) have pointed out that there are four major steps based on the principles of habit formation, which include motivation, demonstration, and practice, and that these steps are: preparation, presentation, application, and follow-up.

In the first step, preparation, the trainee should be motivated to learn. He should become convinced that his person is an important link in the chain of events and that he may play a dual role—providing contaminants and controlling contaminants—and that successful cooperation in the program will affect his job performance record and chances of advancement.

The second step, presentation, includes the "whys" and "hows." A clear understanding of the reasons underlying sanitary handling techniques is fundamental to their application.

The third step, application, gives the trainee a chance to prove to the instructor that he has understood the lesson and is using the appropriate techniques on the job.

The fourth step, follow-up, involves checks on the part of the instructor. Naturally, frequent and thorough checks would be more effective than infrequent and superficial ones.

It should be remembered that recognition of a job well done is essential to keeping employees' performance at a high level.

## CONFERENCES, LECTURES, DEMONSTRATIONS, AND VISUAL AIDS

An early conference on sanitation with the new employee is extremely important and should be scheduled as part of orientation. Naturally, instruction given on the first day cannot possibly convey to the employee all the basic information he needs about bacteria, their reservoirs, activities, and so forth; except, possibly, when programmed instruction is applied (see below). Additional conferences, lectures, demonstrations and visual or audiovisual aids should accompany the employee's on-the-job training as soon as possible. In these sessions, "old" employees might be included. Regular refresher sessions in sanitation are needed by all food service workers.

## PROGRAMMED INSTRUCTION

Programmed instruction by machines is a new and at present much discussed teaching method. The subject matter is prepared by a specialist in a well-organized, simple, effective manner. The learner teaches himself using the material and an appropriate machine.

Teaching machines and programs have, according to Carter (1963), this in common: that continuous active response is required by the learner; that provision is made for informing the student immediately whether each response made by him is correct, making it possible for him to immediately correct his mistakes; and finally, that the rate at which the learner proceeds is determined by his own capabilities.

It seems that the auto-instructional technique will, in the future, solve many training problems, including training in principles and skills of food sanitation.

Carter et al. (1964) developed a programmed course in sanitation in order to investigate the effectiveness of programmed instruction as a technique for teaching nonprofessional food service employees. These authors used a machine which was essentially a slide film projector. The student reads the material presented on a slide and answers questions about what he has read by pushing appropriate buttons; if he answers correctly he may proceed; if not, he is told why the answer is wrong and he is requested to reread the text. The crux of the matter is that the learner cannot proceed to new material until he has chosen the correct answer. Each section contains at the end a test on all the material covered.

Carter et al. (1964) found that although the employees who took the test varied widely in age, level of education, reading skill, and knowledge of subject matter, a statistically significant amount of learning was achieved by the experimental group.

The program has been refined since and is now being used to instruct new food service employees at the University of Missouri Hospital as part of employee orientation. This course, like any conventional type, needs to be followed up with refresher courses. The program itself would have to be updated as new research results and developments in the food field require.

### Objectives and Course Content

The major objectives of a sanitation training course for a nonprofessional food service employee are: to create in him an awareness of the public health aspects of his job and to create in him a feeling of importance of his role within the total sanitation program and an eagerness to do his part.

The subject matter would include, in concise form, the following:
  1) Elements of microbiology, with emphasis on microorganisms which are important from a public health point of view: size,

shape, spores, reproduction; time–temperature relationships of growth and death; and importance of food as medium for bacteria. Principles of food preservation.

2) Parasites in foods.

3) Transmission of pathogens.

4) Foodborne illnesses: causative organisms, circumstances associated with outbreaks, symptoms; reporting; and the role of the health authority.

5) Reservoirs of microorganisms: man (the food handler, the customer); animals (livestock, pets, rodents, insects); environment (sewage, soil, air, water); and food supply.

6) Contamination of food in the food service area from above reservoirs and from secondary sources such as soiled hands, soiled equipment, utensils, and an ill-maintained physical plant. Control measures: personal hygiene; rodent and insect control; efficient plumbing; potable water; removal of soil; avoidance of cross-contamination from raw to cooked food; equipment and utensils sanitation; housekeeping in the areas of storage, food preparation, and service.

7) Multiplication of bacteria in foods and factors affecting multiplication. The meaning of "potentially hazardous foods." Time–temperature relationships; the meaning of "danger zone." Control measures: time–temperature control for all potentially hazardous foods at all stages of storage, preparation, and service.

8) Agencies concerned with food protection. Cooperation with the local health authority.

## Sanitation Manuals

Manuals are available as guidelines to instructors who wish to structure and conduct training programs in food sanitation for food service employees. Manuals have been developed and published by many agencies, a few examples being given under "Additional Readings." The authors of manuals include the U.S. Department of Health, Education and Welfare, Public Health Service; Veteran's Administration; the Departments of Public Health of the various states; and the Health Departments of municipalities, regions, and counties. The instructor seeking information should contact the appropriate health authority of his locality. The references cited at the end of the chapter were given with the intent to provide stimulation regarding possible sources of appropriate material; they are only examples, and by no means exhaustive.

*Visual Aids*

Films, slides, and posters are available through federal and state agencies as well as through commercial channels. Some films may be borrowed without fee, for others rental may be charged, and some are available for purchase.

It is advised that the appropriate State Department of Health be approached, since these agencies are apt to have films available in their film libraries for use in training sessions. Another source is the Communicable Disease Center, Audiovisual Facility, Atlanta, Georgia. The film libraries of universities are another source of films.

In the Film Catalog of the U.S. Public Health Service (PHS Publication No. 776; available through the office of the Superintendent of Documents, Washington, D.C.), audiovisual teaching materials in the area of food sanitation are listed.

Before showing visual aids to a class, the instructor will profit by previewing them critically. Even the best material becomes outdated as research continues to produce new pertinent data. The instructor would do well to correct outdated information and to be prepared for questions from the audience.

Examples of instructional material are given under "Additional Readings."

**References**

Berg, G. (1964). "The Food Vehicle in Virus Transmission." *Health Lab. Sci., 1:* 51–59.

Carter, Evelyn J. (1963). "A Preliminary Investigation of the Effectiveness of Programmed Instruction in Teaching Sanitation to Non-professional Food Service Employees." M.S. thesis, University of Missouri, Columbia, Missouri.

Carter, Evelyn J., Aimee N. Moore, and Cecil L. Gregory. (1964). "Can Teaching Machines Help in Training Employees?" *Jour. Amer. Dietet. Assoc., 44*(4): 271–276.

Eisenstein, A. B., R. D. Aach, W. Jacobsohn, and A. Goldman. (1963). "An Epidemic of Infectious Hepatitis in a General Hospital. Probable Transmission by Contaminated Orange Juice." *Jour. Amer. Med. Assoc., 185:* 171–174.

Forgacs, J., and W. T. Carll. (1962). "Mycotoxicoses." *Advances in Veterinary Sci., 7:* 273–382. Academic Press, New York.

Gibbs, J. P., and W. A. Hansell. (1964). "The Georgia Approach to Self-Evaluation in the Food Service Establishment Industry." Paper presented at the 92nd Annual Meeting of the American Association Public Health, October 8, New York, N.Y.

Hall, H. E., and R. Angelotti. (1965). "*Clostridium perfringens* in Meat and Meat Products." *Appl. Micr., 13*(3): 352–357.

Hartley, R. D., B. F. Nesbitt, and O. Kelly, Jr. (1963). "Toxic metabolites of *Aspergillus flavus.*" *Nature, 198*: 1056–1058.

Lukowski, R. F., and C. E. Eshbach. (1963). "Employee Training in Food Service Establishments." Food Management Program Leaflet 7, GPC 3/63 AMA, Cooperative Extension Service, College of Agriculture, University of Massachusetts.

Piper, Geraldine M. (1965). "President's Report to Members." *Jour. Amer. Dietet. Assoc., 47*(6): 461–465.

Riley, H. D. (ed.). (1964). "Enteropathogenic *Escherichia coli* Gastroenteritis." *Chem. Pediatrics, 3:* 93.

Schmidt, C. F., R. V. Lechovich, and J. F. Folinazzo. (1961). "Growth and Toxin Production of Type E *Clostridium botulinum* below 40°F." *Jour. Food Sci., 26*(6): 626–630.

Trichter, Jerome. (1951). "Development of Self-Inspection for Sanitation in Food Plants of New York City." *Food Tech.,* 5(12): 528–530.

U.S. Department of Health, Education and Welfare, Public Health Service. (1962). "Food Service Sanitation Manual." PHS Publication No. 934 Washington, D.C.

Vester, K. G., and J. W. B. Norton. (1959). "Self-Inspection." *Amer. Jour. Publ. Hlth., 49*(6): 744–751.

Wogan, Gerald W. (ed.). (1965). *Mycotoxins in Foodstuffs.* The MIT Press, Cambridge, Mass.

## Additional Readings

**Examples of Manuals (most recent revisions should be requested)**

Federal Security Agency, U.S. Public Health Service. "From Hand to Mouth." Community Health Series No. 3. Superintendent of Documents, Washington, D.C. 20¢

Georgia Department of Public Health."Food Sanitation."A flipchart. Atlanta, Ga.

Haskell, W. H. "A Training Course in Sanitation for Food Service Workers." Reprinted from *Institutions Magazine,* 1801 Prairie Avenue, Chicago 16, Ill. $2.50

Iowa State Department of Health, in cooperation with Iowa State Board of Control. "Sanitation of Food Service Establishments. A Guide for On-The-Job Training of Personnel." Des Moines, Iowa. Obtainable also through Economics Laboratory, Inc., 250 Park Avenue, New York, N.Y.

Ludewig, Edwin. "Food Sanitation Course. Lecture Notes." New York City Department of Health, 125 Worth Street, New York, N.Y. 60¢

New York State Department of Health. "Guide for Food Handler Training Course" (mimeo) Flipchart. Albany, N.Y.

U.S. Department of Health, Education and Welfare, Office of Education. "Supervised Food Service Worker. A Suggested Training Program." Course Unit II (Safe Food Handling, Essential Health Practices, and Sanitation); Course Unit V (Adequate Storage of Food); Teaching the Course. Superintendent of Documents, Catalog No. FS 5.287:87004. 20¢

U.S. Department of Health, Education and Welfare, Department of the Army, Navy and the Air Force. "Sanitary Food Service. Instructor's Guide." (Appendix 3 contains listing of visual aids and utilization guides for films.)

Public Health Service Publication No. 90. Superintendent of Documents, Washington, D.C. $1.25

Washington State Department of Health. "Sanitation Guide For the School Lunch Program" (mimeo). Seattle, Wash.

Washington State Department of Health. "Food and Beverage Service Workers' Manual." Seattle, Wash.

### Examples of Films

"Dishwashing Dividends." Sound, 16 mm, 19 minutes. Health Film Library, New York State Department of Health, Albany 8, N.Y.

"Epidemiology of Salmonellosis in Man and Animals." Sound, 16 mm, 15 minutes. U.S. Communicable Disease Center, U.S. Public Health Service, Audiovisual Facility, Atlanta, Ga.

"Hospital Food Service Personnel Training: the Individual." Sound, 16 mm, 13 minutes. Health Film Library, New York State Department of Health, Albany 8, N.Y.

"Hospital Food Service Personnel Training: Equipment." Sound, 16 mm, 12 minutes. Health Film Library, New York State Department of Health, Albany 8, N.Y.

"Kitchen Habits." Sound, 16 mm, 13 minutes. U.S. Communicable Disease Center, U.S. Public Health Service, Audiovisual Facility, Atlanta, Ga.

"Outbreak of Staphylococcus Intoxication." Sound, 16 mm, 15 minutes. U.S. Communicable Disease Center, U.S. Public Health Service, Audiovisual Facility, Atlanta, Ga.

"Outbreak of Salmonella Infection." Sound, 16 mm, 13 minutes. U.S. Communicable Disease Center, U.S. Public Health Service, Audiovisual Facility, Atlanta, Ga.

"Principles of Food Sanitation." Sound, 16 mm, 20 minutes. Cine-Tele Distributing Corporation, Los Angeles, Calif. (For rent at the Department of Extension Teaching and Information, Cornell University, Ithaca, N.Y.)

"Safe Handling of Foods in Quantity." Sound, 16 mm, 16 minutes. Department of Extension Teaching and Information. Cornell University, Ithaca, N.Y.

# INDEX